PERCEPTUAL AND MOTOR DEVELOPMENT IN INFANTS AND CHILDREN

THE MACMILLAN COMPANY
Collier-Macmillan Limited,
London

Perceptual and Motor Development in Infants and Children

BRYANT J. CRATTY Ed.D.
University of California
Los Angeles

To Sandy

Acknowledgments

A debt is owed to many people who helped to complete this text. Dr. Namiko Ikeda worked hard during the years 1968 and 1969 collecting laboratory data that contributed to the content. Dr. Jack F. Keogh at U.C.L.A. generously permitted me to use several charts from his monographs, and material in several chapters is based on his findings.

To the donors of a special grant I am also grateful. Their backing permitted me to complete this text and to obtain information that I believe enhanced the chapters dealing with motor development during middle childhood and with visual perceptual development.

Special thanks should also be extended to my beleaguered but capable secretarial staff: Miss Jill Woodmansee, Mr. Jeff Drucker, Miss Sara Dobbins, and Mrs. Anna Carillo. Miss Dobbins aided me in the final revisions of the manuscript.

I would also like to thank numerous professional people throughout the country, physical educators, special educators, and elementary educators who during the past years have asked me to visit with them and who in turn have added to my knowledge of the manner in which children move, grow, and perceive. To my colleagues in Sweden, England, Czechoslovakia, Belgium, Germany, Holland, Spain, Finland, Norway, Chili, and Italy I am also grateful for inspiration and hospitality.

B. J. C.

Vigoroso

Contents

1 INTRODUCTION *1*

    Bibliography   8

2 THE BEGINNINGS OF MOVEMENT IN INFANTS *9*

    Infant Reflexes   10
    Reflexive Locomotor, Swimming, Crawling,
      and Climbing Movements   18
    Voluntary, Independent Locomotion   23
    Summary   26
    Developmental Trends   27
    Bibliography   29

**3 GROSS MOTOR ATTRIBUTES IN
EARLY CHILDHOOD** *31*

    Maturation and Learning   33
    Growth, Structural, and Postural Changes   35
    Prediction of Motor, Emotional, and
      Intellectual Attributes   36
    Emerging Hand, Eye, and Foot Preferences   39
    Locomotion, Variations, and Explorations   43
    Balance   48
    Climbing   52
    Limb Coordination Tasks   53
    Skill with Balls   53
    Summary   60
    Bibliography   62

4 VISUAL PERCEPTUAL DEVELOPMENT 67

Ocular Characteristics of the Infant   70
Visual Attention in the Newborn   73
Perceptual and Perceptual-Motor
    Imprinting?   75
The Modification of Visual and Visual-Motor
    Responses Through Experience   77
Perceptions of Form   78
Perceptions of Movement and Shapes in
    Three-Dimensional Space   81
Trends and Issues   90
Summary   93
Bibliography   95

5 THE BODY IMAGE 101

Feelings About the Body and the Total
    Self-Concept   103
The Performing "Self"   104
Evaluating the Body Image   105
Developmental Trends   112
Summary   118
Bibliography   119

6 MANIPULATIVE BEHAVIORS 123

Hand and Object Regard   126
Contacting Objects   128
The Exploitation of Objects   130
Manual Dexterity in Middle and Late
    Childhood   132
Preferences for Manipulative Activities   135
Summary   135
Bibliography   138

7 SCRIBBLING AND DRAWING 141

Random and Repetitive Actions   143
Enclosing Space   145

The Diagram Phase   148
Combines and Aggregates   153
The Pictorial Stage   155
Printing Letters and Numbers   160
Three-Dimensional Representations in
    Drawing   162
Summary   163
Bibliography   166

**8 MOTOR DEVELOPMENT IN CHILDREN
FROM SIX TO TWELVE** *167*

Measurement Problems   168
Factor Analyses   170
Mental-Motor Relationships   172
Correlative Studies   174
Physical Fitness and Intelligence   174
Age Trends   177
Basic Physical Attributes   179
Reaction Time   182
Locomotor Attributes   189
Running Speed and Agility   199
Agility   202
Skill in the Use of Balls   204
Game Choices of Children   209
Summary   210
Bibliography   213

9 SOCIAL DEVELOPMENT *219*

Infancy   220
Early Familial Influences   221
Gender Identification   223
Parental Attitudes and Performance
    Attributes of Their Children   225
Physical Maturity and Performance as
    Predictive of Social Success   227
Social Characteristics of Children at Play   229
Leadership at Play   231
Cooperation and Competition   234
Social Reinforcement   236

Summary   239
Bibliography   241

**10 EVALUATION AND DISCUSSION OF
SELECTED PERCEPTUAL-MOTOR
PROGRAMS PURPORTING TO ENHANCE
ACADEMIC FUNCTIONS 247**

Perceptual-Motor Training   248
Neurological Organization   253
"Physiological Optics"   257
Comparisons and Conclusions   262
Bibliography   266

**11 MODEL FOR THE STUDY OF
HUMAN MATURATION 273**

The Differentiation and Integration of
    Behavior   274
Summary   288
Bibliography   289

INDEX 293

Introduction 1

Throughout history the developing child has never ceased to elicit wonder and admiration from his observing parents and from others of the tribe at whom he cooed and smiled. Since the dawn of the scientific age scholars from a number of disciplines have also scrutinized the writhings and squirmings of the young.

During the 1920's and 1930's university researchers at Yale, Iowa, Berkeley, and other institutes throughout the country began to collect data on the more observable aspects of human development. At the same time medical scholars here and in Europe began to analyze the reflexive movements seen at birth for clues that might enable them to evaluate the condition of infants whose futures might be marred by the presence of motor or mental abnormalities.

With the coming of new knowledge and techniques in biochemistry, bioelectronics, fetology, and surgery during the 1950's and 1960's, the infant was analyzed with even more sophistication. The health and development of the fetus were more closely monitored, inspected, and at times corrected. The biochemical make-up of the amniotic fluid was analyzed with increasing exactitude. Researchers began to explore the emergence of early chromosome abnormalities, which often lead to insurmountable difficulties.

The importance of environmental experience and stimulation during early infancy has been studied during recent years. A recent television program on the subject pointed out that premature infants are called by name to take advantage of any auditory imprinting that may be important during these early day of life.

Accompanying increased understanding of how children develop is a parallel concern for correcting developmental lags seen as children enter school. Some school districts have instituted developmental screenings composed in part of tasks assessing motor functioning. They are attempting, in this way, to assess deficiencies that are likely to interfere with various abilities important to school success.

Along with this increased interest and new information on the part of those responsible for infant care and training, however, there is sometimes seen a kind of hysterical reaction to the importance of visual-motor, sensory-motor, or perceptual-motor training in education of children. The hyphenated adjective "perceptual-motor" has to some elementary school administrators become like the noisy footfalls that signal the impending visit of an ogre in a children's fairy tale. Parents, visual and motor "trainers," and "educationalists" of a variety of descriptions and biases sometimes bring pressure to bear on school personnel to utilize various kinds of movement tools as magic fertilizers to nurture cognitive flowers from the craniums of normal children. They seem to suggest that a wave of a "balance-beam" wand will cure the effects of unfortunate environmental or hereditary circumstances with which children with various types of disabilities have been plagued.

I do not view perceptual-motor behavior, perceptual-motor learning, or perceptual-motor training as either phrases to be avoided or supernatural cure-alls. Rather, I believe that the perceptions and related movements engaged in by human infants and children are important facets of their personalities. Perceptual and motor behaviors are at times independent from each other and at other times may be joined in interesting ways. Most voluntary movement requires some kind of perceptual activity; the ball to be caught must first be watched, and smoothly executed complex movements are dependent on conscious or unconscious "kinesthetic" feedback of previous components of chains of reactions.

However, one should not fall into the fallacy of assuming that simply because voluntary movement is *in part* "dependent" on various perceptual skills that one can modify *all* perceptual abilities by the insertion of special movement training into the school curriculum. An analogous fallacy would be to suggest that since noise usually accompanies gunfire, all disturbances in adjacent sound waves signal the fact that someone is out to exterminate you.

This text was written in an effort to alleviate some of the hysteria connected with perceptual-motor functioning. I felt that one way in which this might well be accomplished would be to recount some of the more pertinent research findings in as cogent a manner as I can. Furthermore, this text attempts to illuminate the fact that some of the time visual perceptual processes mature and function independently of observable movement behavior. I shall also examine several of the facets of perceptual functioning that are closely associated with motor functioning, visual perception, and the perceptions formed about the body in the following pages.

A model was developed in an effort to explain interactions between perception, movement, and other parts of the developing personality of the child. This model draws on data from factor analytic studies of human performance as well as information from research in which intellectual, motor, perceptual, and verbal aspects of given samples of behavior have been compared. Experimental studies exploring the manner in which emphasis on one component of the human action system (i.e., motor activity) may change another component (i.e., perceptual or cognitive functioning) have also been referred to when formulating the statements in the final part of the text. The reader might refer to this information in the final chapter prior to exploring the material in Chapters 2 to 10.

Some of the discussions that follow outline the manner in which a single channel of development tends to mature and to show its particular pattern of attributes. For example, the chapter on visual perception (4) and those on the gross motor attributes of children from birth to five years (3) and from 6 to 12 years (8) are of this type. Others concentrate more on attributes that represent the functioning of bonds between visual, motor, and at times intellectual qualities. The chapters on manipulative behavior (6) and drawing and scribbling (7) have this latter focus. They represent descriptions of the manner in which visual control and visual inspection of objects associate with impressions of the child's moving hand, forming groups of attributes necessary as the normal child tries to meet society's expectations (e.g., to write his name) and to fulfill his own basic needs (e.g., to tie his shoes).

Several threads may be seen upon study of the pages that follow. For example, I have attempted, when possible, to outline tests that may be used to assess the attributes discussed in the various chapters. Thus, for example, in the body image chapter you will find a survey of most of the available body image tests. I hope through this means to interest researchers in increasing knowledge about various factors related to motor development. These testing techniques are also outlined to clarify statements in the text whose validity and clarity depend to a large degree on the manner in which data have been collected.

Sex differences have been referred to in most of the chapters. Differences in preferences for movement, as well as in manipulative and gross motor skills, have been outlined along with various perceptual differences sometimes seen when boys and girls are compared. Although a separate chapter contrasting boy-girl differences was not included, a text by Maccoby presents these important comparisons in detail (4).

Several terms may be confusing and can be interpreted in several ways, depending on the reader's orientation. The word "movement" itself may be defined in a variety of ways, for indeed most of life's processes involve some kind of movement at some level. The living brain, for example, is never still. A considerable amount of electrical activity continues through the deepest sleep. Emotional behavior is accompanied by endocrine activity and by visceral changes. Silent and "immobile" visual inspection is supported by biochemical and muscular changes within the ocular apparatus. The term "movement" as employed in this text, however, refers to actions observable to others that are supported by the contractions and stabilizing functions of both the larger and smaller skeletal muscles.

Motor performance as used on these pages has a somewhat narrower denotation than does *movement*. Whereas the latter term may encompass gestures and other relatively unstructured actions, *motor performance* refers to the activities inherent in tasks amenable to exact measurement.

The rather global term "perception" also needs to be dealt with in a definitive manner. Perception, as used in the pages that follow, denotes the process of organizing raw sensory data or input, and the term "perceptual efficiency" refers to the accuracy with which various tests of perceptual functioning have been carried out. It is believed to be clearer and more scholarly to refer to specific perceptual attributes emerging from various factorial studies of perception, rather than simply to use the term "perception" in a general way.

The result of these studies suggest that perceptual functioning may be divided into the ways in which individuals mentally organize experience, the speed with which they do so, the way they make selections from among sensory experiences, and the manner in which they modify their perceptual judgments (i.e., perceptual flexibility). These rather global categories may be further divided and related to the manner in which humans deal with specific types of sensory information.

The term "perceptual-motor" is employed in a number of ways in the recent literature. Within this context the term "perceptual-motor" merely denotes the condition in most voluntary acts of a considerable amount of dependency on perceptual abilities. The degree of perceptual involvement in a movement task is dependent on a number of variables, including the age and the past experience of the performer. Factorial studies of how children learn complex coordination tasks generally support the hypothesis that perceptual abilities are more important to progress during the initial stages of learning, whereas later, motor factors (i.e., reaction time, movement speed, measures of kinesthesis) contribute more to performance efficiency (2). Thus, for example, as a child begins to learn to walk, his success is dependent to a large degree on perceptual efficiency, including the accuracy of his visual judgments of the spatial dimensions of the area in which he is walking, of the location of his feet, and of the speed with which the feet are moving. Later, as he reaches early childhood, his ability to walk rapidly, to run, and to otherwise engage in efficient "locomotor" behavior is less dependent on the manner in which he organizes visual data, but rather is more likely to be the result of how fast he can move his feet, how strong his legs are, and how accurately he can judge their positions without the need for constant visual monitoring. Thus his early attempts at walking during the end of his first year may be labeled a "perceptual-motor" task, whereas later, as he moves around his first-grade classroom, walking has become mainly a motor task with little need for the involvement of complex visual-perceptual factors.

In general, the contents of this text deal with "behavior" rather than with the underlying neurological, biochemical, and anatomical bases for behavior. A number of books have attempted to integrate research in neural functioning with behavior, with varying degrees of success, and if the student is interested in this type of material, he may consult references by Konorski (3) and Milner (5). Both of these authors have attempted to relate observable and measurable behavior to neural functioning and to indices of neural maturation. Milner concentrates more on maturational processes. The book by Espenschade and Eckert has also attempted to explain relationships between skeletal-structural changes and movement capacities in the maturing child more completely than has been attempted in this text (1).

Frequent references to concomitant neural changes occurring during infancy and childhood are not found in this book for two reasons: (1) Many of the relationships seen may not be conclusively determined to be causal but may only be paired in time and can be discussed only within various helpful but speculative theoretical "models." (2) I decided to devote this text to observable indices of behavior rather than to the more subtle supportive structures, because, as in all cases when writing a book, of limitations of energy, time, and space.

On reviewing the literature I noted that there are several facets of perceptual, motor, and perceptual-motor development that have been given scant attention by researchers. Largely missing are researches in which motor learning and motor educability have been studied as a function of age. There is little evidence, for example, on just how a child's ability to *acquire* various kinds of skills changes as he matures.

Investigators have not attempted to measure, or compare measures, of kinesthesis obtained from children of various ages. Although it is often considered that possibly the child develops a growing awareness of his body and its functions as he passes from infancy to childhood, there is little evidence that exactly delineates the parameters of that purported change reflected in scores obtained from various measures of "proprioception."

Other factors have received more notice by scholars, but their efforts have at times been inexact and often marred by various theoretical biases they have brought to their laboratories with them. The manner, for example, in which various "drawing" tests are reflective of intellectual function has not been clearly explained, although perhaps this delineation requires a more exact definition of intelligence itself.

As is pointed out in Chapter 8, the lack of cohesive programs in which the factor structure of the perceptual-motor attributes of children may change due to maturation is also apparent upon consulting the available literature. Although I have assumed that somehow the various attribute "families" beget more "children" as a child ages, in the theoretical statements contained in the final chapter, there is not a great deal of "hard" data supporting this contention.

It is also apparent that the researchers collecting data on the motor and perceptual attributes, with few exceptions, have not attempted to locate their efforts within any theoretical framework, nor, upon producing findings, have they attempted to explain them with reference to any old or new conceptual system. These studies are, for the most part, simply descriptions of behavior, which many times are based on relatively poorly defined samples of children within narrow geographical and/or social-cultural confines,* thus making generalizations from the findings most difficult. Despite these limitations of the available studies and the lack of information concerning kinesthetic maturation and changes in skill acquisition, I have attempted to weave a reasonably comprehensive and coherent "rug" of inferences, findings, and clinical observations into a statement about how certain peripheral attributes in infants and children change as they grow older.

It has been my objective to attempt to first outline and discuss recent research findings dealing with perceptual, motor, and perceptual-motor development of infants and children. Furthermore, I have intended to illustrate how in some ways certain perceptual attributes support movement capacities and how in other ways they are independent of each other. Similarly, I have made an effort to illustrate how complex the processes of visual perception and movement are in the maturing child. It is hoped that this latter objective will give chase to some of the simplistic theoretical statements postulated within recent years in which perceptual-motor functioning has been an integral part.

The text was written primarily for educators (physical educators, special educators, and general educators). I believe that achieving movement efficiency is important to the maturing child. I further feel, however, that attempting to change a facet of be-

---

* The campus elementary school has been a favorite playpen for researchers during the years, as indeed I have "played" there occasionally myself.

havior should be preceded by a rather thorough review of the vicissitudes of the behavior one proposes to modify. I hope that the material that follows will prove a firm base from which one may proceed when attempting to structure better programs for the improvement of the motor abilities of children with such difficulties, and for the enrichment of the movement capacities of normal children.

BIBLIOGRAPHY

1 Espenschade, Anna S., and H. M. Eckert, *Motor Development,* Columbus, Ohio: Charles E. Merrill Books, 1967.
2 Fleishman, E. A., "Factorial Analysis of Complex Psychomotor Performance and Related Skills," *J. Appl. Psych.,* **40** (1956), 2.
3 Konorski, Jerzy, *Integrative Activity of the Brain, An Interdisciplinary Approach,* Chicago: University of Chicago Press, 1967.
4 Maccoby, Eleanor E., *The Development of Sex Differences,* Stanford, Calif.: Stanford University Press, 1966.
5 Milner, Esther, *Human Neural and Behavioral Development,* Springfield, Ill.: Charles C Thomas, 1967.

The Beginnings of 2
Movement in Infants

It is a complicated matter to exactly describe the beginnings of motor, perceptual, and perceptual-motor attributes of the human infant. For example, indices of general motor activity in infants may be assessed prior to birth, but of course assessment of perceptual abilities must await birth. Care must be taken, after birth, to differentiate between measures of general activation and scores indicative of some specific kind of motor ability. A similar problem occurs when testing perceptual ability, insofar as it is difficult to separate perceptual from ocular attributes during the first days of life.

It appears, from the available evidence, that indeed infants begin to exercise their movement capacities prior to birth, and that levels of fetal activity are roughly predictive of later motor competency. For example, in 1938 Richards and Newberry recorded fetal activity in 12 infants from one to two weeks prior to birth for five- to six-hour periods and found moderate and positive relationships between the measures obtained and indices of motor development obtained at six months (9). Etta Walters, in a more recent study completed in 1965, also found that prenatal movements, in both duration and intensity, were predictive of motor measures obtained up to the fifth year of life (11).

The classic studies of Fantz and his co-workers have similarly shown that the ability to make perceptual discriminations appears shortly after birth, and other scholars have recently discovered that the human infant displays a remarkably mature set of ocular characteristics during the early days of life. Thus it is apparent that the beginnings of perceptual development are seen near birth, and the first signs of movement characteristics are measurable prior to birth (2).

It appears that general level of activity is a highly individual matter in infants. Irwin, for example, found that the activity levels measured in the more active of 73 infants during the first two weeks of life were 290 times greater than in the least active children within his population (4).* At the same time it is probable that the level of activity evidenced by a newborn child is, to a large degree, genetically determined. Scarr, studying 61 pairs of grade-school twin girls, found that the correlations between measures of reaction time, number of activities selected, number of active games engaged in, and so forth were higher with identical than with fraternal twins (10). She thus concluded that several aspects of activity motivation are inherited.

Meyers and Dingman suggest that by the second year separate cognitive and motor traits can be identified in children and by five an adult pattern of factors begins to emerge (6), whereas Bayley, in a 1968 study, found that only measures of early vocalization could predict later intelligence (the subjects were "followed" from birth to their middle 30's). Indeed she found that the boys who were more active during the 10-to-15-months age period were likely to evidence low verbal ability from ages 4 to 36. The brightest adults were, as infants, according to Bayley, often the more calm and attentive children rather than those who evidenced high levels of motor activity (1).

INFANT REFLEXES

The earliest movements that can be elicited in newborn infants consist of reflexes, involuntary actions triggered by various kinds of external stimuli. Reflexes may be classified in various ways: those involving the total body and its orientation to gravity versus various head and limb movements in which the labyrinths are not involved; those reflexes that are the evolutionary remains of actions seen in animals lower in the phylogenic scale versus the reflexive movements that are later incorporated into the voluntary

---

* A two-dimensional stabilimeter connected with a polygraph was used, with the level of activity recorded in oscillations per minute. Measures were taken for three hours daily. If infants recording over 90 oscillations per minute were removed from the comparison, the most active were 150 times more active than the least active.

movement patterns of older children and adults; and those that differentiate between so-called normal and the pathological motor behavior.

When an infant is born, it is important to determine whether his nervous system is sound by attempting to elicit the expected reflexes. If the reflex is uneven in strength when elicited on both sides of the body or is too weak or too strong, some kind of neurological dysfunction is usually suspected. At the same time, if a "normal" reflex continues to be evidenced for too long a period of time during infancy, or fails to appear at all, the examining physician will probably suspect some type of neurological impairment is present.

Various "pathological reflexes," if present, also indicate the possibility of some kind of irregular neural function. Many of the initial reflexes seen in infants are necessary to sustain life processes between the time the child is no longer nourished within the mother's amniotic fluid and the acquisition of useful voluntary actions. For example, the rooting reflex enables the infant to obtain nourishment as he reflexively turns toward a tactual stimulus applied to his cheek and thus reaches his mother's milk. Other reflexes resemble later voluntary activities. For example, when an infant is placed in certain positions (to be discussed later), he will demonstrate a walking pattern. However, these latter reflexes usually disappear well before their voluntary counterpart is seen.

On the pages that follow only a few of the numerous infantile reflexes will be discussed. Only passing reference will be made to various pathological reflexes. For a more thorough treatment of this topic the reader is referred to texts by Pieper (8) and others (3,5).

THE MORO REFLEX

The Moro reflex (Fig. 2-1) was first elicited by striking the pillow of the infant; subsequently it was found that if the head was shaken quickly, the reflex would appear. When evidencing this reflex, the infant spreads his arms and fingers, and his legs somewhat weakly, and returns both limbs and fingers to a flexed position against the body. At times the infant elicits the reflex as he coughs or sneezes. The beginning of the Moro reflex is opposite to the startle reflex, which is only a flexion without the prior

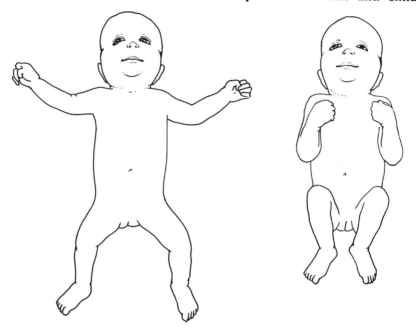

Figure 2-1 The two stages of the Moro reflex.

extension pattern. Also, the Moro reflex can be brought about rapidly and in succession, whereas the startle reflex needs some kind of recovery-from-fright time prior to its being triggered again.

The Moro reflex is seen in the fetus as early as the ninth week after conception and is always present in infants during the first three months of life. If it persists much after the ninth month of life, it may be suggestive of retardation.

TONIC NECK REFLEXES OF THE LIMBS

If the infant's neck is turned, the stretch of the neck muscles triggers an increase of tonus in the limbs on the side toward which the head is facing (Fig. 2-2). The limbs on the other side, in both animals and human infants, usually assume a flexed position.

This reflex is almost always seen in premature babies and during the first week of life in about one half of all normal infants. If it persists, it is taken to be a sign that the higher brain centers are not correctly suppressing the movements mediated by the lower part of the brainstem.

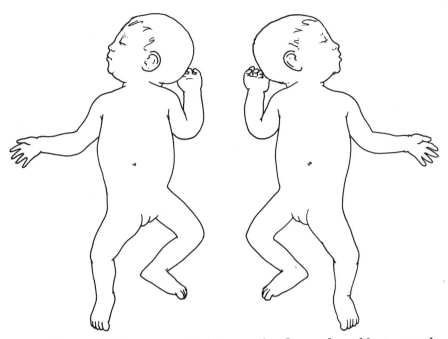

Figure 2-2 The asymmetrical tonic neck reflex, evidenced by increased tonus in the limbs toward which the head is turned.

PALMAR AND PLANTAR GRASP REFLEXES

Touching both palms of the hands and the front part of the bottom of the toes tends to cause flexion of the hands and feet, respectively (Fig. 2-3). This reflex in the hands usually results in a grasping action that excludes the thumb and may be strong enough to support the infant's weight for short periods of time. This reflex has been elicited as early as the eleventh week of gestation and continues in the newborn and becomes progressively stronger between the twelfth day and the third month of life. This reflex usually becomes weaker by the sixth month, disappearing entirely by the end of the first year.

These reflexes are probably the rudimentary remains of the grasping activity that was needed by primate ancestors. Confirming this supposition is the fact that it can be elicited by stroking the palm with a bit of hair. In the palmar reflex, if the infant's hand closes and elicits pressure of much less than 40 gm or more than 120 gm, some kind of neurological dysfunction is usually suspected.

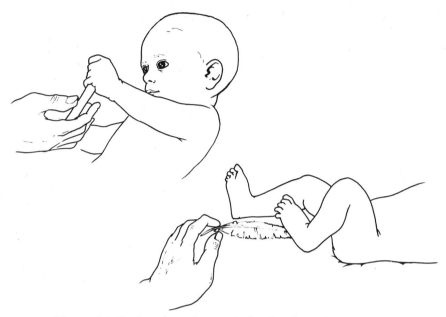

Figure 2-3 Prehensile reflexes of the hands and feet may also be
elicited if the arm is pulled away from the child's body or
if an object is placed in the hand.

"DOLL-EYE MOVEMENTS"

Apparently demonstrating the need of the infant to retain a
stable retinal image are reflexes believed to be triggered by pro-
prioceptors in the neck muscles, in the eyes, and in the otolithic
membranes. In general, if the infant's head is tipped forward, his
eyes will tend to look upward (Fig. 2-4). Similarly, if the head is
held backward, the eyes will look down toward his chin. This
reflex is almost always seen in the premature infant and in normal
infants during the first day of life. In normal infants, however, it
is quickly replaced soon after birth with voluntary eye movements. As with many reflexes, if it persists, it may be indicative
of brain damage.

RIGHTING REFLEXES OF THE HEAD AND BODY

Two related reflexes seen during the first year of life in normal
infants probably contribute to the achievement of later voluntary
turning movements in the crib. One is the neck-righting reflex of

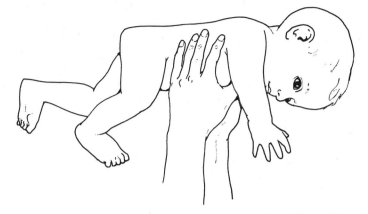

Figure 2-4 "Doll-eye movements." The eyes in this reflex will tend to look upward as the child's head is lowered.

the body, which is elicited by turning the head as the infant is on his back; the trunk will reflexively turn in the same direction (Fig. 2-5). The opposite action, the body-righting reflex of the head, is elicited by turning the legs in one direction, as the child is prone, and eliciting a head-turning movement in the same direction. It is not usual to see this reflex after the first year of life.

THE LABYRINTHINE RIGHTING REFLEX

The labyrinthine righting reflex is seldom seen in the newborn, but it becomes stronger during the middle of the first year. It contributes to the assumption of an upright head and body position and to the child's movement forward during the end of the first year.

Generally the infant evidences this reflex by his tendency to attempt to maintain himself upright by lifting his head upward when the body is tipped downward (Fig. 2-6). Similarly, if the upright infant is held by the shoulders and bent backward, his head will move forward, still attempting to maintain its original position with relation to gravity.

The reflex also may be seen if the upright infant is angled to his left or right. The head tends to maintain the original upright posture with relation to gravity.

This reflex is first seen in about the second month after birth as the infant attempts to look upward while on his stomach. Later the head is aided by the supportive reaction of the arms to the

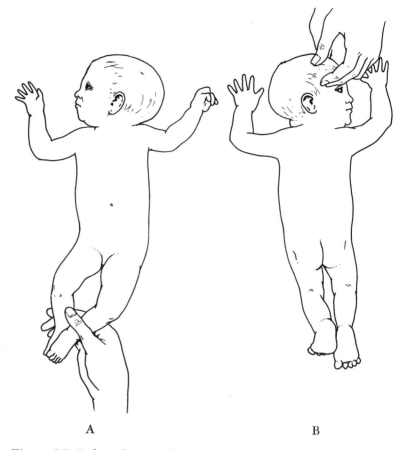

A   B

Figure 2-5 Body-righting reflexes. In *A* the head will turn in the same
direction as the hips are turned. In *B* the hips will turn in
the same direction as the head is moved.

same stimulus as they push on the surface of the crib to permit
the head to remain up for increasing periods of time.

SUPPORTING REACTIONS OF THE ARMS AND LEGS

Similar to the reactions seen in cats, the human infant at about
four months will react when brought toward surfaces by reflexively extending his arms, indicating a readiness to support
himself (Fig. 2-7). By about the ninth month this same reflex
will be seen in the lower limbs as he is lowered toward a surface.
This reflex is dependent on optic stimulation and is absent in the
dark.

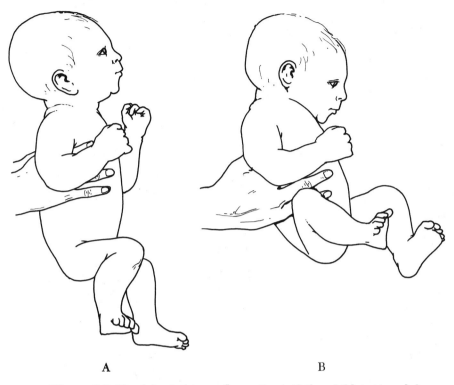

A   B

Figure 2-6 The labyrinthine reflexes. In *A* if the child is tipped forward, his head will remain upright, or backward. In *B*
if the child is tilted backward, the head will remain upright, or forward.

This supporting reflex in the legs may be triggered in one leg
at a time between the ninth and twelfth months if the child's

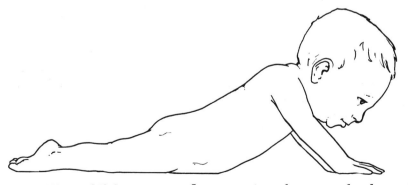

Figure 2-7 Supporting reflex—extension of arms as hands touch a
horizontal surface.

head is turned to one side and then the other, thus eliciting the tonic-neck reflex previously described.

PULL-UP REACTIONS OF THE ARMS

Several months after birth, if held upright by either hand and tipped off to one side or the other, the infant will tend to flex the appropriate arm and try to resume his original upright position (Fig. 2-8). Similarly, if the child is held by either hand and tipped backward, he will flex both arms and attempt to remain upright at the same time. If the infant is held by *both* hands and tipped *forward* from a vertical position, he will evidence the same supporting reaction.

In summary the infant, after the first three or four months, attempts reflexively with his head movements and arm flexions and extensions to maintain an upright posture if placed "off balance" or will try to gain the upright if placed in a front-lying position.

REFLEXIVE LOCOMOTOR, SWIMMING, CRAWLING, AND CLIMBING MOVEMENTS

A number of complicated reflex patterns can be elicited in infants after the first weeks after birth which resemble to a marked degree later voluntary attempts to proceed forward or to climb upward. It has been demonstrated in animals and in humans that these movements are controlled by the spinal cord, with no involvement of the higher brain centers. There seems to be no direct connection in time between these reflexive movements and the infant's later attempts to assume, voluntarily, an upright posture to walk, to swim, and to climb. For example, the so-called "walking reflex" described below terminates in about the fourth to fifth month, whereas voluntary walking does not appear until some time between the ninth and fifteenth months. However, the presence of these interesting reflexes apparently indicates how deeply locomotor activities are ingrained within the human nervous system.

"WALKING REFLEX"

By the end of the second week of life many (about 58 per cent) infants will "walk" if held in an upright position and their feet

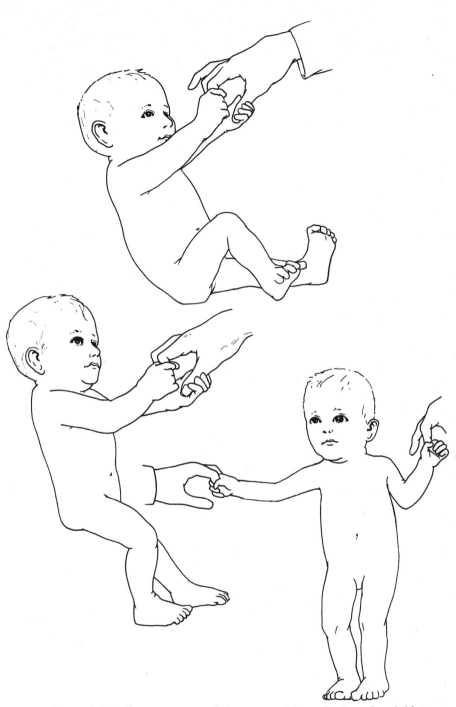

Figure 2-8 Pull-up reactions of the arms evidenced when the child is
placed off balance. He will tend to flex the appropriate
arm or arms to right himself.

19

are permitted to touch a level horizontal surface (Fig. 2-9). This walking pattern involves a distinct knee lift but does not involve other body parts, e.g., an arm swing. The child can be made to "climb" stairs while supported in this manner and can also be

Figure 2-9 Walking reflex (stepping movements as the infant's feet contact small stairs) is elicited either in a horizontal position or when infant is held in an upright position.

made to "walk" while upside down, indicating the lack of involvement of the righting reflex of the labyrinths. As the higher brain centers mature, this reflex disappears and is usually absent by about the fifth month.

"CRAWLING REFLEX"

If the infant is placed face down on a surface and pressure is alternately applied to the bottoms of his feet, he will perform

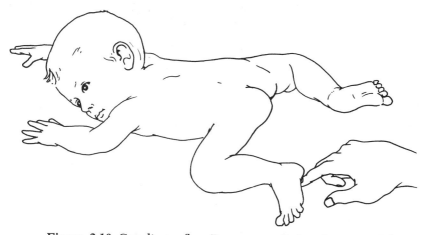

Figure 2-10 Crawling reflex. Pressure applied to bottoms of feet results in a crawling pattern in the arms and legs.

a crawling pattern in his upper and lower limbs (Fig. 2-10). This reflex can be seen at birth and has been elicited in a fetus of seven months' gestation. It usually disappears sometime between the third and fourth months after birth, and there is a distinct time interval between its disappearance and the emergence of voluntary creeping, which occurs sometime between the seventh and ninth months.

Some clinicians have speculated that this reflex is indicative of the remains of a phylogenetic action needed by the primate as he crawled up his mother's stomach to reach her breast.

SWIMMING MOVEMENTS

One of the most interesting reflexes seen in infants is a swimming movement when they are held in or *over* water (Fig. 2-11)! These swimming movements have been filmed by McGraw in infants 11 days old (5). If infants are placed in water, the head must be supported, because they are unable to maintain the head above the water level. These movements are more rhythmic than the previously described crawling movement and usually disappear by about the fifth month of age. These same reflexive swimming movements have also been noted by several experimenters in a number of mammalian species.

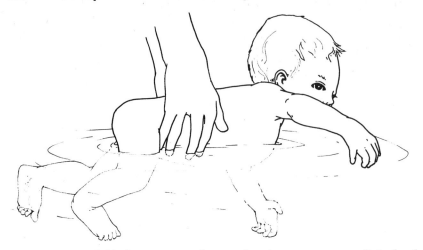

Figure 2-11 Swimming reflex—swimming movements elicited when the infant is exposed to water.

CLIMBING MOVEMENTS

In addition to reflexes that resemble later voluntary attempts to move in a horizontal plane, newborn infants manifest a reflex similar to vertical climbing (Fig. 2-12). With the infant held

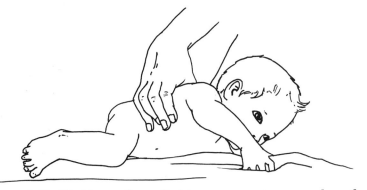

Figure 2-12 Climbing reflex—climbing movements seen when the proper stimuli are present.

vertically, some observers have elicited an alternate upward arm movement and the palmar-grasp reflex in one palm. Some experimenters have noted that reciprocal movements of the legs occur under these circumstances. Others have suggested that this reflex is a remnant of the movement needed by the primate infant to reach the mother's nipple from a position on her lap. Most observers usually place this climbing reflex toward the end of the first year of life and into the second year. It is seemingly associated with the assumption of upright gait and early attempts to walk voluntarily.

VOLUNTARY, INDEPENDENT LOCOMOTION

The various types of independent locomotion are separate from their reflex counterparts. Other reflexes previously described, however, do contribute to some of the initial attempts of the infant to creep and to crawl. Similar to the several-gaited horse, the human infant displays several types of locomotive characteristics at different times. These stages appear at various times in different infants, and their duration depends on both environmental and maturational factors. Most experts, however, suggest that human locomotion is instinctive and triggered through maturational processes even in the absence of environmental supports such as other children to copy or help from a parent.

In the discussion that follows, four types of locomotor behavior will be surveyed. In addition, preceding the section discussing walking, the stages that lead toward an upright stance will be reviewed.

CREEPING

Creeping occurs when the infant has been allowed to remain on his front for prolonged periods of time. In this position the labyrinthine right reflex and the supportive reflex of the arms enable him to look forward. His first attempts to creep, using his arms to pull, are likely to occur as he attempts to reach for an object with both hands at the same time (in the same way he does so while on his back) and fails to touch the object. As his chest and head return to the floor after such an effort, he begins to slide forward and may use his arms to pull himself forward in a series of movements. The legs are usually not involved in early attempts at creeping, and the earlier maturation of the upper part of the body, documented in several types of studies,* is similarly shown in creeping activity.

* For example, studies in which fetal movement is recorded by detectors placed on the mother's abdomen have recorded a significantly greater amount of movement in the upper limbs as compared to the lower ones.

Creeping is usually seen to occur between the fourth month and first year, averaging about the seventh month. Its duration is a highly individual matter and depends on the vigor of the child, the goals he strives to reach, and the surfaces on which he is permitted to creep.

CRAWLING

Crawling develops from creeping. Older infants sometimes prefer to crawl rapidly rather than to walk unsteadily. First attempts to support himself result in a bent-elbow posture, with the feet drawn up under the hips. Later attempts display a strong supportive reflex previously described. Infants who crawl well always move the contralateral extremities in the same direction at the same time, i.e., left arm and right leg (Fig. 2-13). How-

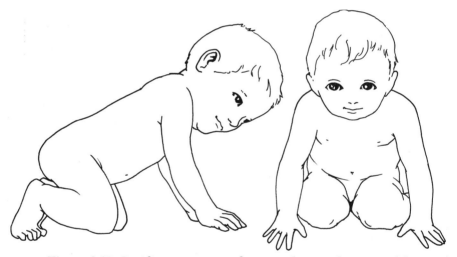

Figure 2-13 Crawling movements begin with a single arm and knee advancing at a time.

ever, before this type of smooth and efficient crawling pattern is manifest, the infant goes through a stage in which only one limb is moved at a time. For example, the left arm will move forward, followed by the right knee; then the right arm will move, and afterward the left knee will inch forward. The pause is usually longer, within the previous sequence, between the movements of the rear leg and the opposite hand than between the first hand movement and the first knee movement. About 20 per cent of all infants move the same side arm and knee when crawling.

Experiments have been conducted in which an infant's lower limbs were restricted during the crawling phase. Despite this restriction (splinting the leg straight, tying both legs together, or similar means), the children persisted in their attempts to move forward. Similarly, when a child has been "taught" to crawl, his success is usually little more than would be expected to occur through maturation.

SLIDING

Some infants develop an unusual method of locomotion involving a slide forward in a seated position, using the heels with which to "dig in." Some use their arms to aid them, and others depend solely on their feet for propulsion in this unusual position. Generally this method is bypassed by the infant as he attempts upright gait immediately after learning to crawl.

STANDING UP

Despite the manner in which the infant learns to creep, and then to crawl, from a front-lying position, he usually begins to assume an upright posture starting from a back-lying position. By the fourth or fifth month of life an infant has learned to turn over from his back to his stomach by first turning the head, which permits the body to follow, probably by eliciting the body-righting reflex previously described.

The first attempts to turn from front to back can be explained by a chaining together of several reflexes. An ocular-following reflex is triggered as the infant is attracted by a moving object and follows it with his head and eyes. This, in turn, elicits the body- or the head-righting reflex (depending on whether he started on his stomach or back), and in this manner he turns over in spite of himself.

If the infant is on his stomach, he begins to reach for objects and to bring his feet under his body, as described previously, and he finishes on his back. By about the seventh month, he tries to sit up for increasingly longer periods of time, and by the tenth month he may succeed in sitting. His first attempts to sit unaided will sometimes meet with failure if his arms continue to flail at objects that attract his attention, thus disturbing his balance.

Having assumed a seated position, he will continue to attempt to gain the upright, depending on the presence of social reinforcers such as opportunities to hang onto furniture and other convenient handholds. He may then proceed to walk, supporting himself constantly with his hands.

By the twelfth to fifteenth month the child will be able to rise to a standing position from a back-lying position without external aid. This difficult skill is mastered usually a month or two after he begns to perform an independent upright gait.

UPRIGHT GAIT

After the infant has pulled himself upright, sometime between the tenth and fifteenth month, he begins to move laterally around the periphery of his handholds (e.g., the coffee table). His first attempts at unsupported forward steps are sometimes frustrated by his own excitement, and he may fall to the floor. Early attempts at upright steps in infants are characterized by a wide stance, giving him a wider base of support; the feet are turned outward, and the knees are slightly flexed, as seen in our simian ancestors. Similarly, the first steps taken by the infant are not regular, nor are they accompanied by regular reciprocal arm movements.

His spine is flat during his first attempt to walk, but with continued practice the typical lower lumbar curve seen in the mature child becomes apparent.

Studies with birds, animals, and infants who were not permitted the opportunity to observe others of their species move in their characteristic manner suggest that human locomotion is probably an innate and not a learned skill. Although environmental supports such as the interested parent and available furniture can be expected to accelerate the acquisition of a child's walking skills to a slight degree, attempting to force him to walk before his nervous system is mature enough to perform its task is as likely to be unsuccessful in *accelerating* his progress as is the attempt to somehow delay his progress in walking by imposing restrictions on his efforts.

SUMMARY

In general the available experimental and observational clinical literature suggests that the infant manifests a number of kinds of reflexes that, although resembling locomotor activities, are different from them and are also separated from them by a time interval. Some of these reflexes, however, such as the supporting and labyrinthine righting reflexes, contribute in direct ways to the assumption of an upright posture and thus to erect locomotion.

Upright gait is preceded by several other stages that may appear for varying periods of time in individual infants or may be absent entirely. The prewalking activities include creeping, crawling, and sliding.

Upright locomotion, although hastened by various environmental factors, seems largely the outcome of the readiness of neural maturation. Accurate limb and body movement follows a general progression of head to foot development. Initially only the head, neck, and arm regions function with accurate voluntary control. For example, in creeping the legs are frequently not involved, and prebirth movements occur more often in the upper part of the fetus's body. In crawling and walking control of the arms seems also to precede the development of accurate control of the legs.

DEVELOPMENTAL TRENDS

Three trends in the motor development of infants and children are frequently cited in the literature. It is often written, for example, that the development of voluntary control proceeds from the head to the feet, often termed a "cephalocaudal" progression. It is also frequently stated that control of the larger muscles precedes the acquisition of control of the smaller muscles. The third principle asserts a general tendency for children to mature in a proximal-distal manner, i.e., for motor functions closer to the midline of the body to become more accurate than those farther away.

It seems to me, however, that these principles need to be carefully evaluated using current available research data as reference points. For example, it is obvious that a child's hands have response capacities that radically exceed those of the feet; thus to compare the acquisition of hand control to that of foot control involves contrasting highly dissimilar portions of the infant's action system. It is true that a child seems able to control head movements before arm movements, and these in turn appear to become more proficient prior to leg movements. It is equally true, however, that the child's controlling eyes are located nearer his hands than his feet, and that the response capacities of the upper and lower limbs are not alike.

Concerning the statement that "fine" control follows the acquisition of control of the larger muscles, again a thorough consideration should be made of the available evidence concerning visual-manual and locomotor and trunk control. For example, innumerable studies indicate that although minimal control of the trunk muscles is seen earlier than accurate hand-eye control, a satisfactory case could be made for the fact that upper-limb control and gross-motor control develop in relatively parallel and equal ways. Hand regard is seen as early as the third month of age, but locomotor activity does not occur until about the twelfth month.

Thus the evidence suggests that these three principles should be examined in detail before they are accepted without question. In general they are true some of the time, if careful delineation of the fine or gross motor control attributes under consideration is clearly made. Head and neck control clearly precedes the acquisition of hand and leg control; however, leg and arm control are not really comparable components of the infant action system owing to the differences in proximity to the visual system and to the aforementioned dissimilarities in their basic response capacities. Thus the evidence suggests that the principle of cephalo-caudal development is more valid than are the second and third principles. Further clarification of the evidence for these three axioms should occur upon consideration of the data in the chapters that follow.

Approximate Time Behavior Occurs	Behavior Indicative of the Orgins of Movement in Infants
Gestation	Moro reflex appears
	Fetal activity prior to birth indicative of later motor competency and vigor
Birth	Birth reflexes, including Moro, startle, palmar grasp, rooting, crawling reflex, etc.

	Seeks novel stimuli, variable activity levels evidenced
	Walking reflex seen
30 days	
	Arm-supporting reflex seen
60 days	Labyrinthine righting reflex appears
	Separate perceptual-motor and cognitive traits identifiable
90 days	Pull-up reactions in the arm (reflex)
	Walking reflex terminates
	Infant can turn over from back to stomach
6 months	Moro reflex terminates
	Voluntary creeping appears
	Swimming reflex disappears
	Voluntary crawling appears
	Crawling reflex disappears
9 months	Supporting reflex in the legs seen
	Palmar and plantar grasp reflexes disappear
	Righting reflexes of the head and body disappear
12 months	
	Supported walking
	Can arise from a back-lying position to a standing position, independent locomotion

BIBLIOGRAPHY

1 Bayley, Nancy, "Behavioral Correlates of Mental Growth—Birth to Thirty-Six Years," *Amer. Psych.*, **23** (Jan. 1968), 117.

2 Fantz, Robert L., "Pattern Discrimination and Selective Attention as Determinants of Perceptual Development from Birth," in *Perceptual Development in Children*, H. Kidd Aline

and Jeanne L. Rivoire (eds.), New York: International Universities Press, 1966.

3 Illingworth, R. S., *The Development of the Infant and Young Child,* London: E. & S. Livingstone, Ltd., 1967.

4 Irwin, O. C., "Amount of Mobility of 73 Newborn Infants," *J. Comp. Psych.,* **14** (1932), 415.

5 McGraw, M. B., *The Neuromuscular Maturation of the Human Infant,* New York: Hafner Publishing Co., 1966.

6 Meyers, C. E., and Harvey F. Dingman, "The Structure of Abilities at the Preschool Ages: Hypothesized Domains," *Psych. Bull.,* **57** (1960), 514–32.

7 Milner, E., *Human Neural and Behavioral Development,* Springfield, Ill.: Charles C Thomas, 1967.

8 Pieper, Albrecht, *Cerebral Function in Infancy and Childhood,* New York: Consultants Bureau, 1963.

9 Richards, T. W., and H. Newberry, "Studies in Foetal Behavior," *Child Dev.,* **2** (1938), 79.

10 Scarr, Sandra, "Genetic Factors in Activity Motivation," *Child Dev.,* **37** (1966), 663–73.

11 Walters, C. Etta, "Prediction of Post-Natal Development from Foetal Activity," *Child Dev.,* **33** (1965), 801–808.

Gross Motor Attributes **3**
in Early Childhood

Toward the end of the first year of life the child is usually beginning to walk. His motor behavior undergoes marked changes during this time in his life, and as he enters the second year he will begin to show a number of variations in his locomotor activities; he will usually begin to jump, to run, and to hop. At the same time he will show the beginnings of skills that will later be developed to high levels in childhood and adolescence. During his second year he will begin to handle play equipment and balls if they are made available to him.

During his third and fourth years he will usually begin to manifest the beginnings of social interactions at play (see Chap. 9), and a variety of individual differences will modify the manner in which the child is observed to move. The obese child of nursery school age performs in a different manner than his thinner peer (47). Children will begin to evidence differences due to play experiences to which they are exposed, whereas several observers have noted both subtle and obvious differences in the manner in which little boys and girls appear to move and to perform skills (49).

These years represent a period of experimentation on the part of young children. They are learning how to learn motor skills, and thus they will often exhibit a variety of ways of performing relatively simple motor tasks. This variability of "work methods" makes it difficult for experimenters to collect reliable data during these ages. The test and tester may be reliable, but their young subjects are not. For example, when throwing accuracy is tested, the preschool child will sometimes launch it underhand and at other times side-arm, while occasionally adopting an overhand pattern of throwing (Fig. 3-1).

Figure 3-1 Initial attempts at throwing are marked by variability, as is true with other motor skills on the part of the preschool child.

During this period the child will begin to display various asymmetries in the manner in which he moves. Hand preference becomes apparent in most children, and ear and eye preference are also measurable. The child will prefer to hop on one foot consistently and in other ways establish movement characteristics that will tend to persist into childhood and adulthood (3,7,13,14, 17).

His movements toward the end of the first five years will become more integrated. He may begin to jump with his arms and to throw with the proper weight shift. By the end of his fifth year additional movement capacities will emerge, although he cannot rhythmically hop very well, skipping is not mastered until another year or more passes, and his abilities to throw accurately and to catch small balls both remain relatively undeveloped.

Overall, however, the first five years of life present a time of marked changes. The infant begins to assume the physical dimensions of a child; he becomes independent to a marked degree in various self-care skills, and his early attempts at making sounds have proliferated into a reasonably extensive vocabulary. The round toddler becomes a linear runner. The child of four or five will often substitute thought for movement, and at the same time he gets ready to begin school and to learn to read and to write. His movement abilities have multiplied, and the several channels of development (see Chap. 11) have "sprouted" numerous branches. In this chapter the child's ability to engage in activities involving the larger skeletal muscles is examined in some detail. His manual abilities when dealing with objects and his early attempts at scribbling and drawing are outlined in Chapters 6 and 7.

MATURATION AND LEARNING

A number of studies often cited in summaries of the literature have been carried out with twins in which an attempt has been made to determine whether instruction can significantly alter motor skill acquisition or whether maturational factors seem to predominate. Gesell and Thompson report, for example, the results of attempting to teach one of a pair of twins block handling and climbing activities over a period of six weeks (16). The training was begun toward the end of their first year of life (46 weeks). At the end of the training period the twins were observed for an additional period of time. It was found that the twin who had not been given special training progressed more during the three weeks following the experimental period than did the "trained" twin during the six weeks he was exposed to special instruction. Studies in which children have purportedly been trained to excel in more precise skills have produced similar results. For example, Hicks and Ralph (20) found that children between two and three years of age who were trained in the Porteus Maze task did no better after seven weeks of training than did an untrained group; in fact the untrained group improved more during the duration of the experiment.

The importance of maturation in the acquisition of movement attributes is further underlined by the findings of the study by Hilgard in which two-year-olds were exposed to special training in ladder climbing, buttoning tasks, and the use of scissors for a period of 12 weeks (23). A matched group of controls who were given no training produced scores comparable to those of the trained group after only one week of practice at the termination of the experimental period (23).

A longitudinal study of the now famous twins, Jimmy and Johnny, by McGraw involving special training in a variety of climbing tasks produced somewhat conflicting results. Purposely selecting the twin who apparently lagged somewhat behind his brother in development, McGraw reported that the trained child appeared to change significantly and he developed locomotor and climbing abilities superior to those of his untrained brother, despite the fact that both started walking at the same time (35).

Minerva also attempted to determine whether training or maturation contributed most to motor development by cotwin control methods in a study carried out in the 1930's (38). Initially Minerva compared the performance of four sets of identical twins and the scores of six fraternal twins on a series of motor tasks including jumping over a cord, throwing accuracy (at a distance of about 3 ft), and ball-rolling accuracy. The twins were four and one-half years old. This preliminary testing produced the finding that in general the throwing task and the jumping task were remarkably similar in the identical-twin pairs, and the purportedly more complex task of ball rolling did not show the influence of the identical inherited characteristics of the identical twins.

After this initial testing Minerva selected one from each group and gave them a six-month period of motor training involving a variety of tasks, including the ones initially tested for. At the end of this period of time, when the children were about five, it was found that natural improvement in the more complex throwing tasks proceeded more slowly in the untrained subjects than in the trained twins. Jumping, on the other hand, did not evidence much improvement because of training. Minerva concluded that the more complex tasks are modifiable through training, but the more basic locomotor functions are not (38).

I have conducted a study the results of which point to the validity of Minerva's conclusions. Using father-son scores in motor ability tests collected while both were freshmen at Pomona College, it was found that moderate-to-high father-son correlations were obtained when the results of their broad jumping and 100-yd-dash scores were compared. On the other hand, the more complex ball-throwing and vaulting scores when analyzed revealed no similar relationship (6).

Data from investigations on the effects of inordinate deprivation of movement experiences of children in early childhood have produced similar results. For example, Dennis found that constricting the movements of Indian children by attaching them to their mother's backs apparently exerted little effect on their subsequent attempts to learn to walk (9,10).

It thus appears that despite reasonably restricting conditions and lack of special training children will generally display the emergence of basic locomotor attributes at the expected ages. More complex activities, including throwing, are probably more modifiable with special attention. In general it has been found in Los Angeles that the children from culturally deprived environments, although not usually deficient in gross motor activities, often demonstrate a lag in abilities needed when drawing, or engaging in fine manipulations. With further investigation the exact determinants of the manner in which training may modify different abilities in different children of various types may be found.

GROWTH, STRUCTURAL, AND POSTURAL CHANGES

A number of structural, muscular, and postural changes occur in children between the ages of one and five that exert important influences on their movement capacities and potentials.

The bent-kneed walk, with the feet wide apart, for example, changes to a marked degree as the legs prove more able to support the body weight with the knee locked during the second and third years of life. By the fifth year the child can stand and walk with straight legs. From the first to fifth year the length of the body increases, as reflected in both long-bone and trunk growth. Generally, girls seem to mature more rapidly, as reflected in their longer legs and arms, although boys are about 4 per cent heavier than girls in this age period. The child's head height contributes less and less to his total body height during these years. At the age of two his proportionately large head contributes about one fourth of his total height, and by the age of five and one-half it is only about one sixth of his total height.

Differences in body-build proportions are apparent during this period of life, and Walker, among others, has confirmed the expected finding that body build is related to motor proficiency even in the nursery school child (47).

The overall growth rate of the child decelerates during the years one through five. In general, about twice as much growth occurs between the ages of one and three as occurs between the ages of three and five. After the age of five, however, the rate levels off to a marked degree, until the pubertal "spurt" occurs following late childhood.

These growth, postural, and structural changes influence performance to a marked degree. As the head becomes relatively smaller, the child's performance in balance tasks is undoubtedly facilitated. As his legs get longer, he becomes able to engage in a larger variety of accurate locomotor activities, and as his shoulders widen and his arms lengthen, he becomes able to throw with greater mechanical efficiency.

PREDICTION OF MOTOR, EMOTIONAL, AND INTELLECTUAL ATTRIBUTES

An increasing number of investigators have followed children from birth to maturity, and some of them have focused on the manner in which early indices of perceptual-motor functioning or generalized motor activity may be used to predict later intellectual, motor, and/or emotional ratings. In general, their findings suggest that general behavior tendencies are often predictable for adulthood and late adolescence from an assessment of behavior in infancy and during the preschool years; on the other hand, it is apparent that more specific measures of later intelligence are not reflected in various batteries of psychomotor tests administered early in life.

For example, Honzik *et al.,* investigating the "stability of mental test performance" between various age groups, found no highly predictive correlations between early measures of psychomotor competency and scores collected in intelligence tests later in life (25). Even between the ages of two and five years the correlation between scores was only +.32. Bloom, summarizing this literature, suggests that not until the age of eight years are children's I.Q. measures likely to be correlated with later intellectual measures. It is thus apparent that whatever is measured in tests of childhood efficiency administered early in life is different from the traits sampled in late childhood and adolescence.

General activity level in children was investigated by Scarr in a recent study (40). She first suggested that tendencies to activity in children might be divided into several subcategories, including measures of reaction time, the number of activities engaged in during a specific time interval, the number of active games chosen by children, as well as measures of anxiety and patience. As she found that the pairs of measures of these kinds collected from identical twins were more highly correlated than the scores on those measures made by fraternal twins, the author concluded that "activity level" and "tendencies for vigorous action" are largely inherited.

The findings of the interesting study titled *Birth to Maturity* seem to support the assertions made by Scarr. Inspection of data collected from a survey of samples of parent-child behavior by 89 children for a period of 25 years resulted in conclusions that tendencies toward passivity on the part of some of the boys studied during their nursery school years were reflected in different occupational choices and relatively passive kinds of behavior later in life. These boys tended to pick "intellectual" rather than "physical" occupations, and in other ways were significantly different from children who were observed to be vigorous in their playing protocols in the nursery school playground (28).

Kagan and Moss (28), the authors of this study, reported an interesting "sleeper effect" that was apparent in their findings. It was noted that behavioral tendencies measured during the school years (from the ages of 6 to 14) in no way either reflected nursery school activity levels or predicted adult behavior. The classroom seemed to have a restraining effect on their subjects, and the action patterns seemed repressed and relatively similar. Generally the groups identified earlier as either vigorous or passive were not significantly different from each other in the vigor levels they displayed during these middle years of childhood.

In one of the more detailed longitudinal studies of human development recently completed by Bayley, a number of early behavioral indices were tested to find out whether they were predictive of later indices of intellectual competency and emotional stability. Fifty-four subjects were tested from birth to their thirty-sixth year of life. During the first 15 months they were evaluated monthly, and after that evaluation was less frequent (2).

In general infantile behavior was found to consist of six separate measurable attributes including:

1. Visual following—seen during the second to third month.
2. Social responsiveness—evaluated between the third and seventh months.
3. Perceptual interest—seen from the first to third and fifteenth to seventeenth month.

Figure 3-2 Activity level may be evaluated in a number of ways, including the duration of time spent and energy expended in instrumented activity rooms as shown in *A*, and in situations which are instrumented with force platforms (*B*) in which the number of squares the child "visits" is recorded.

4. Manual dexterities—evaluated during the fourth to seventh month.
5. Vocalizations—seen developing from the fifth to fourteenth month.
6. Object relations—found between the tenth to seventeenth month.

It was found that only early vocalization demonstrated any clear-cut correlation with later I.Q. scores, and this occurred only in the case of the girls. The brighter men, it was found, displayed a tendency to be relatively calm, as babies. Active male babies tended to score high in various tests of intelligence administered in infancy but produced lower scores on intellectual tests taken later in life (2).

In summary, these types of data suggest that attempting to predict adult characteristics from early indices of any type is an extremely tenuous undertaking. Since it is obvious that infants possess response capabilities different from those of adults, it should be equally apparent that when evaluating infants, children, adolescents, and adults relatively dissimilar measures must be employed. There are a lot of data, found in several places in this text, that indicate that human attribute patterns tend to proliferate as a function of age (Chap. 11). Taken together it is plain that comparing different measures of different attributes obtained from human subjects whose neuromotor and cognitive functions exhibit increasing variability and which change with maturity should not be expected to yield high correlations, if sampled at various times as they mature.

There are basic motor indices of normal neural maturation sought in every maturing infant and child. However, it is not very accurate to suggest that the many subtle facets of total human personality emerging later in life are highly predictable from these early movement, perceptual, and perceptual-motor assessments.

EMERGING HAND, EYE, AND FOOT PREFERENCES

All mobile organisms move in an asymmetrical manner if external cues are removed. Also, animals up and down the phylogenic scale, even using vision, tend to evidence various asymmetries of function. The rat shows paw preference that cannot be eradicated; the grasshopper has his favorite scratching leg; and the lowly mealworm will move in a spiral manner if his eyes are covered (7).

It is thus not surprising that the human infant and child will begin to manifest various asymmetrical ways of moving, seeing, and hearing. Hand preference and eye preference have been the subjects of much scientific and pseudoscientific speculation during the past 40 years.

Separating fact from fallacy is not an easy matter, for these preferences represent complex qualities within the human action system. For example, some speak of hand dominance as indicative of the side of the cortex controlling most or many of life's functions. In truth, however, most authorities feel that hand preference bears little relationship to cerebral control of speech, and that changing hand preference in a child will probably exert little influence over other perceptual, verbal, auditory, or cognitive functions (13,15,19).

At the same time hand, eye, and foot preferences are interesting and important to study for what they reveal about human action. The culture usually demands that, by the age of five or six, a child write his letters and numbers, and for these tasks he must choose only one of his hands. As he learns to throw, again a single hand must be employed, and kicking a ball also requires some decision concerning leg use.

The research indicates that hand and foot and eye preferences in children have several dimensions. For example, the emergence of these unilateral tendencies might be considered on a time scale. In general, most authorities believe that hand preference emerges quite early in life and is seen as children begin to swipe at objects during their third and fourth months. For example, Lippman found that reaching responses of children by the age of one year were usually (72 per cent) carried out with the right hand (33). These preferences may not be as marked as the child begins to learn to walk and must attend to his feet, but by the age of six, hand preference is well established in some children, and they are reasonably consistent in hand usage for given tasks (14,15).

It has been hypothesized that this early emergence of hand preference is related to the side toward which the infant habitually moves his head when exhibiting the tonic neck reflex; however, inspection of the data concerning the percentage of time the reflex is seen to the left and to the right indicates that the division is about equal, whereas about 90 per cent of all children are usually seen to utilize their right hands in manipulative tasks.

Most authorities believe that hand preference is both inherited, probably a mendelian recessive trait, and to a lesser degree molded by the culture as the child matures (19). Substantiating the first statement is the fact that about 42 per cent of all children with left-handed parents are left-handed; about 17 per cent of the children from marriages in which one of the parents is left-handed swing from the starboard side; and only about 2 per cent of the children from marriages of right-handed parents are left-handed.

Data suggesting that these inherited preferences are also molded by the culture are derived from studies of handedness at various ages that showed that there is a tendency to find a decrease in left-handedness in older children and adolescents and adults when contrasted to hand use in younger children (19). In addition, it has been found that older children are less likely to perform tasks with their left hands in tests of hand preference where performance might elicit social censure (22).

Hand preference, however, is not easily evaluated. Most children and adults usually fail to exhibit consistent hand preference in all one-handed tasks to which they are exposed. Rather it is usually found that individuals exhibit degrees of handedness and will perform some tasks with one hand and other activities with the other. Some evaluative scales have rated hand preference on a seven-point scale (19), from those who are completely left-handed, through various degrees of unilateral hand preference, to individuals who are right-handed in everything they do.

Eye preference also seems inherited, upon comparing father-mother preferences with those exhibited by their children, and yet at the same time there is likely to be little correspondence between hand and eye preference. About 50 per cent of normal children are what is termed "cross-dominant" (exhibiting left eye–right hand preferences, or the reverse), and the other 50 per cent of a normal population of children evidence same eye-hand preference. Although some clinicians writing in the 1930's speculated that cross-dominance was indicative of some kind of perceptual and/or intellectual malfunctioning, more recent research data illuminating these relationships are not supportive of this type of global assertion (3). A more thorough discussion of the relationship of hand-eye preferences to educational problems is found in Chapter 10.

Leg preference it not usually as marked as is hand preference, and yet it is more likely to correspond to hand usage than is eye preference. At times children will be seen to kick and otherwise engage in *learned* motor skills with one foot and yet, when given general directions to hop on one foot or to stand on one foot, they may evidence a *preference* for the other foot. Lack of perfect correspondence between leg use in various tasks is reflected in the findings of studies by Keogh (30) and Jenkins (26). About 94 per cent of their subjects preferred to kick with their right foot, only about 65 per cent used their right foot when engaging in hopping tasks of various kinds.

There are persistent findings that suggest that left-handedness may in some way be indicative of some kinds of minimal or moderate neuromotor problems.* For example, Flick has produced findings based on the assessment of 453 children that suggest that children who are left-eyed and -handed perform poorly on perceptual-motor and intellectual tasks. A greater incidence of ambidexterity and left-handedness is usually found in groups of retarded children than in normal children (13). However, it is difficult to determine whether retarded children have difficulty remembering which hand they are accustomed to using when performing various tasks because of their inability to retain the *concept* of a left and right hand, or whether fluctuations in hand use are actually linked with subtle neurological processes that are in turn related to mental or perceptual functioning.

Further clouding an assessment of the information dealing with hand, eye, and foot preferences is the fact that these attributes are evaluated in a number of ways, some of which may elicit different findings. Care must be taken, for example, when evaluating handedness to present reasonably difficult one-handed tasks to the child tested, or he is likely to evidence a 50-50 hand preference in simple tasks (i.e., picking up something placed directly in front of him). Eye preference has been evaluated using a number of measures, some of which are of questionable validity and reliability. The difficulties in determining leg use have been previously discussed. Therefore, when drawing conclusions concerning the manner in which an individual child or group of children is performing, one must take into consideration the quality of the evaluative devices employed.

In summary, the research suggests that hand, eye, and foot preferences are extremely complex manifestations of a number of relatively independent asymmetries inherent in the human action system. These preferences emerge relatively early in the life of a child, and often appear and disappear in cycles during the first years of life. Eye, hand, and foot preferences seem, initially, to be determined by heredity and are later molded by subtle social and cultural pressures. It would seem that affixing sinister clinical diagnoses to children who evidence purported

* The author's left-handedness has been linked to dyslexia in recent years by innumerable proofreaders.

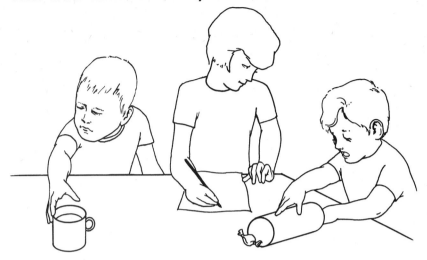

Figure 3-3

cross-dominance is less than sound, as is attempting to remedy perceptual, motor, and intellectual malfunctions by attempting to alter hand, eye, and foot use (Chap. 10).

LOCOMOTION, VARIATIONS, AND EXPLORATIONS

STAGES IN THE DEVELOPMENT OF WALKING BEHAVIOR

The initial attempts of the infant to walk are marked by wide-spaced feet and an irregular rhythm. He seems to have difficulty in balancing his large head on his body, as his body is unaccustomed to maintaining the upright position. The toes usually turn outward to further enhance his balance. Many times he will prefer to maintain his more efficient crawl than to exert the effort to walk. Generally, the more wiry baby will walk earlier than the more obese baby. Girls will usually walk before boys.

As walking proficiency is gained, the child begins to assume a narrower and more rhythmical gait, and he places his feet straight ahead with the heel of one foot directly in front of the toes of the other foot. The walking rhythms of children of approximately two years of age have been measured, and they generally assume a pattern of about 170 steps per minute, with the steps about half the length of those seen in adults (1,12).

The child of two years of age must visually monitor his walk, and he continually watches the placement of his feet so that he will be able to deal with obstacles in his path by circumventing them. By the age of three years, however, he will walk without the need for close visual inspection of his moving feet.

Efficient walking is seen in the child as his balance becomes better. His arm action is integrated into the alternate rhythm of his feet placement, and leg strength and ability to lock the knees are gained during the support phase of the gait cycle.

VARIATIONS IN LOCOMOTION

Soon after learning to walk the child will often attempt to vary the manner in which he moves in an upright position. By about the middle of his second year he will become able to walk sideward and will do so from time to time. A little later he may decide to walk backward occasionally.

At times the child will be seen to walk on his tiptoes when he is first gaining an upright walking posture; however, it is not common to see this modification until the middle of the second year. During his third year of life he may be seen to seek vertigo by spinning and becoming dizzy.

RUNNING

The child of 18 months will often be seen to evidence a somewhat hurried walk that resembles a run. This is not a genuine run, however, because the child's leg power and balance do not permit him to leave the ground with both feet at the same time.

Between the ages of two and three years the child will evidence a true run but will generally lack the ability to efficiently start and stop quickly. But by the ages of four and one-half or five years his running ability will increase markedly, and a good reciprocal arm action will be seen in the running pattern.

By the age of five years a child will evidence the ability to run with reasonable speed. The average velocity measured in a number of studies of five-year-old children suggests that they can travel approximately 11.5 ft per second (26).

JUMPING

As in his first attempts to run, the young child remains in contact with the ground with one foot when he first tries to jump. He will usually be seen at approximately 18 months of age to step off low objects. Shortly afterward the child will step off with

Figure 3-4 Progression in running proceeds in a reasonably predictable manner from the second to the sixth year.

one foot and will remain momentarily suspended in the air for a short period of time.

The child will employ the two-feet take-off at about two years of age, and initially this will be accompanied by a retraction of the arms to the rear rather than by the more efficient arm swing forward as is seen in older children. Jumping over barriers will occur after the child begins to jump down from low heights. Guttridge has found that approximately 42 per cent of preschool children can jump well by the age of three years and that approximately 72 per cent may be considered reasonably skillful jumpers by four and one-half years of age (18).

Data collected from five-year-old children reveal that on the average the children can broad-jump a distance of almost 3 ft, using a two-feet take-off and landing. Girls are slightly less able in this task than are boys. When asked to jump over a low hurdle, again using a two-feet take-off, five-year-old children can usually clear a height of about 1 ft. The means vary from 10.25 in. to 14.4 in. In the hurdle jump the scores posted by the girls are likely to be equal to those achieved by the boys.

HOPPING, SKIPPING, GALLOPING

One-foot hopping, skipping, and galloping are other variations of locomotor abilities evidenced by children as they pass from

Figure 3-5 First attempts at jumping involve a one-foot step-down as shown (A). Then the child will engage in a two-foot take-off (B) and later become able to jump over obstacles with a one-foot (C), and later a two-foot take-off and landing (D).

infancy to the school years. It is sometimes found that these tasks are sex-linked: boys may prefer to gallop while feeling that skipping is too feminine for them to attempt; on the other hand, girls sometimes skip well but have not experimented with the more forceful-appearing masculine activity of galloping.

Hopping

Hopping may be performed in place on one foot, in an alternate manner from foot to foot, and for a distance, as in the frequently employed 50-ft hop test administered to children.

By the age of three and one-half years most children can hop from one to three steps on their preferred foot if no evidence of either precision (hopping into squares), rhythm (alternate hopping from foot to foot), or distance is required of them. By the age of four years most children can hop from four to six steps on one foot, and by five years of age the number of consecutive hops is usually extended to between eight and ten.

Rhythmic hopping, however, executed as the child is required to pass from foot to foot without hesitation, is more difficult, and few (approximately 10 per cent of all five-year-old boys and a slightly greater percentage of the girls at this age) can execute even a simple two hops–two hops rhythm, moving from the right foot to the left foot without breaking the rhythm pattern (30,31).

By the age of five years, however, many children have gained the necessary endurance, balance, and strength to enable them to hop for some distance at a reasonably rapid speed. Most can hop 50 ft in about ten and one-half seconds. Sex differences are also seen in this type of hopping task, with the girls excelling the boys. They will usually traverse 50 ft, hopping on one foot about 3.4 seconds faster than the boys; and at the same time more than 80 per cent of the girls exposed to this task by researchers have completed 50 ft successfully, whereas only from 62 to 69 per cent of the boys have been able to do so (24,30).

The precision with which five-year-old children can hop forward for a distance of 15 ft has also been evaluated by Holbrook, Keogh, and Stott (24,30,43). The scoring was the percentage passing and the percentage failing to execute this task using both the right and the left feet in different trials. Failure was also scored if a child deviated from the 18-in.-wide pathway that he was to follow, and if he evidenced an extensive amount of hand-arm movements to maintain his balance during his two traversals.

As in the other tasks outlined that required precise hopping movements, the girls were found to be superior to the boys by the age of five years. The ability to hop accurately on both feet in separate traversals was usually found to be too difficult for most five-year-old boys, with only about 37 per cent passing, whereas the majority of girls of the same age found the task relatively easy, with about 73 per cent passing. Approximately three times more boys than girls were found in one study of this type of task to be unable to hop on either foot. Most children of this age, however, seem to be able to discern which is their best hopping foot with little difficulty when confronted with this type of task.

Skipping and Galloping

These more complex variations of forward-hopping patterns are sometimes seen in children as young as four years of age. However, skills in both skipping and galloping are not generally achieved until about six and one-half years of age (Chap. 8). Guttridge, however, observed rudimentary galloping by approximately 43 per cent of the four-year-old children she studied (18).

Early attempts at skipping during the fourth and fifth years usually take the form of skipping on one foot and of walking on the other foot. Only approximately 20 per cent of the five-year-old children observed in the various investigations are usually found to evidence the ability to skip with proficiency.

BALANCE

A number of balance tasks have been presented to children during the preschool years. These include line-walking (dynamic balance), beam-walking, and posturing on one foot while standing either on the floor or on a narrow beam with the arms and/or body held in various positions. Balance is a rather common measure of the "health" of the nervous system employed in neurological examinations of children. It generally reflects the efficiency and the integration of the muscular system (particularly the reflexes that enable children to unconsciously adjust their postures to the upright), of ocular control, and of the vestibular apparatus (inner ear).

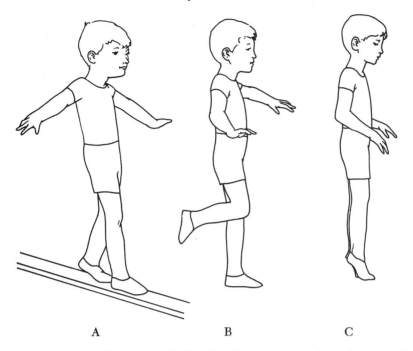

A   B   C

Figure 3-6 Balancing ability has been evaluated in beam-walking tasks as shown (A), as well as in the ability to maintain control in various positions (B, C).

Children gain the ability to walk lines with reasonable accuracy at a remarkably early age. The ability to walk a reasonably straight pathway is achieved at about the third year. Fifty per cent of the three-year-old children tested by Bayley in 1935 were able to walk a distance of 10 ft on a 1-in.-wide line without "falling off" (1). It is not until nearly four years of age, however, that children are able to walk a circular line, according to Wellman (48).

It has been found in studies we have carried out in our laboratory that five-year-old children on the average can maintain reasonable control while posturing on one foot, even with their arms folded. The girls proved to be slightly superior to the boys in this kind of static balance task; the boys could on the average maintain their balance with their arms folded for about three seconds, and the girls were able to perform the task for about two seconds longer (8).

Both Holbrook and Keogh evaluated static balance by requiring children to stand for ten seconds on one foot with their hands on their hips (24,30). The task was scored on a pass-fail basis. Marked differences are seen upon comparing data, with the five-year-old children in Holbrook's study performing considerably poorer (only 40 per cent passing) than the children tested by Keogh (85 per cent passing). The girls were generally superior to the boys in this type of task.

Several researchers have required children to maintain an immobile heel-toe position, with their eyes closed and their hands on their hips (the Romberg position). It was seen that the test scores obtained from various studies evidence marked differences in the abilities of children of similar ages. The tests of this nature have often proved difficult to score reliably.

Several researchers have utilized the walking board with children in an effort to ascertain their ability to balance in a more dynamic fashion, such as to balance while moving through space. Bayley has chronicled the ways in which balance-beam abilities emerge in younger children by using a beam 7½ meters long, 6 cm wide and 10 cm high (1). It was found that two-year-old children attempted to stand on the beam, and children slightly older attempted to walk with one foot on the beam and the other foot on the floor. By approximately the third year the children could walk by alternating the placement of their feet at least part of the way. By the age of four and one-half years they could slowly traverse the entire length of the beam. During the following year their speeds increased, and at five and one-half years of age they could walk the beam in about four seconds.

Keogh, in a series of studies of balancing, found that five-year-old children could be tested successfully using balance beams 2 in. in width. Beams of this width could be utilized to evaluate static balance in children by asking them to posture in a relatively immobile fashion either by using one foot or by being either parallel to the length of the beam or across the length of the beam (29).

In general, the studies of balance in preschool children demonstrated the fact that prior to the age of two years a child cannot be expected to undergo much stress when asked to maintain an upright position. He has enough difficulty accomplishing this, either while walking normally or while walking beams. However, by the age of three years, children can usually walk lines for a short distance and can attempt tentatively to walk beams that

Figure 3-7 Balancing ability proceeds from the ability to walk lines for short distances and to stand on wide balance beams, as shown in *A* and *B*, to the ability to walk curved lines (*C*), and to assume more difficult postures (*D*), and to walk narrower balance beams (*E, F*).

are about 4 in. in width. By three years of age children can usually take one foot off the ground for short periods of time, posturing on the other, from three to four seconds, without losing balance.

The visual-motor systems of the four-year-old child for maintaining balance improve rapidly. He can traverse beams from 3 to 4 in. wide and can maintain a posture on one foot for increasing periods of time. By the age of five years a child can be expected to traverse balance beams of decreasing width; he can posture on one foot for increasing lengths of time, with and without the aid of his arms.

CLIMBING

Climbing tasks require a reasonable amount of bravery on the part of the maturing infant and, in addition, involve the integration of arm and leg movements. Climbing tasks employed in the various studies have included stair climbing and ladder climbing.

The first climbing behavior is usually seen as the infant, while still unable to walk, crawls up available stairs. When the infant begins to walk, he will generally learn to climb stairs without alternating his feet, and if he is supported by either a handrail or an adult, he will walk up stairs in an upright position. By the middle of his third year he begins to alternate his steps by placing one foot at a time on a riser. At about the end of his fourth year and about the beginning of his fifth year, if he has assistance and increased courage, he will attempt to descend stairs.

Ladder climbing shows a similar progression. The child will move from a marked-time type of climbing (placing both feet on a single rung before ascending to the next rung) to movement in which the feet are alternated up the rungs (placing one foot on one rung and the other foot on the next higher rung).

Proficiency at climbing, as measured, is a function of the height and the width of the risers of the stairs and of the nature of the ladder that confronts the child. Separating the extent to which courage, dependent behavior versus independent behavior, and motor abilities contribute to success in climbing achievement of children, however, is a rather difficult undertaking.

LIMB COORDINATION TASKS

A recent investigation of various kinds of limb coordination tasks carried out by Keogh further illuminates sex differences in the performance of five-year-old children. Thirty boys and 30 girls of five years were exposed to five groups of tasks involving tapping and clapping in rhythm while seated, foot and arm movements while standing, and hopping movements while walking forward. Although at times the reliability of scoring individual items left something to be desired and it is hoped that this will be rectified in future investigations, the overall averages of the percentage passing and failing at age five have important implications for program planning and evaluation of children of this age group (32).

In the less difficult tasks it was found that 60 per cent of the five-year-old girls earned passing scores by engaging in five cycles of the various tasks, whereas only 32 per cent of the five-year-old boys could successfully complete them. When the more difficult tasks were analyzed, the differences were even more marked, with only 4 per cent of the five-year-old boys passing and 18 per cent of the girls achieving passing scores.

For example, in a "jumping jack" task, 7 per cent of the five-year-old boys could complete five cycles without breaking rhythm or performing incorrectly, whereas 40 per cent of the five-year-old girls could do so. Foot tapping and hopping in place evidenced similar pronounced sex differences. The findings of this investigation are surveyed further in Chapter 8. However, these findings further illustrate the marked differences seen in tasks reflecting accuracy of movement when scores achieved by females are compared with those of the males at the age of five years. With further refinement, these types of tasks, I believe, will have value in the evaluation of children in the early elementary school grades with suspected motor difficulties.

SKILL WITH BALLS

From the time he is born, the infant appears fascinated with movements that he observes close to his crib (Chap. 4). It is only after several years, however, that he can accurately match movements with these dynamic events, and his ability to impart velocities to them (throwing) precedes his ability to intercept them (catching).

Proficiencies in ball throwing, ball catching, and ball kicking are influenced to a marked degree by cultural expectations. One of the first things an athletic father will often do with his budding offspring will be to attempt to place a ball in his hands either by throwing it or by rolling it to him. In many cultures around the world in which soccer is popular, various foot-eye coordinations are valued by parents. Thus success and failure at ball-throwing tasks are predictive to a remarkable degree of the amount of social esteem received or withheld from a child on the playground while interacting with his peers and parents.

THROWING

Ball throwing emerges from the manipulative phase that is labeled the "exploitation of objects" in Chapter 4.* The infant may find that a hand-held object is suddenly "pulled away" from him as he rapidly swings his arm in a sudden movement. The sound the missile makes as, for example, it strikes a vase and the visual display and other effects that the object elicits will probably encourage him to make renewed voluntary attempts to duplicate the throwing action. His first attempts at throwing are usually a rigid underhand motion. During the second, third, and fourth years the child will usually evidence a wide variety of throwing patterns, as he will seem to be searching for efficient work methods in this type of complex motor task.

During early childhood the throwing efficiency of the child improves as he begins to incorporate first a weight shift in his throwing and, later, a step with the foot opposite to that of the throwing arm. A detailed cinematographic evaluation of throwing behavior, carried out by Wild in 1938, revealed the fact that the child passes through several stages while acquiring skill and efficiency (49).

Primarily forward and backward motions of the body and of the arms are seen in the simple patterns elicited from the two- and the three-year-old children in this investigation. The body remains facing the direction of the throw, and there is

---

* Some writers have suggested that throwing may be the emergence of an inherent type of protective mechanism that was once necessary for the survival of prehuman ancestors.

either little or no weight shift. By the middle of the third year the child will usually evidence some bodily rotation accompanying the arm movement, but without any marked weight shift. The body rotates to the right when the left hand is used and rotates to the left when the right hand is used. By the ages of five and six years, the child will be seen to take a step and make a pronounced weight shift as he releases the ball. Improved velocity and accuracy will result from these refinements in the throwing pattern.

Investigations of throwing velocity, throwing distance, and throwing accuracy have been reported with frequency in the literature. Wellman found in an early study the distances that 50 per cent of the subjects within various age ranges were able to throw both large and small balls (48). She found that, by the age of two and one-half years, children can throw a ball that is 9½ in. in circumference a distance of from 4 to 5 ft; by about three and one-half years of age, another 2 ft is added to the distance of the throw; and by about four and one-half years of age, her subjects were able to throw the same small ball a distance of from 12 to 13 ft. A larger ball with a circumference of 16¼ in. proved more difficult to throw during the third and fourth years; in general, it was thrown about 2 ft less at each age than was the smaller ball. See Figure 3-9.

CATCHING

As in the analysis of throwing behavior described above, several researchers have observed catching behavior in preschool children and have attempted to differentiate between various levels of proficiency. Wellman has defined three levels of proficiency: one level in which the arms are held straight and the elbows are held stiff in front of the body, as is usually seen in young children below the age of three and one-half years; a second level in which the elbows remain fixed but the hands are open to receive the missile, as is usually seen in children about the age of four years; and a final level in which the arms and elbows are held to the sides of the body permitting them to "give" when the ball arrives. This final level was seen in about 50 per cent of Wellman's subjects at the age of about five and one-half years when the subjects were asked to catch a larger ball.

In a study in our laboratory, in which the catching abilities of

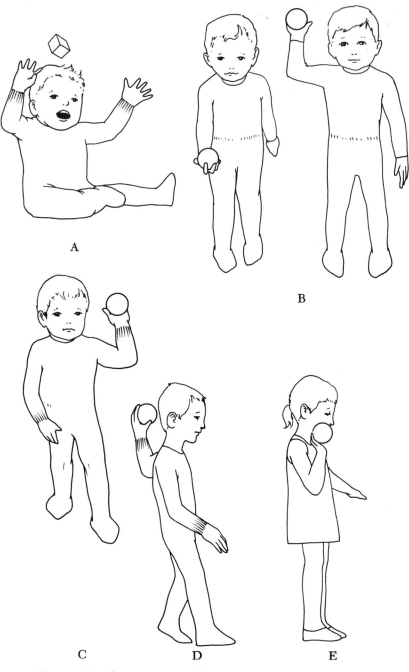

Figure 3-8 Throwing proceeds from the accidental letting go which
may instigate the action in an 18-month child (*A*), to the
variable performance seen in the two- to four-year-old
(*B*), to a throw with a step with the same-side foot as
shown in *C* above, to the correct mechanical effort accompanied by a step with the foot opposite the throwing
arm (*D*). Sex differences in throwing behavior are often
seen into late childhood, with the girl less likely to involve
her entire body in the action (*E*).

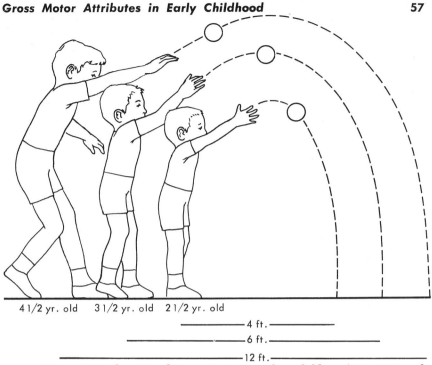

4 1/2 yr. old   3 1/2 yr. old   2 1/2 yr. old

——————4 ft.——————

—————————6 ft.—————————

————————————12 ft.————————————

Figure 3-9 Throwing distance increases when children (2½, 3½, and 4½ years old) are asked to throw a small ball.

five-year-old children were evaluated, it was found that by five years of age the average child can catch a large playground ball that is 8 in. in diameter from three to four times out of five attempts, when the ball is bounced to him from a distance of 15 ft so that it arrives chest-high. Contrary to what might be expected, the boys were not as proficient as were the girls in this task.

An advanced part of this test required that the child intercept with a direct forward movement of his first finger a ball on a string swinging through a 180-degree arc before the ball completed its third swing. The string was held by the tester in such a way that the ball swung an arm's distance from the child and directly in front of him. The ball was restarted by the tester after each attempt was made by the child to intercept it (18). We have found in this test that the six-year-old can contact the ball about once out of five tries, the seven- and eight-year-old about twice out of five times, and children nine to eleven years of age about three times out of five.

Holbrook and Keogh both have collected data using three catching tasks (24,30). In the first task, the child was required to

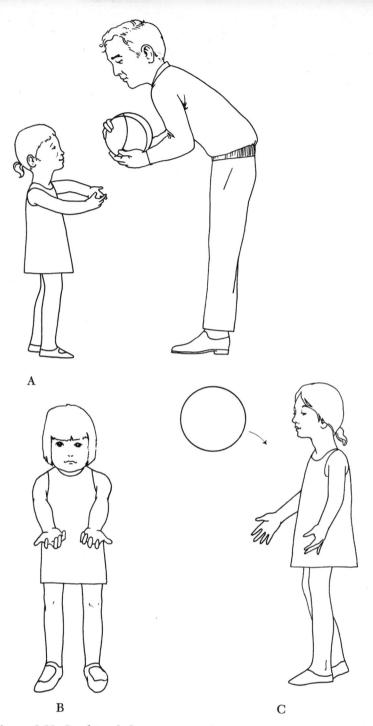

A

B   C

Figure 3-10 Catching behavior passes through several stages from *A*
in which the child passively awaits the ball to be placed
in an arm-cradle, to *B* in which a stiff elbow receptive
position is assumed, to a more mature pattern (*C*) in
which the child's arms are relaxed and to the sides of
the body.

bounce a tennis ball once with both hands and to catch the ball once with both hands. In the second task, the child was required to bounce a tennis ball once with both hands and to catch the ball once with one hand. In the third task, the tester dropped a table tennis ball, and after the ball bounced one time, the child was required to catch it. This third task proved too difficult for five-year-old children to complete, for they generally watched the ball bounce several times before even attempting to intercept it.

The first two tasks that utilize tennis balls were found to be scorable when administered to five-year-old children and revealed the following proficiencies. In the first task, the five-year-old children were successful slightly more than 50 per cent of the time, with the boys slightly superior to the girls. The means of the sexes, however, were not statistically significant. In the second task, the five-year-old children were successful only about 33⅓ per cent of the time. Hand preferences did not seem critical in these tests. The data were tabulated by separating the scores into those achieved by the left and right hands and those achieved by the preferred and nonpreferred hands.

The study by Williams, reviewed in Chapter 6, points out how difficult five-year-old children find the anticipation of the pathways of small balls thrown from a distance (50). In this investigation it was found that virtually none of the children tested at five years of age could correctly identify the place that a tennis ball, projected from a ball-throwing machine some distance away, would land, when the children were permitted to see only the initial part of the ball's arc.

An investigation of ball-bouncing conducted by Wellman demonstrated that children can probably deal better with balls that they themselves have propelled than with balls that were thrown by another person, whose directions, velocities, and trajectories are not as predictable (48). By the age of five years a child can usually bounce a large playground ball at a distance of 3 ft along the ground.

The available data thus suggest that by the age of five years children may begin to evidence reasonably mature throwing patterns. Their abilities to hit targets accurately and to intercept balls thrown from some distance away pose far more difficult problems of perceptual and motor integration. It is also probable, as would be expected, that children can better deal with balls whose pathways they have initiated through bouncing than they can anticipate the trajectories of missiles over which they have exerted no direct influence.

SUMMARY

From birth to the age of five years the child undergoes obvious changes in his ability to move, and in the level of skill he exhibits in various tasks. By the end of his first year his horizons for movement are expanded to a large degree as he moves into a vertical plane, achieves an upright stance, and learns to walk.

During these years a proliferation of movement attributes involving movements of the larger muscles is seen. Numerous ways are learned to throw balls, and several types of missiles, including balls, beanbags, and the like, are dealt with. The child's locomotor behavior similarly evidences a variety of substages, including walking in various directions, on various surfaces, at different velocities, and with numerous individual variations that are unique to himself.

His structures change during these years from the flat-backed, immobile infant dominated by reflexes to the straight-legged, curved-spined, mobile child. Sex differences emerge, including the manner in which the total body is employed by the boys when throwing and engaging in similar tasks, as opposed to the more limited movements of the girls. Increased accuracy is seen in the hopping and skipping behaviors of the girls as opposed to the less adroit behavior of the boys. Body-build differences represent another group of variables influencing the movement capacities of children within this age range. The slow obese child is a marked contrast to the thin and active lithe child.

By five years of age the child can jump about 1 ft in the air, can catch a large ball, can broad-jump about 3 ft, and can balance statically and dynamically. He is beginning to throw efficiently and can run in a well-coordinated manner. His neuromotor system is nearing completion. His physical maturity is starting to emerge. He requires only experience to further enhance his capacities for movement.

Approximate Time of Appearance	Selected Behaviors
1 year	Walking unaided
	A rapid "running-like" walk Will step off low objects
2 years	Walking rhythm stabilizes and becomes even Jumps crudely with two-foot take-off Will throw small ball 4–5 ft
	True running appears
	Can walk sideward and backward
3 years	Can walk a line, heel to toe, 10 ft long
	Can hop from two to three steps, on preferred foot Will walk balance beam for short distances Can throw a ball about 10 ft
4 years	Running with good form, leg-arm coordination apparent, can walk a line around periphery of a circle
	Skillful jumping is apparent
	Can walk balance beam
5 years	Can broad-jump from 2–3 ft Can hop 50 ft in about 11 seconds Can balance on one foot for 4–6 seconds Can catch large playground ball bounced to him

BIBLIOGRAPHY

1 Bayley, N. A., "The Development of Motor Abilities During the First Three Years," *Monogr. Soc. Res. Child Dev.*, **1** (1935), 1–26.

2 Bayley, Nancy, "Behavioral Correlates of Mental Growth, Birth to Thirty-Six Years," *Amer. Psych.*, **28** (January 1968), 1–17.

3 Belmont, Lillian, and H. G. Birch, "Lateral Dominance and Right-Left Awareness in Normal Children," *Child Dev.*, **34** (1963), 257–70.

4 Bloom, Benjamin S., *Stability and Change in Human Characteristics,* New York: John Wiley & Sons, 1966.

5 Cowan, E., and B. Pratt, "The Hurdle Jump as a Developmental and Diagnostic Test," *Child Dev.*, **5** (1934), 107–21.

6 Cratty, B. J., "A Comparison of Fathers and Sons in Physical Ability," *Res. Quart.*, **31** (1960), 12–15.

7 ———, "Why Johnny Can't Right . . . Write," in *Perceptual Motor Behavior and Educational Processes*, Springfield, Ill.: Charles C Thomas, 1969.

8 ———, and M. M. Martin, *Perceptual-Motor Efficiency in Children,* Philadelphia: Lea & Febiger, 1969.

9 Dennis, W., "The Effect of Restricted Practice upon the Reading, Sitting and Standing of Two Infants," *J. Genet. Psych.*, **47** (1935), 17–32.

10 ———, "Infant Development under Conditions of Restricted Practice and of Minimum Social Stimulation: A Preliminary Report," *J. Genet. Psych.*, **53** (1938), 149–58.

11 ———, and M. G. Dennis, "The Effect of Cradling Practices on the Age of Walking in Hopi," *J. Genet. Psych.*, **56** (1940), 77–86.

12 Espenschade, Anna S., and Helen M. Eckert, *Motor Development,* Columbus, Ohio: Charles E. Merrill Books, 1967.

13 Flick, G. L., "Sinistrality Revisited: A Perceptual-Motor Approach," *Child Dev.*, **37** (1966), 613–22.

14 Gesell, A., "The Ontogenesis of Infant Behavior," in *Manual of Child Psychology* (2nd ed.), L. Carmichael (ed.), New York: John Wiley & Sons, 1954.

15 ———, and L. B. Ames, "The Development of Handedness," *J. Genet. Psych.*, **70** (1947), 155–75.

16 ———, and H. Thompson, *Infant Behavior: Its Genesis and Growth,* New York: McGraw-Hill, 1934.

17 Gieseck, M., "The Genesis of Hand Preference," *Soc. Res. Child. Develop. Monogr.,* **5** (1936), 102.

18 Guttridge, M. V., "A Study of Motor Achievements of Young Children," *Arch. Psych.* **244** (1939) 1–178.

19 Hecaen, H., and Julian de Ajuriaguerra, *Left-Handedness, Manual Superiority and Cerebral Dominance,* New York: Grune & Stratton, 1964.

20 Hicks, J. A., and D. W. Ralph, "The Effects of Practice in Tracing the Porteus Diamond Maze," *Child Dev.,* **2** (1931), 156–58.

21 Hildreth, G., "Manual Dominance in Nursery School Children," *J. Genet. Psych.,* **73** (1948), 29–45.

22 ———, "The Development and Training of Hand Dominance: I. Characteristics of Handedness; II. Developmental Tendencies in Handedness; III. Origin of Handedness and Lateral Dominance," *J. Genet. Psych.,* **75** (1949), 197–275.

23 Hilgard, J. R., "Learning and Maturation in Preschool Children," *J. Genet. Psych.,* **41** (1932), 36–56.

24 Holbrook, S. F., "A Study of the Development of Motor Abilities Between the Ages of Four and Twelve, Using a Modification of the Oseretsky Scale," Doctoral Dissertation, No. 5537, Ann Arbor, Mich.: University of Michigan, University Microfilms, 1953.

25 Honzik, M. P., J. W. MacFarlane, and L. Allen, "The Stability of Mental Test Performance Between Two and Eighteen Years," *J. Exper. Educ.,* **17** (1948), 309–24.

26 Jenkins, L. M., *A Comparative Study of Motor Achievements of Children Five, Six and Seven Years of Age,* New York: Teachers College, Columbia University, 1930.

27 Jones, T. D., "The Development of Certain Motor Skills and Play Activities in Young Children," *Child Dev. Monogr.,* Teachers College, Columbia University, **26** (1939), 1–180.

28 Kagan, J., and H. A. Moss, *Birth to Maturity: A Study in Psychological Development,* New York: John Wiley & Sons, 1962.

29 Keogh, J. F., *Motor Performance of Elementary School Children,* Monograph, University of California, Los Angeles, Department of Physical Education, March, 1965.

30 ——, *Analysis of Individual Tasks on the Stott Test of Motor Impairment,* Technical Report 2–68, USPHS Grant, HD 01059, University of California, Los Angeles, Department of Physical Education, 1968.

31 ——, "Rhythmical Hopping Tasks as an Assessment of Motor Deficiency," Paper to the International Congress of Sports Psychology, Washington, D.C., 1968.

32 ——, *Developmental Evaluation of Limb Movement Tasks,* Technical Report 1–68 (USPHS Grant HD 01059), Monograph, Department of Physical Education, University of California, Los Angeles, 1969.

33 Lippman, H. S., "Certain Behavior Responses in Early Infancy," *J. Genet. Psych.,* 34 (1927), 424–40.

34 McGraw, M. B., *Growth: A Study of Johnny and Jimmy,* New York: Appleton-Century, 1935.

35 ——, "Later Development of Children Specially Trained During Infancy," *Child Dev.,* 10 (1939), 1–19.

36 ——, *The Neuromuscular Maturation of the Human Infant,* New York: Hafner Publishing Company, 1966.

37 Metheny, E., "Breathing Capacity and Grip Strength of Preschool Children," *Univ. Iowa Stud. Child Welfare,* 18 (1941), 1–207.

38 Minerva, A. N., "Psychomotor Education and General Development of Preschool Children: Experiments with Twin Controls," *J. Genet. Psych.,* 46 (1935), 433–54.

39 Rarick, L. G., *Motor Development During Infancy and Childhood,* Monograph, Madison, Wis.: College Printing & Typing Co., Inc., 1961.

40 Scarr, Sandra, "Genetic Factors in Activity Motivation," *Child Dev.,* 37 (1966), 613–37.

41 Shirley, M. M., *The First Two Years: A Study of Twenty-Five Babies. Vol. I. Postural and Locomotor Development,* Minneapolis: University of Minnesota Press, 1931.

42 ——, *The First Two Years: A Study of Twenty-Five Babies. Vol. II. Intellectual Development,* Minneapolis: University of Minnesota Press, 1933.

43 Stott, D. H., "A General Test of Motor Impairment for Children," *Dev. Med. Child Neuro.,* 8 (1966), 523–31.

44 ——, and F. A. Moyes, *Test of Motor Impairment* (3rd rev.), Guelph, Ontario, Canada; Department of Psychology, University of Guelph, 1968.

45 Updegraff, R., "Preferential Handedness in Young Children," *J. Exp. Educ.*, **1** (1932), 134–39.

46 Victors, E. E., "A Cinematographical Analysis of Catching Behavior of a Selected Group of Seven and Nine Year Old Boys," *Dissert. Abstracts*, **22** (1961), 1903–1904.

47 Walker, Richard N., "Body-Build and Behavior in Young Children. Body-Build and Nursery School Teacher's Ratings," Monograph of the Society for Research in Child Development, Gesell Institute of Child Development, **3** (1952), 27–84.

48 Wellman, B. L., "Motor Achievements of Preschool Children," *Child Educ.*, **13** (1937), 311–16.

49 Wild, Monica R., "The Behavior Pattern of Throwing and Some Observations Concerning Its Course of Development in Children," *Res. Quart.*, **9** (1938), 20–24.

50 Williams, H. G., "The Perception of Moving Objects by Children," Unpublished study, University of California, Los Angeles, Perceptual-Motor Learning Laboratory, 1967.

Visual Perceptual 4
Development

During the past few years a number of researchers have explored the emergence of various visual behaviors in infants and children. As the focus of this text is on perceptual-motor activity, it is appropriate to review some of this recent information because much of the time movements are visually monitored and directed.

Inspection of contemporary findings and investigations, however, reveals that the relationships believed to exist between visual and motor behavior are actually more complex than is supposed. Several theories of visual perception and of perceptual development expounded during the 1940's and 1950's have had to be re-examined on inspection of this recent evidence (22). When the visual attributes of children as young as five years of age are assessed using factor analytic techniques, it is apparent that the previous lists of cues purporting to aid in the organization of visual space may need to be revised (58).*

As researchers have formulated newer techniques to evaluate the perceptual competencies of infants of younger ages, it is becoming evident that a great deal of visual behavior, including fixating, visual discriminations of various types, and tracking, occurs far earlier in the life of the human than was formerly supposed (18,32,67).

It is also evident that some components of visual development are independent of motor development, and that generally the latter precedes the former. Although it is true that the infant engages in visually directed reaching and manipulative behaviors,

* Invariance, interposition, texture, et cet.

as described in Chapters 4 and 7, it is also true that he tracks moving objects, fixates, and focuses on objects at various distances in a remarkably mature manner well before he exhibits coordinated locomotor and/or precise manipulative activity (32,53,67).

A number of paradoxes become apparent when inspecting the investigations that deal with these complex facets of human functioning. The infant is able to discriminate between triangles and other geometrical figures near birth, but the triangle is one of the more difficult figures for him to draw and is not completed accurately until a year or two after he becomes able to draw a square and a circle at about six or seven years of age. The child of three or four years of age seems to be intent on "tying down" various geometrical figures in an up-down orientation; that is, he will quickly inform an investigator whether various figures are either "upside down" or "right side up," but does not recognize familiar figures before the age of five unless they are placed in an exact upright position (23,24,25,27). At the same time this same child, if asked to draw letters or place several geometrical figures in some prescribed relationship to each other, will ordinarily scatter the letters or figures all over the page without any apparent need and/or ability to align them within exact spatial dimensions (11).

There are several important facets of visual development that have not been accorded extensive treatment by researchers.* However, a survey of the available data does lead to the identification of several stable phases that the child passes through as he learns to utilize his ocular apparatus and begins to structure and interpret objects and events that confront him as he moves from infancy to childhood.

For example, it is apparent that during the early days of life the infant reacts to generalized shapes and undifferentiated objects; later these objects are examined and dissected into parts; as the child matures further he begins again to reassemble and to synthesize the parts into wholes. Several examples will be found on the following pages that illustrate the emergence of these three phases (5,12,50).

The available evidence also suggests that the visual perceptual attributes develop earlier than, and at times apparently indepen-

---

* Largely absent, for example, are studies dealing with the manner in which children of various ages make judgments of movements of one object and of the relative movements of more than one object in space.

dent from, the movement attributes that will later be paired with these perceptual attributes. For example, the infant is seen to track moving objects at birth, and by the sixth month he performs this task quite well for increasingly longer periods of time when objects move in arcs through his space field at various speeds (52). It is several years later, however, before the child is able to intercept a ball by catching it with his hands (11); it is still longer before he is able to simultaneously relocate his body and ready his grasp when anticipating the pathway of a thrown missile (69). To cite another example, within the first month of life the child is able to visually discriminate between the relative distances of two objects and can tell the difference between three- and two-dimensional figures (4). On the other hand, it is not until the age of 10 or 11 that children are able to draw three-dimensional cubes and cylinders (38).

There is a tendency for the child's visual apparatus to become more flexible as he matures. Initially his accommodation distance, for example, seems "locked in" (67). A few weeks later the child can fixate at several distances and is able to track with increased facility. He employs binocular cues gained from the simultaneous viewing of three-dimensional objects. Also, he becomes able to employ "movement parallax cues" obtained from his neck and head musculature as he moves his head while looking at stable and at moving objects (5).

On the pages that follow several facets of visual perceptual development are examined. Initially information relative to the early visual attributes of infants is outlined. Within this same section some early indices of perceptual selection and discrimination are also discussed.

Next, information relative to the manner in which children organize static forms is reviewed. Within this section, as in the others, experimental methods will be covered, as the type of responses and data obtained are dependent not only on the maturation of the subjects, but also on the care taken when collecting the responses. The final portion of the chapter contains a discussion of the manner in which children organize perception of depth, of distance, and of movement in space.

The human infant, high on the phylogenic scale, is an extremely complex animal. The visual apparatus, interacting with intelligence, movement, and verbal behavior, represents one of the more intricate components of the human action system. It will therefore become apparent to the reader that the material that follows contains more questions than answers. At the same time, the amount of recent research activity has begun to paint reasonably clear outlines of the processes and the subprocesses involved as the maturing child looks, sees, and forms understandings.

OCULAR CHARACTERISTICS OF THE INFANT

The facility with which the infant organizes his visual world depends on his rudimentary intelligence, as well as on the sophistication of the visual apparatus. Thus it seems appropriate initially to examine the manner in which the ocular attributes of infants mature, before exploring the ways in which the child interprets visual events.

It is apparent that the infant is born with several basic ocular attributes. These include the ability to fixate briefly on stable objects and the tendency to briefly track slow-moving objects with both eyes through relatively short arcs. The newborn infant can generally accommodate at a distance of about 7½ in., and this accommodation seems to be initially "locked in" at this distance. More adjustable focal lengths emerge after several weeks. At birth the human infant has been estimated to be fixating on objects about 3 to 5 per cent of the time during his waking hours.

A number of recent investigators have studied tracking behavior in the newborn and have generally been surprised to find an inordinate amount of relatively efficient ocular concordance (both eyes working together) in children only a few days old (67). Haith, for example, carefully observing 41 infants from three to five days of age, found that their attention was attracted to the movement of a light presented during five-second intervals. The criterion he utilized to determine when the child was distracted in this manner was to record the termination of non-nutritive sucking movements when the moving light was displayed. Although he found no sex differentiations, stable individual differences were recorded (32).

In addition to the presence of fixation and tracking behaviors, which seem independent of one another, a number of immature structural characteristics are present in the newborn infant's ocular apparatus. For example, the cones in the center of the eye are relatively undeveloped; the cells in the fovea are plumper and less numerous than those of the adult, and only one layer of cells is usually present during the first days after birth (52). It is thus likely that, as Vernon explains, the child is undergoing the first phase of his perceptual development when he may acquire only a vague awareness that "something is there" (61), owing to this incomplete development of the receptors that afford a clear representation of external stimuli on the center of the retina.

At the same time, the infant's eye exhibits no "pupillary unrest," which is normally seen in the adult eye. Not until the fifth or sixth month does the infant's pupil evidence rapid fibrillations as he looks at objects or becomes aroused emotionally; and not until the age of two years do these rapid movements reach the speed seen in adults (from 30 to 120 per minute) (52). Although it is not clear what functional connection these movements of the pupil have to visual perceptual behaviors, some observers have speculated that they support visual alertness and involve a type of sophisticated scanning behavior helpful when the organism is under emotional, perceptual, and/or intellectual stresses.

Also absent at birth is the tendency for the head and eyes to work in unison. Characteristically, the head will lag behind as the eyes follow an object moving across the space field (52,67).

By the time the infant is a month old he will visually pursue objects through increasingly longer arcs, with more facility usually exhibited in the horizontal than in the vertical plane. The length of the arc through which an infant at this age will watch movement has been estimated to be about 90 per cent. Increasing also is the amount of time each day that the infant spends looking at his emerging world. And even during these early days the visual environment to which he is exposed will significantly influence the duration as well as the quality of the visual inspections he will engage in (19,36,67).

Operationally the visual behavior of the infant of 30 days is changing. He begins to include other components of his muscular system with his eye movements. The head is more likely to move with the eyes. These head movements probably afford him movement parallax cues. These cues, paired with the visual stimulation he is receiving, afford him richer information concerning the objects and events to which he is exposed.

During the second month, the infant's ability to accommodate at various distances increases significantly. His retina will develop further, and the second layer of cones in the retina will appear.

By the third month, the infant will evidence changes in accommodation comparable to those seen in adults (33).*

By the second and third months the infant can track vertically and horizontally, and he becomes aware of the shapes and relative distances of objects. Also by this time the eye-blink response to approaching objects may be seen (52,67). Generally this reflex is more likely to first be elicited as an object is brought toward the eyes from the front, and not until two or three months later will peripherally approaching objects cause this protective reflex to be triggered.

During the third and fourth months the child is seen to engage in coordinated movements of the head and eyes, and the eye blink occurs in a coordinated manner, unlike the earlier uncoordinated, one-eye-at-a-time blinks observed immediately after birth.

Also during these months the infant will discover the movements of his hands and feet and will begin to spend a considerable amount of time examining them. This phase of visual-motor development is covered in detail in Chapters 4 and 5 and will not be dealt with extensively at this point. At the same time, hand regard is the first step in an extremely important chain of events that leads toward oral as well as manual examination of the shapes, textures, and weights of objects coordinated with simultaneous visual activity.

By the sixth month of life the infant is visually alert about 50 per cent of the time (67). He will visually track targets through a wide range of angles, in several directions, and at many speeds. In general, he begins to exhibit a number of competencies in the use of his ocular apparatus that are comparable to those of adults. He can accommodate and track well, and, in addition, he can fixate in a coordinated manner for increased periods of time on stimuli to which he gives status. Eye and head movements similarly appear to become coordinated and efficient when the infant is looking and turning toward objects.

Forehead wrinkles will appear, and other facial muscles will be seen to interact with the ocular apparatus as the infant engages in visual behaviors of various types.

---

* Visual accommodation is the adjustment of the ciliary muscle, which in turn modifies the shape of the crystalline lens. A recent technique tests the eyes without the use of drugs and evaluates the infant's capacity to accommodate to a target moving toward and away from the eyes (dynamic retinoscopy) (67).

During these first six months, the infant is exhibiting the ability to perceptually discriminate, to form judgments of size, shape, and speed, and also to attend to stimuli for increasing periods of time. Also, various visual-manual operations are well underway by this time (Chaps. 4 and 5).

VISUAL ATTENTION IN THE NEWBORN

Several experimenters, exhibiting a great deal of ingenuity, have begun to study the factors influencing the duration and quality of visual attention in the infant. These scholars appear to be searching for the variables that contribute to learning. In their research they have explored the neurological basis of attention, as well as various parameters of the stimulus conditions to which the infants are exposed. They have also studied the nature of various physiological modifications occurring as the infant's attention is "caught" by various kinds of visual displays (55).

A number of techniques have been utilized to measure attention in infants, and a variety of stimuli have been placed before the newborn infant in these experiments. Although it is possible to photograph the reflection on the cornea of objects at which an infant is looking, most investigators have been able to obtain reliable measures of attention by simply clocking the duration an infant's eyes are observed to look at an object. The measures that may be obtained by utilizing this method of recording infant attention include total fixation time, longest fixation, first fixation, and number of fixations within a given interval. Lewis and his colleagues found that the best general indices are the longest fixation and the first fixation (45).

Several types of stimuli have been presented to children in order to study attentive behavior, including the human face, representations of distorted and blank human faces, grids of varying degrees of complexity, and various targets. Age and sex differences have been explored as variables influential of attention in infants (17,18,42).

In addition to simply clocking the duration of time an infant seems to look at various stimuli, researchers have also recorded various other changes accompanying visual regard. For example, it has been found that the heart beat characteristically slows down during the initial phases of attention to a new stimulus in infants, children, and adults (42).

Some experimenters have also demonstrated that peripheral dilatation of the blood vessels in the face occurs during attentive behavior. Other postural and facial behaviors have also been studied in conjunction with attention. It is difficult to determine, however, when collecting these relatively crude physiological and behavioral measures, just *why* an infant is attending to a given stimulus. For example, he may be frightened by the presentation, interested in what is seen, or just passively attempting to categorize what the experimenter has decided to reveal to him (42).

In general, however, the evidence from studies of attention may be summarized as follows:

1. The most prolonged periods of attention are likely to be elicited by reasonably complex stimuli and stimuli to which the infant has not been exposed on prior occasions (16,17,19).

2. Presentations of the human face are likely to elicit fixations of longer duration than will the presentation of designs (42,45).

3. Infants show marked changes in visual preferences during the early months of life, especially when different patterns are shown to them.

4. Early experience is likely to influence visual preference changes, and some experimenters have suggested that the quality and nature of visual attention in infants are likely to prove to be more helpful in assessing later intelligence than are the traditional measures of perceptual-motor efficiency presently employed (19).

5. Relatively few sex differences are seen in visual attention during the early months of life (42).

6. Objects of intermediate complexity and intermediate brightness are preferred to objects that are extremely complex in design, or are too bright, or are not sufficiently illuminated (42).

Further experimental and theoretical attempts are being made to more exactly delineate the factors contributing to infantile attention and, more importantly, to study the meaning of attentive behavior. A number of questions are being asked by experimenters. For example: Are the duration and quality of attention related to early and later intellectual performance? What are the relationships between the acquisition of ocular control, visual-motor integrations, perceptual development, and attentive behavior? What is the meaning of the general finding that infants seem to prefer novelty and complexity during the first days of life?

Kagan has hypothesized that the reasons for attention may be at least twofold. The infant may regard visual stimuli in order to "savor" the experience because it represents some unique and unfamiliar representation of a classification of objects and things new to the infant (an "emergent schema"). Kagan also speculates that attention may be given by the infant to stimuli that are related to more familiar groups of events ("older schema"). In this latter instance the child is assumed to be attempting to categorize the stimuli within familiar cubicles (42).

There is no doubt that these studies of infantile attention should, when extended, prove highly interesting to students of child development. Their findings, in time, may also unlock doors important to understanding the genesis of intellectual as well as of perceptual-motor development.

PERCEPTUAL AND PERCEPTUAL-MOTOR IMPRINTING?

Since the turn of the century the triggering of apparently "wired-in" behavioral tendencies in animals has been studied. This phenomenon, termed "imprinting," may be manifested in several ways, depending on the response capacities of the species studied and on the environmental or experimental conditions to which they are exposed. Examples of this type of behavior include the following response in chicks, sexual overtures between animals of two different species, and various nest-making tendencies in birds.

In general, the research on this facet of behavior indicated that in animals:

1. Imprinting occurs within rather exact time intervals within the life of the animal. For example, the following response will usually be elicited to a moving stimulus in chicks only between the ninth and twentieth days of life (3).

2. Movement, or other attempts to activate the animal, will often elicit more pronounced imprinting than if the animal is not aroused to an optimum level (60).

3. The onset of fear responses during the early days of an animal's life will often make imprinting difficult or impossible (3).

Imprinting may be differentiated from classical learning by the fact that the latter modification of behavior may occur any time during the life of an animal. Imprinted behavior is difficult to extinguish, whereas learned responses are not. Massed practice seems to facilitate imprinting but may impede learning (10).

Some writers (10,30) within recent years have speculated that a similar type of triggered behavior may emerge in human infants under various conditions present in the early environment. Several kinds of evidence have been cited to support this hypothesis. For example, it has been suggested that masculine and feminine characteristics of behavior are the result of early imprinting (31). Others have described various tendencies toward emotional stability and instability in early adolescence as appearing to be the result of the manner in which the individual was raised during the first six months of life (6,8,9,29). Some researchers have noted that verbal behavior and speech patterns seem the result of early exposure to various auditory stimuli (7).

Investigations of the emergence of the tendency of infants to reflect the smile of an adult also suggest that optimum time during which this response may be elicited is similar to that seen in the studies of animal imprinting previously cited (59). The controversial wolf-child histories of India similarly reflect the possibility that some kind of animal-like imprinting may occur early in the lives of these unfortunate children (21).

It is thus possible that interacting with the innate perceptual and perceptual-motor qualities with which the infant is endowed, and with the responses that are the result of learned experience, are some kinds of imprinted behaviors. And although little solid evidence may be found in the literature supporting this assumption, there are several indirect indices that in truth the human "animal's" behavior may be in part the result of imprinting (31).

More questions are raised by this kind of speculation than are answered by the available data. For example, it may seem likely that the more complex human animal may be susceptible to imprinting of more than one type of behavior, and that imprinting in human infants may occur at several optimum times, extending through infancy, childhood, and adolescence (10). Gray, for example, has suggested that the early period may begin with the onset of the smiling response at the age of six weeks and terminates with the fear of strangers usually seen at about the sixth month of life (30). Imprinting to sex-appropriate behavior may occur just prior to the fourth year; imprinting to the peer group, shortly thereafter. Imprinting to a member of the opposite sex (i.e., falling in love) may be triggered by biochemical changes occurring in late adolescence and early adulthood (10).

It would seem that with further experimentation some of the assumptions made in this section may be confirmed, modified, or rejected. At the same time it is believed that an effort might be made to determine just what, if any, types of perceptual tendencies, motor characteristics, and other behavioral characteristics are susceptible to various visual environments to which the child is exposed early in his life. It also would be illuminating to find out the manner in which concomitant motor activity may contribute to or detract from the automatic influence of various experiences encountered during the first weeks of life.*

THE MODIFICATION OF VISUAL AND VISUAL-MOTOR RESPONSES THROUGH EXPERIENCE

Several scholars during recent years have reported the effects of early handling on the development of animals (3,53), and the various material deprivation studies contain inferences that the quality of early experiences to which the infant is exposed will significantly alter his later behavior. Brody, for example, noted that infants who were handled more often were consistently more attentive visually than those who were not handled as much (8). Additionally, the former exhibited a significantly greater amount of visual motor behavior during the early weeks of life.

In 1962 an investigation was carried out, utilizing reasonably exact assessment procedures, the purpose being to determine the influence of various degrees of visual enrichment of the early environment of infants. The researchers obtained base-line data on 63 infants to determine the time in life in which visually directed reaching occurred and the time during which the eye blink to approaching objects was seen. The duration of time in which the infants displayed visual attention was also plotted, together with the emergence of visual tracking and increased flexibility of accommodation. Some of these normative data were referred to in the initial section of this chapter (67).

---

* In general, the animal studies indicate that concomitant motor activity (i.e., walking up inclines and over hurdles) positively influences imprinting in animals (the following response in chicks) (60).

Following the establishment of average parameters for various visual and visual-motor behaviors, the experimenters sought to create conditions that would conceivably modify the time of the appearance of such behavior in the life of infants. One group of children was left in rather bland surroundings and used as controls. A second group was afforded 20 minutes a day of extra handling by the nurses from the sixth through the twenty-sixth day of life. The changes noted in this group were a significantly greater amount of visual attention and the delay of hand regard by eight days.

A second experimental group was given even more visual and motor stimulation of various kinds. Not only were they afforded extra handling similar to that given to the other experimental group, but their crib liners were removed, so that the ward activities could be seen. Their mattresses were flattened, which facilitated hand, arm, and trunk movements. Multicolored bumpers were substituted for flat white ones, and, finally, a special visual stabile containing contrasting colors and forms was suspended over their cribs from the thirty-seventh to the one hundred and twenty-fourth days.

Following regular and frequent observations it was determined that hand regard and swiping behavior in this second group were delayed by two weeks and by five days, respectively. However, when visual-manual activity was begun, accurate prehension was achieved 45 days ahead of the controls.

It is thus probable that with increased amounts of attention by adults, such as more handling and providing an enriched visual environment, measurable changes can be elicited in the visual and motor behaviors of infants. At the same time the data emanating from this study suggest that although visual attention will tend to delay the *onset* of manual activity, an excess of external visual stimulation will lead toward increases in visual attention by the infant, which in turn will result in qualitative and quantitative changes in his visual-motor behaviors early in life.

PERCEPTIONS OF FORM

Apparently the ability to discriminate between various geometrical forms occurs quite early in the life of an infant. For example, Ling, in 1941, demonstrated that infants of six months could discriminate between various geometrical figures (47). The stimuli themselves were used as reinforcers and were sugar-coated, three-dimensional forms. He furthermore found that the discriminations were not affected by changes in size orientation. As Ling's experiment extended over a period of six months, however, the effects of maturation versus learning are difficult to separate when evaluating the findings. Also contributing to the positive findings was the fact that the forms used were three-dimensional. Several experimenters have found that three-dimensional shapes are easier for children to discriminate than two-dimensional forms (36,40).

Watson (65) evaluated the ability of infants, 15 to 20 weeks old, to differentiate between four different orientations of the human face. The criterion for recognition was increased smiling on the part of the infants. In general, the "upright" face received more response. However, whether or not an infant responds to a configuration within various spatial orientations is probably due to whether or not it is familiar to him. In this same investigation by Watson, the infants did not respond to other geometrical figures placed in "upright" positions with greater frequency than to those that were rotated to the left or right prior to presentation. Other data similarly indicate that if an object is meaningful to the perceiver, he seems more sensitive to its relative position in space. If not, he will probably fail to recognize it or its orientation.

The available evidence indicates that children, as they mature, seem to organize the various dimensions of their space field in a reasonably orderly sequence (22,43,54). First to mature are the vertical dimensions, followed by the recognition and organization of the horizontal. The more complex oblique or diagonal dimensions of the space field are the last to become organized by the child (39).

Children of two years are as likely to look at figures, pictures, etc., upside down as in the correct position. By three and four years of age vertical lines can be distinguished from horizontal lines, and the six-year-old and older child generally evidence little difficulty in dealing with discriminations involving vertical, horizontal, and oblique lines (54).

Several findings concerning form discrimination in children seem to contradict one another. For example, children can often identify forms and objects that are inverted and otherwise removed from the usual upright orientation better than adults.

However, their ability to discriminate between "b" and "d," "p" and "q," and other asymmetrical numbers and letters often is faulty until the age of seven (13,14).

A similar paradox is seen when the findings of Ghent are considered (23,24,25). He found that children of three and four years evidenced no hesitation when asked to determine whether a group of nonsense configurations were upright or upside down. They seemed to scan the figures from top to bottom and usually placed figures with their focal points toward the bottom. Ghent speculated that this appeared to be related to their tendency to scan the figures from top to bottom. In extensions of these investigations, Ghent found that nonsense geometrical figures, which were aligned as children would be expected to orient them, were more quickly and easily recognized than if they were inverted from the expected orientation.

There thus seem to be differences in the way children prefer figures to be placed in space and the manner in which they require them to be placed in order to recognize them. At the same time, children of three and four years of age, as has been pointed out, exhibit marked difficulty when asked to draw figures, letters, or numbers within exact spatial dimensions (i.e., a straight line).

Letter and number reversals are common in children of five and six years of age. Thus the left-right dimensions of the space field seem more difficult to organize than are the up-down dimensions. Davidson, in a 1935 survey of this type of spatial confusion in letter discrimination, found the following (14):

Percent of Children Evidencing Confusions in the Comparisons Shown in Kindergarten and First Grade *

	N	d-b	d-p	d-q	b-p	b-q	q-p	q-b	q-d	b-d
Kindergarten	48	93	50	35	40	42	96	43	27	87
Grade 1	111	65	19	13	19	15	62	11	13	60

Several writers have speculated that the ability to make correct left-right orientations in space is somehow dependent on and influenced by the child's ability to make left-right discriminatons about his own body parts (44). Although these two perceptual attributes in populations of children are seen to mature at about the same time in life, at about the sixth and one-half to seventh

* From Helen P. Davidson, "A Study of the Confusing Letters B, D, P, Q," *J. Genet. Psychol.,* **47** (1935), 458–68.

years,* in data collected from neurologically handicapped children by Ayres, (1) and in an unpublished study within our own laboratory, no significant correlations were found to exist between the tendency to reverse figures in space and left-right judgments about the body and its parts (11).

PERCEPTIONS OF MOVEMENT AND SHAPES IN THREE-DIMENSIONAL SPACE

By the age of two years the child's ocular apparatus is mature in many ways. The eyes track through a wide range of angles and speeds and many children are well coordinated in these efforts. The size and weight of the eyeball approach adult dimensions; pupillary reflexes and fibrillation also are nearly mature (52). At the same time the perceptual development of the infant is far from complete. In general he is only beginning to deal with parts of objects with which he is confronted, instead of synthesizing visual experiences in two- and three-dimensional space. His perceptions of movements, when more than one object is present, are less than adequate. His most obvious problem is the inability to coordinate his motor efforts when attempting to deal with rapid movement in his space field.

It is probable, however, that at two years the infant is capable of judgments that indicate he has acquired both size constancy and distance constancy. Size constancy is the perception of an object as having stable and consistent shape despite the way it is viewed, and the resultant change in stimuli reflected on the light-sensitive retina. At the same time it is probable that the human infant by his second year is beginning to form relatively consistent judgments of the distance of objects despite the fact that he may be observing objects of various sizes in space, placed a similar distance from him (4,5,12).

The findings from investigations of Bower indicate that infants between 50 and 60 days old are capable of making these relatively sophisticated perceptual judgments (5). Bower conditioned infants to make head-turning responses by rewarding them with

* The left and right of the body seems to be a concept not easily acquired, and children evidence an improvement in this type of judgment at a linear rate through childhood, until about the age of 12, at which time they persist in making the chance errors likely to be evidenced by adult subjects. See Chapter 7.

a "peek-a-boo" by the experimenter when responding to objects placed at various distances and to objects of various shapes and sizes. It was found that the infants were responding to real size and distance cues, not merely to changes in the retinal image of objects (i.e., to apparent size and distance change created by confronting the child with smaller objects rather than moving an object of a similar size further away). Bower concluded that it is doubtful whether the human infant ever depends solely on the simple retinal image when formulating judgments about visual space. Rather, she concludes, the young child organizes visual information in a rather sophisticated manner near birth. She attributes these apparently well-developed capacities near birth to the fact that the human infant is rather high on the phylogenic scale.

Bower further tried to ascertain the manner in which the infant formed these complex types of perceptual judgments by immobilizing the heads of some of her subjects, and in other subjects by patching one eye. Thus she attempted to determine the relative help of movement parallax cues (kinesthetic sensations arising from the neck, accompanying apparent movement in space of objects), the role of binocular cues obtained from the simultaneous regard of objects by both eyes at the same time, and of monocular cues obtained when one eye viewed the objects under the various experimental conditions. It was found that the most important cues were obtained by the infant when he was permitted to move his head while viewing the objects to which he was exposed, and next in order of importance were binocular cues.

In extensions of these investigations, Bower tried to find out whether these infants, two months old and younger, could react to both size and spatial cues at the same time. She found (in common with similar findings using other perceptual and motor tasks, which will be discussed in the pages that follow) that requiring the infants to organize two types of reasonably complex classifications of cues at the same time tended to "overload" their perceptual capacity. They could only be conditioned to size-shape cues, *or* to distance cues, but not to both at the same time.

Bower concluded that infants can often handle the same information as can adults, but are able to absorb less information at the same time. With maturation, she suggests, the improvement in the capacity to process increasing quantities of information is achieved.

Bower employed infants younger than those utilized by other researchers when attempting to determine the accuracy of similar perceptual judgments. She used an extremely crude response, head turning, to verify the quality of perceptual judgments formed by her subjects. Others have tested children at older ages whose perceptual awareness was confirmed by more complex verbal and gross motor behaviors.

For example, Walk, in 1961, in the classic "visual-cliff" studies, utilized the ability of infants to crawl to confirm the degree to which they are aware of depth in their visual field (63). Walk used 36 infants, from 6 to 14 months old, in an interesting series of investigations. These followed a number of similar investigations in which the depth perception of chicks, goats, lambs, pigs, turtles, dogs, and monkeys were studied by determining whether they were willing to walk over a "visual cliff" formed by clear glass that served as an extension of a high table on which the animals were placed. It was found that in all young animals the awareness of the difference between the height of the table and the floor was generally enough to make them refuse to travel over the "cliff" (62). The human infants usually balked at the task despite the presence of their mothers on the opposite side of the glass surface offering them attractive objects. Of all the animals tested, only the turtles were somewhat inaccurate in their perception of the depth cues present in the experimental conditions. Walk concluded that cues obtained with a single eye were just as important as binocular cues in these early attempts to discriminate depth on the part of the immature subjects (28).

Other techniques have been utilized assessing the presence and accuracy of depth perception in children of two and three years. Johnson and Beck, for example, presented pictures observed through a device that made them appear in three dimensions. Invariably the two-year-olds attempted to reach for the objects by extending their hands past the picture-holding device, which was attached to their eyes (40).

Evidence presented by Cruikshank in 1941 has also been frequently cited in the literature to substantiate the fact that at six months children begin to evidence the organization of depth cues (12). In this study, infants of various ages were presented one rattle at a distance of 75 cm, and later they were confronted with a rattle of the same projected size at a distance of 25 cm. It was found that infants younger than six months would reach for the more distant one about one half the time, whereas after the one-half-year mark was reached, the subjects would tend to manually seek only the closer one (12). Ten years later Misumi found that stable differential responses to distance were evidenced by nine months as the child would consistently reach for the nearer of two red balls despite differences in size (49).

In investigations in which adult subjects have been employed, it is becoming increasingly apparent that judgments concerning the relative placement of objects within the distant space field are relatively independent of those involving depth (the relative "closeness" of two or more objects to the observer). This same differentiation seems to occur during late infancy and early childhood (2).

For example, it has been noted in nursery school children that their play seems dependent on perception of depth, rather than distance, with the latter remaining relatively undeveloped (57). It has been hypothesized that while the sizes of nearby objects are judged in terms of the child's manipulative capacities, distances immediately adjacent to the individual are scaled in units corresponding to the body's motions, i.e., steps.

Judgments in distant space, on the other hand, seem to be phylogenically of a different order. In humans, apparently, two separate sets of cues are utilized to judge distance and depth, and when the two attributes are compared (based on scores collected from subjects as young as five years), no significant correlations are usually obtained (58).

Thus even after the infant organizes near space, a job important for his safety and survival, it is several more years before he assimilates and organizes the cues that enable him to accurately structure and deal with distance.

Other independent factors, based on comparisons of scores in 40 tasks administered to young children by Smith, revealed other separate visual-perceptual attributes. For example, visual acuity was found to be independent of the perception of distance and depth, and the ability to "fractionalize" space was a fourth attribute independent of the first three named. The latter attribute involves the accuracy with which a child could estimate what is one half the distance between himself and a more distant object.

It was found that this general pattern of independent attributes remained relatively constant as children matured into adulthood (58).

THE SYNTHESIS AND SELECTION OF VISUAL EXPERIENCES

In the investigation by Bower previously discussed, it was pointed out that the infant subjects, ranging in age from 40 to 60 days, evidenced an inability to attend to too many cues at a time as they formed discriminations of size, shape, and distance (5). Innumerable other types of studies with children have similarly demonstrated the manner in which children first attend to the parts of an object, or event, prior to combining the parts into an organized whole. Data emanating from studies in which children from two years of age and older have been utilized are based on more accurate responses, as the children can verbally respond to the manner in which they are forming various perceptual judgments.

An interesting experiment by Elkind and his colleagues in 1964 (15) demonstrates the emergence of "part perception" into "whole perception" as children mature. Two-dimensional drawings were utilized in this investigation, drawings of common objects that were formed by other independent parts. For example, a heart formed by the curved necks of two giraffes was employed; a scooter made of candy parts and a bird whose components were vegetables were other drawings in the series (Fig. 4-1). It was found that the four- and five-year-olds would report receiving only the parts from which the total drawings were constructed; they might say for example, "I see vegetables." There seemed to be a separation of whole and part perception at these ages. By the age of seven children would seem to alternate in their organization of the interesting figures and would say, "I see candy," and, looking at the same picture, would state, "It is a scooter," etc.

By the age of eight, however, 60 per cent of the children, and by nine years 78 per cent, would apparently perceive both the wholes and parts at the same time, as evidenced in their statements that, "It is a man made of vegetables," or "It is a heart formed by giraffes' necks," etc.

This same whole-part phenomenon is illustrated in the findings of an investigation by Ling in 1941 (47). Using 125 subjects from

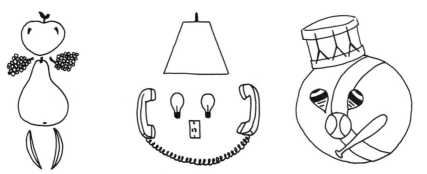

Figure 4-1 Illustrations used to evaluate whole versus part perception by Elkind. [From D. Elkind, R. R. Koegler, and E. G. Koegler, "Studies in Perceptual Development: II. Part-Whole Perception," *Child Dev.*, **35** (1964), 81–90.]

the ages of four to seven, who were asked to make judgments concerning the differences in sizes between various geometrical figures, it was found that the younger children had little difficulty determining which of two triangles was larger, but evidenced confusion when size discriminations of two dissimilar geometrical figures were present at the same time (i.e., a rectangle and a circle).

Other experimental data that reflect this trend from the perception of parts to wholes are found in studies of the efficiency with which subjects of various ages can select figures that have been "embedded" into complex designs. When this type of problem is presented to five- and six-year-olds, only the more intelligent can deal with them successfully. This capacity seems not to mature until the late teens, although marked improvement is often seen in the mean scores collected from children in late childhood, between the ages of 10 and 13 (46).

When children of various ages are asked to select letters from more complex backgrounds, as would be expected, definite maturational trends can be identified (26). Gibson, for example, found significant differences in the performance of children in the second, fourth, and sixth grades, and in that of adults. Not only was more accuracy achieved with age, but the selections were made more rapidly by the older children and by the adults.

It is difficult, of course, to determine whether increased success as a function of age in the above experiment was due to the increased use of letters by the older subjects or to some facet of perceptual maturation.

PART-WHOLE INTEGRATION OF VISUAL-MOTOR TASKS

Investigations carried out in our laboratory during the past several years with various drawing tasks, and tasks involving the interception of balls swinging on strings, also illustrate the manner in which maturation results in the ability to synthesize and integrate various independent perceptual impressions and the motor and visual perceptual components of a coordinated act.

For example, in the drawing task described in Chapter 7, four-year-olds are characteristically seen to concentrate on making the figures as accurate as they can, or they attempt to place the figures with reasonable accuracy overlapping the initial large square that they draw. But they are apparently unable to attend to both accuracy and location, as are the five-, six-, and seven-year-olds.

A subtest of a six-category battery of perceptual-motor tests involves attempting to touch a ball swung through a 180-degree arc on a 15-in. string, an arm's distance away from the child and even with his chin. The four-year-olds tested can often watch the ball with their eyes moving in a coordinated manner, as it swings back and forth in a horizontal plane; or they can with ease touch the ball with their first finger when it remains hanging immobile. Not until the age of seven years, however, do the children seem able to integrate the visual and motor act and touch the ball in even two out of five separate attempts.

Thus within several kinds of perceptual and perceptual-motor tasks one is able to discern the manner in which maturation contributes to increasing the capacity of children to process and organize increasingly larger "hunks" of incoming data. The following sections contain descriptions of several other experiments in which the same tendency to a synthesized experience with greater facility as a function of age is further illustrated.

THE PERCEPTION OF MOVING STIMULI

It has long been noted in experiments with adults that when more than one object is caused to move in the space field, either simultaneously or at different times, they often interpret the dynamic "event" as involving some kind of physical causality. It will be reported that one object seems to be "pushing," "going into," or "throwing" another object.

In developmental studies in which this tendency has been investigated it has been noted that younger children do not tend to exhibit inclination to attribute causal effects to moving stimuli as much as do adults. For example, in a study by Piaget and Lambercier carried out in 1958, it was found that noncausal types of responses were elicited from seven- and 9-year-olds, and in fact one half of the 13-year-olds who responded voiced similar reactions to two stimuli made to move at the same speed. The children were more likely to perceive some causal effect occurring between two moving stimuli only if they actually made physical contact, whereas the adult subjects would often infer causality in which gaps of space were sustained between two or more moving stimuli (50).

In an interesting study by Wapner and Werner (64) this same effect was evaluated developmentally when subjects were exposed to pictures of familiar objects placed on moving belts some of which were drawn in positions suggesting motion, while others were not. Marked developmental differences were noted in the responses obtained. The children constantly overestimated the speed of the objects whose configurations denoted speed; their perceptions of speed of movement seemed altered by the qualities inserted into the drawings. The adults, on the other hand, correctly matched speeds of the drawings containing inferred movement and the "static" drawings without any of the distortion voiced in the children's responses.

THE INTERCEPTION OF MOVEMENT

In a study conducted in 1965 by Williams, who was at that time in our laboratory, the ability of children to estimate the terminal location of small balls projected by a mechanical device was evaluated (69). The subjects consisted of children of both sexes from the ages of 5 to 12 years. The children were placed one at a time under an overhead platform so that they observed only the initial arch of balls projected at the end of the platform; the balls landed over the subjects' heads out of sight on top of the apparatus. Additionally the children stood on an apparatus containing switches connected to clocks that were activated when they removed their feet. The clocks were connected to a ball-throwing machine so that the time could be measured between the initial projection of the ball and the moment the children's feet left the starting point. The children were asked to quickly and accurately attempt to determine where the ball would land by moving their bodies in position to catch it, if it would descend to them, and if the overhead platform was not in the way. Thus a speed (reaction time) and accuracy measure (distance between where the child finally stood and where the ball would actually descend) could be obtained (Fig. 4-2).

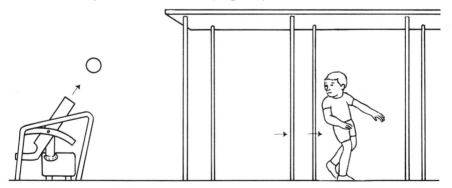

Figure 4-2 Children of various ages were evaluated by Williams, in their ability to accurately judge the landing position of balls, when they were not permitted to see the final part of the trajectory (Williams, 18).

Children in the first two years of elementary school (six, seven, and eight years) tended to react quickly and inaccurately. They seemed excited and moved rapidly off the switches on which they were standing, but apparently had no clear idea where the ball's arcs would terminate. Several even were concerned that the ball would land across the street and declared that they "could not get through the fence and leave the schoolyard."

By the age of nine, however, the children seemed to perceive the difficulty of the problem. They reacted considerably slower, but became significantly more accurate in their judgments of the landing spots than their younger brothers and sisters.

The children in the final elementary school grades evidenced the kind of mature integrated perceptual-motor functioning previously described in other contexts. They moved rapidly off their "marks" and made their judgments with accuracy.

The findings of other experiments have also demonstrated the difficulty children of eight and nine still have in integrating time and space. For example, they will often judge two balls rolling down two runways as moving at the same speed upon arriving across from each other, even though one of the pathways is straight and the other crooked! Or conversely, they will estimate that two balls under similar conditions have moved at the same distance.

It thus appears, upon surveying the available evidence, that complex spatial perceptions involving the perceptual anticipation of rapidly moving objects in space, coupled with locomotor and manual responses necessary to contain them, are not seen to mature until late childhood. Prior to that time accurate visual tracking or locomotor and manual behaviors are reasonably well developed, but they do not work quickly and accurately in concert.

TRENDS AND ISSUES

The available evidence delineates numerous gaps in the theoretical and practical knowledge of the manner in which the human infant and child perceptually mature. There are, however, investigations whose data are suggestive of future work that might be carried out to fill in our understanding of these complex processes.

In general, the role that movement plays in perceptual development of infants and children is not well understood. For example, the studies carried out based on the sensory-tonic theory of perception with children of various ages often results in conflicting findings. Some studies indicate that with increased age children seem more likely to be dependent on postural tonus while making visual judgments, but other studies show the reverse to be true.

Although the work of Olin Smith has begun to delineate the factor structure of the visual perceptual attributes of the child of five years and older, little is known about the manner in which younger children's visual and perceptual attributes evolve, fragment, and diffuse (58). Although it has been speculated that in the newborn infant fixation and tracking are relatively independent processes, and that later judgments of size and distance are related, in opposition to the separation of these attributes seen in studies with adults, the exact parameters of early perceptual maturation have not been researched extensively.

The role of manipulative experience in the formation of perceptions of objects in near space is not well understood. Pick and his colleagues, for example, have produced data that indicate that tactual perceptions of space and visual organization of shape are independent perceptual operations in children (51). On the other hand, Held and his colleagues have inferred that some kind of voluntary (self-induced) movement is imperative to the organization of basic visual perceptual judgments (34,35).

At the same time it has not been clearly delineated just *how* infants and children arrive at more complex judgments about visual space. Undoubtedly both cognitive and perceptual attributes contribute to the formation of spatial impressions, but the manner and consistency with which a given child adheres to either method of dealing with his world are not well understood (26). French (20) polled adult subjects after they completed a perceptual battery of 14 tasks to determine whether they were cognitively analyzing the operations involved, or whether they were "perceptual types." Separate analysis of the two group scores indicated that the correlations obtained between various perceptual scores and a test of mathematical reasoning were moderately high, whereas the second group seemed to be depending on visual spatial attributes in the performance of several tests with the battery.*

The interaction of perceptual versus cognitive processes in the formation of visual judgments by young children has not been researched. It is probable that, as children mature, an increasing percentage revert to cognitive processes when forming perceptual judgments, but the manner in which this trend is manifested has not been objectified.

Studies carried out with animals indicate that visual function is highly influential of various indices of maturation of the visual system. For example, in one investigation it was found that the optic nerve of chicks in an eye that was covered at birth evidenced a considerable delay in the acquisition of its myelin sheath when contrasted with that of the second eye, which was left exposed. In the previous pages some of the anatomical characteristics of the maturing eye were briefly covered. However, few data are available describing exactly the manner in which functional perceptual behaviors correspond to various signposts of neurological and anatomical aging within the ocular apparatus of infants and children.

Another unresolved question concerns the manner in which various cues contribute to the formation of accurate judgments about size, distance, and the like by children of various ages, although an earlier reviewer (71) suggests that with the addition of cues more accurate judgments are likely to be made on the part of younger children. More recent evidence by Smith indicates that often children can make accurate judgments about distance and size when viewing objects through tubes that preclude the utilization of auxiliary visual cues (58). Furthermore, few clear-cut maturational trends were noted in Smith's data.

Further work on topics dealing with developmental perception should also lead toward more valid and scholarly theories than are presently found in the literature. A cogent theory of perceptual development should encompass data obtained from factoral analyses and at the same time take into consideration such variables as learning and the intellectual strategies employed by children, as well as giving strong consideration to the assumption

---

* The criterion task was Thurston's Cubes Test.

that visual perception is a multifaceted rather than a unifactoral facet of the child's personality.

SUMMARY

In summary the research evidence suggests that:

1. A considerable amount of ocular activity may be seen in the newborn. This initial visual behavior can be classified into tracking and visual regard. Both can apparently be modified significantly by the presentation of various stimuli to the infant, and in relatively permanent ways by the modification of the infant's visual environment (32,52,67).

2. Behavior exhibiting figure and size constancy has been evidenced in infants of two months (5). These early perceptual judgments are apparently supported by cues arising from binocular fixations, as well as stimuli caused by movement parallax received as the child scans objects with concomitant head movements.

3. The organization of lines in space proceeds in a relatively predictable manner, with horizontal and vertical preceding oblique (43).

4. With continued maturation there is a trend that indicates several shifts in perceptual characteristics, from the initial vague awareness that some things are present in the space field as wholes, passing through an analytical phase in which only the parts of objects or specific characteristics of moving and static forms are dealt with, to the final phase in which a great deal of visual perceptual and visual motor integration is evidenced (61). This final organizational level is evidenced in data arising from studies of ball throwing, figure group perception, and whole versus part perception of complex pictures, and from investigations in which passive judgments of time and space are made by subjects of various ages. Complete integration of the visual motor apparatus when dealing with and anticipating the pathway of rapidly moving small objects is probably not complete until early adolescence, depending on experience (58,68,69).

5. With increased experience comes increased differentiation of perceptual attributes. But by the age of five years a number of separate visual perceptual factors emerge, which remain relatively stable through adulthood (58).

Approximate Time Behavior Occurs	Selected Visual, Perceptual Behaviors
Birth	Rudimentary fixation, reflexive tracking for brief periods
3 months	Accommodation becomes more flexible, head and eyes coordinate Seeks novel visual experiences Evidences size and shape constancy in perceptual judgments
6 months	Visually tracks through 90° in horizontal and vertical planes Visually alert about 50 per cent of the time, awareness of depth in visual-cliff studies
1 year	Mature pupil fibrillation appears
2 years	
	Distinguishes vertical from horizontal lines
5 years	
	Distinguishes between lateral, vertical, and horizontal lines
7 years	
	b, p, d, q confusions resolved
9 years	
10 years	Can intercept balls thrown from a distance

BIBLIOGRAPHY

1 Ayres, A. Jean, "Patterns of Perceptual-Motor Dysfunction in Children: A Factor Analytic Study," Monogram Supplement, *Percept. Mot. Skills,* **3-V** (1964), 18.

2 Baird, J. C., "Retinal and Assumed Size Cues as Determinants of Size and Distance Perception," *J. Exp. Psych.,* **66** (1963), 155–62.

3 Beach, F. A., and J. Jaynes, "Effects of Early Experience Upon the Behavior of Animals," *Psych. Bull.,* **51** (1954), 239–326.

4 Bower, T. G., "Slant Perceptions and Shape Constancy in Infants," *Science,* **151** (1966), 832–34.

5 ———, "The Visual World of Infants," *Sci. Amer.,* **215** (1966), 80–97.

6 Bridges, K. M. B., "Emotional Development in Early Infancy," *Child Dev.,* **3** (1932), 324.

7 Brodbeck, A. J., and O. C. Irwin, "The Speech Behavior of Infants Without Families," *Child Dev.,* **12** (1946), 145–56.

8 Brody, S., *Patterns of Mothering,* New York: International Universities Press, 1951.

9 Casler, L., "Maternal Deprivation: a Critical Review of the Literature," *Monogr. Soc. Res. Child Dev.,* **26** (1961), 1–64.

10 Cratty, Bryant J., "Human Imprinting," in *New Perspectives of Man in Action,* eds., Roscoe C. Brown, Jr., and Bryant J. Cratty, pp. 74–87, Englewood Cliffs, N.J.: Prentice-Hall, 1969.

11 ———, and Margaret Mary Martin, *Perceptual-Motor Efficiency in Children, The Measurement and Improvement of Movement Attributes,* Philadelphia: Lea & Febiger, 1969.

12 Cruikshank, Ruth M., "The Development of Visual Size Constancy in Early Infancy," *J. Genet. Psych.,* **58** (1941), 327–51.

13 Davidson, Helen P., "A Study of Reversals in Young Children," *J. Genet. Psych.,* **44** (1934), 452–65.

14 ———, "A Study of the Confusing Letters B, D, P, Q," *J. Genet. Psych.,* **47** (1935), 458–68

15 Elkind, D., R. R. Koegler, and E. G. Koegler, "Studies in Perceptual Development: II. Part-Whole Perception," *Child Dev.,* **35** (1964), 81–90.

16 Fantz, R. L., "The Origin of Form Perception," *Sci. Amer.,* **204** (1961), 66–72.

17 ———, "Pattern Vision in Newborn Infants," *Science,* **140** (1963), 296–97.

18 ——, "Pattern Discrimination and Selective Attention as Determinants of Perceptual Development from Birth," in *Perceptual Development in Children*, eds., Aline H. Kidd and Jeanne L. Rivoire, New York: International Universities Press, 1966.

19 ——, and S. Nevia, "The Predictive Value of Changes in Visual Preferences in Early Infancy," in *Exceptional Infant: Vol. 1, The Normal Infant*, Seattle: Special Child Publications, 1967.

20 French, J. W., "The Relationship of Problem-Solving Styles to Factor Composition of Tests," *Ed. Psych. Measmt.*, **25** (1965), 928.

21 Gesell, Arnold, *Wolf Child and Human Child*, New York: Harper & Row, 1941.

22 ——, Frances L. Ilg, and Glenna E. Bullis, *Vision: Its Development in Infant and Child*, New York: Paul B. Hoeber, 1949.

23 Ghent, Lila, "Recognition by Children of Realistic Figures Presented in Various Orientations," *Canad. J. Psych.*, **14** (1960), 249–56.

24 ——, "Form and Its Orientation on Child's Eye View," *Amer. J. Psych.*, **74** (1961), 177–90.

25 ——, and Lilly Bernstein, "Influence of the Orientation of Geometric Forms on their Recognition by Children," *Percept. Mot. Skills*, **12** (1961), 95–101.

26 Gibson, E. J., "Developmental Study of Visual Search Behavior," *Percept. Psychophysics*, **50** (1966), 169–71.

27 ——, and V. Olum, "Experimental Methods of Studying Perception in Children," in *Handbook of Research Methods in Child Development*, ed., P. H. Mussen, pp. 311–23, New York: John Wiley & Sons, 1960.

28 ——, and R. D. Walk, "The Visual Cliff," *Sci. Amer.*, **4** (1960), 67–71.

29 Goldfarb, W., "The Effects of Early Institutional Care on Adolescent Personality," *J. Exp. Ed.*, **12** (1943), 106–29.

30 Gray, Philip H., "Theory and Evidence of Imprinting in Human Infants," *J. Psych.*, **46** (1958), 155–66.

31 Green, Richard, and John Money, "Effeminacy in Prepubertal Boys, Summary of Eleven Cases and Recommendations for Case Management," *Pediatrics*, **27** (1961), 2.

32 Haith, M. M., "The Response of the Human Newborn to Visual Movement," *J. Exp. Child Psych.*, **3** (1966), 235–43.

33 Haynes, H., R. White, and R. Held, "Visual Accommodation in Human Infants," *Science*, **148** (1965), 528–30.

34 Held, R., and J. Bossom, "Neonatal Deprivation and Adult Rearrangement; Complementary Techniques for Analyzing Plastic Sensory-Motor Coordinations," *J. Comp. Physiol. Psych.*, **54** (1961), 33–37.

35 ———, and A. Hein, "Movement Produced Stimulation in the Development of Visually Guided Behavior," *J. Comp. Physiol. Psych.*, **56** (1963), 872–76.

36 Hershenson, M., "Visual Discrimination in the Human Newborn," *J. Comp. Physiol. Psych.*, **58** (1964), 270–76.

37 Howard, I. P., and W. B. Templeton, *Human Spatial Orientation*, New York: John Wiley & Sons, 1966, Chap. 13.

38 Ilg, Frances L., and L. B. Ames, *School Readiness*, New York: Harper & Row, 1965.

39 Jeffrey, W. E., "Discrimination of Oblique Lines by Children," *J. Comp. Physiol. Psych.*, **62** (1966), 154–56.

40 Johnson, Betts, and L. F. Beck, "The Development of Space Perception: I. Stereoscopic Vision in Pre-School Children," *J. Genet. Psych.*, **58** (1941), 247–54.

41 Kagan, J., "Infants' Differential Reactions to Familiar and Distorted Faces," *Child Dev.*, **36** (1966), 519–32.

42 ———, "The Growth of the 'Face' Schema: Theoretical Significance and Methodological Issues," in *Exceptional Infant, Vol. 1, The Normal Infant*, ed., Jerome Hellmuth, pp. 335–48, Seattle: Special Child Publications, 1967.

43 Katsui, A., "A Developmental Study on the Perception of Direction in Two-Dimensional Space," *Jap. J. Psych.*, **33** (1962), 63–70.

44 Kephart, N. C., *Slow Learner in the Classroom*, Columbus, Ohio: Charles E. Merrill, 1964.

45 Lewis, Michael, J. Kagan, and J. Kalafat, "Patterns of Fixation in the Young Infant," *Child Dev.*, **37** (1966), 331–46.

46 Line, William, *The Growth of Visual Perception in Children*, Cambridge: University Press, 1931.

47 Ling, Bing-Chung, "Form Discrimination as a Learning Cue in Infants," *Comp. Psych. Monog.*, **2** (1941), 17.

48 Long, L., "Size Discrimination in Children," *Child Dev.*, **12** (1941), 247–84.

49 Misumi, J., "Experimental Studies on the Development of Visual Size Constancy in Early Infancy," *Bull. Fac. Lit. Kyushu Univer.*, **1** (1951), 91–116.

50 Piaget, J., and M. Lambercier, "Récherches sur le Développement des Perceptions: 33 La Causalité Perceptive Visuelle chez L'enfant et chez l'Adulte," *Arch. Psych.*, **36** (1958), 77–201.

51 Pick, H. L., R. E. Klein, and Anne D. Pick, "Visual and Tactual Identification of Form Orientation," *J. Exp. Child Psych.*, **4** (1966), 391–97.

52 Pieper, Albrecht, *Cerebral Function in Infancy and Childhood,* New York: International Behavioral Sciences Series, Consultants Bureau, 1963.

53 Riesen, A. H., "Plasticity of Behavior: Psychological Series," in *Biological and Biochemical Bases of Behavior,* eds., H. Harlow and C. Woolsey, pp. 425–50, Madison: University of Wisconsin Press, 1958.

54 Rudel, R. G., and H. L. Teuber, "Discrimination of Direction of Line in Children," *J. Comp. Physiol. Psych.*, **56** (1963), 892–97.

55 Sanders, A. F., "The Selective Process in the Functional Visual Field," *Institute for Perception Monograph,* Soesterberg, Netherlands, 1963.

56 Smith, O. W., "Problems for the Theorist Who Would Account for Everyday Perceptions of Depth and Distance," presented at N.R.C. Vision Committee Conference on Perceived Depth and Distance, Washington, D.C., 1961.

57 ———, "Spatial Perceptions and Play Activities of Nursery School Children," *Percept. Mot. Skills,* **21** (1965), 260.

58 ———, and P. C. Smith, "Developmental Studies of Spatial Judgments by Children and Adults," *Percept. Mot. Skills,* Monograph Supplement, 22, No. 1 (1966), 3–73.

59 Spitz, R. A., and K. M. Wolf, "The Smiling Response: A Contribution to the Ontogenesis of Social Relations," *J. Gen. Psych.*, Monograph No. 34 (1946), 57–156.

60 Thompson, W. R., and R. A. Dubanosky, "Imprinting and the Law of Effort," *Animal Behavior,* **12** (1964), 2–3, 213–18.

61 Vernon, M. D., "The Nature of Perception and the Fundamental Stages in the Process of Perceiving," in *Pattern Recognition,* ed., Leonard Uhr, New York: John Wiley & Sons, 1966.

62 Walk, R. D., and E. J. Gibson, "A Study of Visual Perception in the Human Infant with a Visual Cliff," presented at East. Psychol. Assn., Atlantic City, N.J., April 1959.

63 ———, and ———, "A Comparative and Analytical Study of Visual Depth Perception," *Psych. Monog.*, **75**:15 (1961), 519.

64 Wapner, S., and H. Werner, *Perceptual Development: An Investigation Within the Framework of Sensory-Tonic Field Theory*, Worcester: Clark University Press, 1957.

65 Watson, J. S., "Perception of Object Orientation in Infants," *Merrill-Palmer Quart.* **12** (1966), 73–94.

66 Weinstein, S., E. A. Sersen, L. Fisher, and M. Weisinger, "Is Re-Afference Necessary for Visual Adaptation," *Percept. Mot. Skills*, **19** (1964), 641–48.

67 White, Burton L., and Richard Held, "Plasticity of Sensorimotor Development in the Human Infant," in *Biological and Biochemical Bases of Behavior*, eds., H. Harlow and C. Woolsey, Madison: University Wisconsin Press, 1958.

68 Williams, Harriet G., "The Development of Certain Aspects of Visual Perception in Children," unpublished study, University of Toledo, 1968.

69 ———, "The Perception of Moving Objects by Children," unpublished study, University of California, Los Angeles Perceptual-Motor Learning Laboratory, 1967.

70 Wohlwill, J., "Developmental Studies of Perception," *Psych. Bull.*, **57** (1960), 249–88.

71 ———, and M. Weiner, "Discrimination of Form Orientation in Young Children," *Child Dev.*, **36** (1964), 1113–25.

The Body Image 5

The development of the child's awareness of his body, its parts, its movement capacities, and its relationship to environmental supports begins probably before birth. A study by Walters, for example, presents evidence that the child who engages in prolonged and vigorous prebirth movements can be counted upon to be advanced motorically during the first few years of life (33). Thus it would seem that the child begins learning about his capacities for bodily movements several months before he is separated from his mother.

Workers in the field of children's prosthetics sometimes attach something having size and weight to the stumps of children born without limbs so that the infant begins early in life to incorporate this into his body image. If this is not done, it is often found that the child may later reject a workable prosthesis when he becomes capable of using one. It would thus seem that visual-motor integrations begin to operate near birth in the formation of the child's perceptions of himself and his capacities for movement.

Formulating an acceptable definition of body image presents a formidable problem because of the variety of ways in which the term is utilized in the psychiatric, psychological, and child development literature. To some, the body image is a global concept encompassing all the movement capacities as well as the sensory impressions created by these movements. To others, the definition is a more operational one and includes simply the score obtained on a given test of body image, which might include evaluating the ability of the child to name body parts, to draw a human figure, or to construct a manikin.

It is apparent that if one were to accept the former definition, a discussion of body image would encompass a book larger than the present one. And yet it seems apparent that the body image of a child is composed of more than simply the ability to respond quickly and accurately when asked to identify body parts. The question of acceptability of either type of definition rests on the more basic question of whether the study of perception should include only those judgments that an individual can make at the conscious level (3).

The concept of body image, even if measured and defined in rather exact operational terms, may be further fragmented into the individual's perceptions of his body size and shape, judgments of the body's ability to perform, subjective feelings concerning the worth of the body and its parts, the body as exemplifying a masculine or a feminine manner of appearing and acting, or more subtle feelings about the body, i.e., the rigidity or penetrability of its psychological boundaries. Although most of the above components of the body image have been measured with varying degrees of success, relatively little attention has been paid to assessing these qualities from a developmental standpoint. The major focus of such measures has been on adults and children with various personality disorders.

Further problems related to body image revolve around the relationships between body build and/or the child's perceptions of the acceptability of his body and other psychological and social attributes. The relationship between body build and various personality traits has been the subject of increasing experimental attention. Similarly, relationships between social adjustment and body build have also been the subject of several research studies within recent years (8,11).

More global questions, of course, include those that attempt to elucidate the role of the child's or adult's perceptions of his body into a more comprehensive survey of the self-concept. Just how much does an individual's perceptions of his body and its functions influence and/or interact with his total perceptions of himself as an individual?

On the pages that follow, I will not attempt to answer all the questions posed in the preceding paragraphs. A rather operational look will be taken at the methods available for measuring various components of the body image, as well as the manner in which these measures reveal various developmental trends. The definition of body image offered for your consideration is as follows: The child's body image includes all measurable responses the child makes relative to his body's size, shape, components, perceived capacities for movement, and interactions with the environment. It is hoped that this rather comprehensive statement will assume more definitive outlines as the reader reviews the information that follows.

FEELINGS ABOUT THE BODY AND THE TOTAL SELF-CONCEPT

An important question that has been dealt with by various workers is the relationship between a child's feelings and perceptions about his body and his total self-concept. Moderate correlations have been obtained between measures of feelings about the body obtained from children (29) and scores purporting to evaluate a more global opinion of their total self-concept.

Piers and Harris, in a test of "The Way I Feel About Myself," found when subjecting their data to factor analysis that six components emerged, including one factor named Physical Appearance and Attributes. This factor was evaluated by yes-no responses to such questions as "I am good-looking," "I have a pleasant face," "I have a bad figure," and "I am strong." The other factors included Behavior (I do bad things), General and Academic Status (I am good in my school work), Anxiety (I cry easily), Popularity (I have many friends), and Happiness and Satisfaction (26).

In 1953, Secord and his colleagues developed tests they termed measures of "body cathexis" and of "self-cathexis." On the initial test, 46 body parts were presented to their subjects, and they were asked to rate them with regard to their feelings about these body parts using a five-choice scale, ranging from "I wish a change could be made," through "I have no particular feelings one way or another," to "I consider myself fortunate." The authors hypothesized that the scores they obtained on this body cathexis scale would be related to the manner in which their subjects expressed their feelings about the more general self-cathexis scale, which included items like "life goals," "morals," "moods," "ability to meet people," and similar more global components of the human personality.

Their findings point to moderate relationships between the total self-concept and an individual's feelings about his body. The correlations ranged from +.58 for men to +.66 for women. It was believed by Secord that women develop more anxiety about their bodies, and it was shown that they expressed less neutral feelings about their body parts than did the men in their sampling.

Unfortunately, neither Secord nor Piers and Harris seem to have carried out extensive work with children using their assessment devices. Nor have any other studies with which this writer is familiar used these or similar tools to evaluate developmental changes evidenced in children's feelings about their body and about their total self-concept.

Studies of these questions could be carried out by exploring the change in self-concept and body concept as a function of age and sex. Subjective observations of these changes are often seen in the literature; it would seem that with a more objective approach offered by these evaluative devices of this nature more precise educational guidelines could be formulated. Readers interested in more comprehensive discussions of research dealing with the total self-concept are referred to recent texts by Hamachek (18) and Wylie (36).

THE PERFORMING "SELF"

The body is perceived by the maturing child as a vehicle of physical performance. Thus, a portion of his perceptions about himself and his body is related to the quality of the performance his body permits him to achieve. A recent summary of the literature dealing with aspiration level as it relates to physical performance (11) discussed several investigations that indicated that a child's perceptions of himself as a performer vary as a function of age.

The manner in which the male perceives his performance capacities seems intimately related to his total personality complex. And early experiences with success and failure in physical performance, it has been hypothesized by more than one investigator, are influential on personality traits that persist into adulthood. Jones, for example, in a longitudinal study of late and early maturing boys states that during adulthood their physical differences largely disappeared, but psychological differences remained. The late maturers when adults still seemed to be engaging in immature attention-getting behavior, and the early maturers were more poised socially, seemed more secure, and were more successful in their professional undertakings. Mussen suggests that "in our culture, the boy in whom physical development is retarded is exposed to a sociological environment which may have adverse effects upon his personality development." Apparently being in a disadvantageous competitive position in athletic activities, as well as being regarded and treated as immature by others, may lead to negative self-conceptions, heightened feelings of rejections by others, prolonged dependent needs, and rebellious attitudes toward parents.

As well-adjusted children mature, they begin to establish more accurate concepts of their performance capacities. Their estimates of their future performance on tasks become more realistic (2), and they engage less in overcompensatory behavior as reflected in self-estimates as they grow older. If, on the other hand, they perceive themselves as inept, or are insecure for other reasons, their aspirations, as reflected in vocalized feelings about performance capacities, are frequently unrealistic, or are not voiced at all.

EVALUATING THE BODY IMAGE

Many strategies have been employed by experimenters when attempting to evaluate the body image. Included in the following discussions are tests of the verbal identification of body parts and tasks involving imitation of gestures, as well as others. Chapter 7, dealing with drawing behavior, also contains an evaluation of the draw-a-person test as a measure of body image.

DRAW-A-PERSON

A frequently used clinical tool for the assessment of personality, psychotic symptoms, and what might also be termed body image involves requiring the child to draw a picture of a person. The manner in which the child reacts is a function of the nature of the directions and his artistic ability, as well as innumerable factors inherent in the situation. Tests of this nature are questioned by several writers who have attempted to objectively assess their worth. Brengelmann, for example, suggests that when such drawings are utilized as assessments of personality, the ratings obtained "have been largely specific to the investigator," making "comparisons between investigators, and therefore, recognition of general trends in expressive behaviour difficult." Similarly, Swenson, who reviewed 87 studies that employed variations of the "draw-a-person" test, concluded that "definitive research on the basic meaning or significance of human figure drawings is lacking" (32).

This type of criticism has not prevented several investigators from attempting to assess intelligence through figure drawings of children (16), nor others from making various attempts at personality assessment and body image development by using such a measure. Consideration of the findings of these investigators, however, should be interpreted within the limitations outlined above. (See Chapter 7.)

Kephart, in a film titled *Body-Image,* suggests that the figure drawings of children reveal that initially the child perceives the face and some of its parts, primarily the eyes. Later in his development, he states, the child begins to gain an awareness of the limbs and their placement, revealed in drawings that include a balloon-like face from which the arms and legs directly protrude in the form of "sticks" (Fig. 5-1). Further developmental steps,

Figure 5-1 In the first attempts to draw the human form the legs usually project directly from a large head. The trunk is excluded.

Kephart asserts, include some indication of a trunk, and final development of the body image is reflected in the inclusion of legs and arms, hands with more details, and limbs that have been "fleshed out" in contrast to their earlier "spaghetti-like" appearance. A child is also shown in the film who has been required to arrange the parts of a manikin into a human figure. In this latter instance the trunk also is left out of the final reproduction, and the legs are shown arranged so that they protrude directly from the bottom of the head. It is difficult to validate Kephart's statements with reference to experimental data, insofar as he presents no accompanying studies to which we might refer to confirm his assumptions.

Ilg and Ames, at the Gesell Clinic, have used a modification of the draw-a-person test by presenting an incomplete man to children of various ages and asking them to draw in the missing body parts. From an analysis of the children's drawings, they suggested, one is able to trace the evolvement of the body image. Their data are subjected to exhaustive analysis; however, to summarize, it is found that by the age of five about 50 per cent of both boys and girls are able to add hair, eyes, ears, neck, arm, fingers, a leg, and a foot to the drawings in the proper places. Many children are able to perceive these parts and place them in context by the age of four. Not until the ages of eight and nine, however, were the children in this investigation noted to draw lines indicative of the facial expression they wish their picture to project (20).

VERBAL IDENTIFICATION OF BODY PARTS

Others have taken a different approach to the evaluation of the child's awareness of his body and its parts. This second type of evaluation has utilized the child's verbal responses to various directions as a means of evaluating corporal awareness. These instruments have their genesis in the neurological test devised by Head in the 1930's.

Benton and others have constructed tests whose scores depend not only on the accuracy of the response, but also on the speed with which the child identifies body parts when asked to do so. The Benton test also asks the child to point to the body parts of a picture and make correct identifications, and in all of the scoring carried out in this test more credit is given if the child consistently reverses his concepts of left and right, even though inaccurate responses are given, than if he evidences no such consistent reversal. This writer is unaware, however, of research in which the Benton test has been utilized to identify developmental trends in normal children. The major area in which it has been utilized is to assess children with various kinds of perceptual dysfunction.

We must turn to data supplied by Ilg and Ames for a somewhat sketchy picture of the manner in which children begin to identify body parts verbally as they mature. Awareness of the parts of the face, of the arm and hands, as well as of various left-right components of the body was utilized in their evaluation. By the age of five, about 80 per cent of the children they tested were able to name their eyes, when they were touched by the examiner, and about 50 per cent were able to name their eyebrows under similar conditions. By the age of seven, 70 per cent of these children correctly identified their eyebrows.

These investigators also obtained information concerning the manner in which the ability to identify the hand and its parts develops in children. The thumb seems easiest for children to identify, for over 90 per cent of the children in the study correctly identified it by the age of five years. From 60 to 70 per cent of the children correctly identified the hand when asked to do so by five years, whereas the middle finger and little finger were usually not named by the four-year-olds. The ring finger was usually not named before the age of seven.

PERCEPTION OF LEFT AND RIGHT

Further data collected by these investigators provide insight concerning the manner in which children begin to perceive their various left-right dimensions. After pointing to a hand or body part, the investigators asked, "What is the name of this to you?" It was found that from 74 to 66 per cent of the girls and boys at the age of five failed to identify correctly their left and right hands; by the age of six years, 62 per cent of the girls and 56 per cent of the boys still failed to make this kind of discrimination. By seven years, however, only 14 per cent of the girls and 16 per cent of the boys were unable to correctly identify their left and right hands.

The reasons given by the children that enabled them to make these left-right discriminations were classified by the experimenters. The most frequent reason given was that the hand was connected with a motor function of some kind—its use. "I use it to salute the flag, to eat with, to write with," etc., were frequent responses given by the children.

Ilg and Ames requested other right-left discriminations to be made relative to other body parts. It was found that the left ear and eye were identified correctly (or were accorded consistent opposite identifications) by about 50 per cent of the five-year-olds and by about 68 per cent of the six-year-olds in their investigation. By chance, children of course can be expected to give correct responses concerning left and right dimensions of their body about 50 per cent of the time!

By the age of six, 64 per cent of these children were able to identify correctly the left and right hands of the examiner; by seven years 74 per cent were able to do so; and by the age of eight years, 95 per cent could successfully project themselves into the reference system of the examiner.

Although the development of unilateral hand use is seen as early as the seventh *month* of age according to some authorities, it seems as though a cognitive awareness of the body's left-right dimensions is gained considerably later, at about the age of six or seven *years*. An awareness of up and down and of the sense of front and back is acquired during the preschool years, from three to four years, and an awareness of left and right develops during the first years at school (17).

Binet suggests that this kind of left-right recognition occurs at about the age of seven; Terman places it at six years, and Piaget agrees with him. According to Gallifret-Granjon (15), the recognition of a child's own left and right occurred at six years of age in 86 per cent of the cases he surveyed, and the recognition of left and right in an observer did not occur until the age of eight. The recognition of the relative position of three objects, using Piaget's test, does not occur before 10 or 12 years of age (17).

An important study concerning left-right orientation from a developmental standpoint was carried out by Spionnek (17), who found that these perceptions of the body evolve through several stages.

1. Stage One

The child cannot distinguish between the two sides of his body, from birth to about three and one-half years.

2. Stage Two

The child becomes aware that his left and right limbs are found on either side of his body but is unaware of their location, which body parts are called "left" and which ones are "right." This stage usually occurs between the ages of four and five years.

3. Stage Three

The child realizes that the left and right limbs and organs are found on opposite sides of his body without knowing that they are right or left parts (between the ages of six and seven years).

4. Stage Four

During the fourth stage the child comes to know precisely which parts of his body are right and left (between the ages of eight and nine years).

Employing operant conditioning, Spionnek has demonstrated that by five years of age children can be taught to correctly identify their left and right body parts. This is two years before children could normally be expected to make these kinds of judgments.

Data from an unpublished study by the author and one of his students also demonstrated that left-right discriminations in children classified as minimally neurologically handicapped could be significantly improved through training in various movement activities that incorporated various left-right decisions on the part of the child (i.e., "Roll over your left shoulder," "Jump and turn to your right," etc.) (11).

In experiments in which two choice answers are required (i.e., left or right) it may not be assumed that "correct" answers are being elicited unless a population of children responds with accuracy about 75 per cent of the time. It is thus apparent upon a review of this research that not until about the age of seven can normal children correctly identify their left and right body parts and sides with consistency.

THE IMITATION OF GESTURES

Tests of the type discussed above have been criticized insofar as they seem at times to be merely vocabulary tests. Can a child point to his thigh when asked to do so because he has an awareness of where his thigh is, or simply because he knows the meaning of the word? In most of these tasks, verbal "bridges" need to be built between the examiner's request and the response made by the child before the latter's response can be made correctly.

In an effort to produce a body image test in which the child's vocabulary would play a relatively inconsequential part, Bergés and Lézine developed a test by which children's bodily awareness is assessed by noting the accuracy in which they can imitate hand and limb gestures of the examiner. The test has been divided into two sections including both simple and complex gestures. In the initial portion of the test, simple hand and arm positions are assumed by the examiner, and the child is scored according to the proficiency he exhibits when imitating these. In the "complex gesture" section, the child is asked to imitate more difficult finger and arm gestures, some of which require the imitation of the tester's movements (6).

In the imitation-of-simple-gestures portion of the test, it has been found that three-year-olds are able to perform only about one half as well as six-year-olds, and at the age of four years, the children evidence about 75 per cent of the proficiency of children two years older.

When responses to complex gestures are evaluated, the three-year-olds are found to be only one third as proficient at copying these more complicated patterns, several of which involve movement, as are six-year-olds.

It was found that the simplest gestures for the children to copy were those in which static positioning was involved usually employing the arm and/or hand. More difficult were gestures in which two body parts were employed at the same time, i.e., "raise right arm and extend left horizontally." And the most difficulty was encountered by the children when they were asked to imitate gestures in which the limbs positioned in two planes, i.e., "parallel hands in different places with the left hand forward."

However, this type of test constructed by Bergés and Lézine might also be criticized as a valid measure of body image as indeed it is probably more a test of visual perception of the examiner's movements. In any case it represents an interesting approach to this kind of measurement problem and with refinement might even prove more useful in the future.

OTHER TESTS

Innumerable other measures have been utilized in efforts to assess the child's awareness of his body and his feelings about its shape and function. The somatic apperception test developed by

Adams and others, for example, utilizes a manikin and/or outlines of the body having various conformations (1,27). These tests attempt to ascertain how the individual feels about his body by noting discrepancies between the *ideal* body outline he selects and the outline he selects as his own. At other times, these judgments are compared to anthropometric measurements of the individuals making the selections.

Other measures range from the projective test, based on responses to the Rorschach used by Cleveland and Fisher to ascertain "barrier score," to tests of the extent to which the individual interposes rigid psychological boundaries between himself and his environment, to the more objective test devised by Dillon in which the subject is asked to adjust wooden frames via a pulley system until they seem to replicate his body's width and height. Unfortunately, these kinds of measures are seldom utilized with children. Developmental studies in which they have been employed are presently not available.

DEVELOPMENTAL TRENDS

A review of the literature reveals the following trends relative to the developmental stages through which children pass relative to gaining a conscious awareness of the names of various body parts and of their left-right dimensions. The manner in which the child's perceptions of his body are constructed is summarized below. The information upon which this table is based was gained from a survey of the available developmental literature, relating to measures of body image, some of which has been reviewed on the preceding pages.

Body Perception by Children (7 steps)

Age	Perceptions Formed
0–2 years	At the end of this period, the child can sometimes identify gross body parts verbally; can touch "tummy," back, arm, or leg when asked to do so; seems aware of toes before leg
2–3 years	Becomes aware of front, back, side, head, feet, and can locate objects relative to these body reference points; begins to gain awareness of more body parts, i.e., thumb, hand, feet, etc.; parts of face learned

4 years	Becomes aware that there are two sides of the body, and knows their names, but not their location; more detailed awareness of body parts gained; can name little finger and first fingers
5 years	Knows that there is a left and right side of the body, but is usually confused concerning their location; can locate self relative to objects, and objects relative to self; trunk appears in figure drawings
6 years	Begins to distinguish left and right body parts and to locate body relative to the left and right of things and objects relative to the left and right of the body; becomes aware of little finger and ring finger and names them
7–8 years	Concept of laterality well established; begins to correctly distinguish the left and right of other people and name correctly their left and right movements; facial expressions appear in figure drawings; limbs are filled in and details appear in figure drawings
9–10 years	Adopts other individual's perspective with ease; can describe the arrangement of objects from another's point of view

I have devised a body image rating scale incorporating some of the major concepts found in the previous studies. It has been validated using normal children from four to seven years of age. Two primary concepts underlie this scale: (1) The body image is formed at the conceptual level, as well as at the dynamic level, as the body interacts with objects in the environment. (2) Correct assessment of developmental stages in the acquisition of the body image requires that both static and dynamic judgments be made (i.e., "As I walk around you, tell me when I am nearest your left and right side").

The scale is meant as an assessment device, as well as to be suggestive of various training procedures. Its 16 steps are not mutually inclusive. For example, it is of course known that young children from the ages of three and four, while organizing their body planes, also acquire an awareness of some of the body parts.

The scale, together with evaluative exercises underlining each step, is presented below.

1 IDENTIFICATION OF BODY PLANES (FRONT, BACK, SIDE)
   a Touch the front of your body _____
   b Touch the top of your head _____
   c Touch your back _____

2 BODY PART IDENTIFICATION (LIMBS, ETC.)
   a Touch your feet _____
   b Touch your arm _____
   c Touch your leg _____

3 OBJECTS IN RELATION TO BODY PLANES
   a Where is the ball—in front of you, behind you, or by your side? _____
   b Is the ball by your feet or by your head? _____
   c Is the chair to your side, to your back, or to your front? _____

4 BODY PLANES IN RELATION TO OBJECTS (FRONT, BACK, SIDE)
   a Touch the wall with your side _____
   b Lie on the mat on your back _____
   c Place your back nearest the chair _____

5 MOVEMENTS OF THE BODY
   (a) Trunk Movement While Fixed
      i Bend forward to the front _____
      ii Bend to the side; bend to the other side _____
      iii Bend slowly backward _____
   (b) Gross Movements in Relation to Body Planes
      i Where is your side? _____ Can you move sideways? _____
      ii Can you move forward and backward? _____ Can you move sideways? _____
      iii Can you jump up? _____
   (c) Limb Movements
      i What can you do with your arms? Straighten arms _____ Bend arms _____ Lift arms at your shoulder _____ Turn your arms (rotate them both ways)

ii What can you do with your legs? Straighten legs
_____ Bend one leg at your knee _____
Lift one leg at your hip _____

6 LATERALITY OF BODY
   a Touch your left leg _____
   b Touch your right arm _____
   c Balance yourself on one foot _____

7 LATERALITY IN RELATION TO OBJECTS
   a Here is a chair; put your left side nearest the chair

   _____

   b Put your left foot in the box _____
   c Go up to the wall and put your right side nearest the wall;
     now move in and touch the wall with your left side

   _____

8 OBJECTS RELATED TO LATERALITY
   a Is that box by your side? _____
   b Is that stick touching your right or your left foot?

   _____

   c Which arm is nearest the ball? _____

9 LATERALITY TO MOVING OBJECTS
   a You stand still and I'll move around you. You tell me where
     I am. When am I at your back, at your left, at your right?

   _____

   b Now I'll move a little faster. You tell me where I am

   _____

   c Stand still and tell me where the rolling ball is to your
     body. Is it to your left, your right, your back, or your front?

   _____

10 MOVING BODY'S LATERALITY TO OBJECTS
   a You walk around this chair and tell me where the chair is in
     relation to you _____
   b (Use two chairs around which to walk a figure eight.)
     Walk around the chairs and tell me where you are. When
     are the left and right sides of your body nearest the chairs?

   _____

11 The Left and Right of Objects (Personal Reference System)
   a Point to the left side of the table _____
   b Point to the right side of the chair _____
   c Show me the right and left sides of the paper _____

12 Static Directionality with Other People (Projection into Another's Reference System)
   a (Person opposite subject.) Show me my left arm _____
   b Touch my right elbow _____
   c Touch my left ear with your left hand _____

13 Laterality of Other People in Relation to Static Objects
   a Which side of my body is nearest the chair? _____
   b As I walk around the figure eight (the two chairs) tell me which side of me is nearest to the object _____

14 Relation of Static Objects to Laterality of Other People
   a (Experimenter moves chair to a static position.) Where is this chair in relation to me? _____ Is it at my left or at my right? _____
   b Where is the ladder in relation to me? _____

15 Moving Objects in Relation to Others' Laterality
   a Tell me where the ball is as it moves around my body. Is it to my right, my left, my front, or my back? _____
   b Where is the moving rope? Is it to my front, my back, my left, or my right? _____

16 Laterality of Others' Movements
   a Tell me, am I walking to my left or my right? _____
   b Which way am I moving? _____

Several workers have claimed that the body image is important to the effective performance of motor skills. Critical to Kephart's theory is the notion that a well-established concept of left and right dimensions on the part of the child about his body transfers to his perceptions of correct dimensions in visual space. If a child's frame of reference from which he makes such spatial judgments is not well established, particularly with regard to left-right discriminations, he will frequently confuse various left-right dimensions of words and of letters. "No" will be perceived the same as "On," and further confusion will be seen as the child attempts to make accurate judgments relative to the difference between d's and b's.

Data supporting such a contention are somewhat scarce. In a recent study of Jean Ayres, no significant correlation was found between a test of body image emphasizing laterality and a score in a test of how well the children organized visual space (4).

However, the findings of Davidson (13) suggest that children at the age of five exhibit the same right confusion when attempting to discriminate between b's and d's as they exhibit when attempting to name their left and right hands. This relationship does not necessarily infer causality, however. It would appear that further more definitive research on this subject would be helpful.

The theory of perception that best supports the relationship between bodily perceptions and judgments made in visual space was outlined by Werner and Wapner, in 1949. In general, they contend that bodily tonus influences various spatial judgments, and in support of their argument they have presented evidence that experimental alternations of neck muscle tension will influence an individual's perceptions of the verticality of luminous rods in otherwise dark rooms or his perceptions of the vertical made kinesthetically and/or with tactile cues. Further investigations within this "sensory-tonic theory of perception" in 1957 by Wapner showed that the tendency of tonal alterations to influence spatial judgments was less pronounced in late than in early childhood. These data can be taken to indicate that although, during the early years of life (from birth to seven), children are somewhat dependent on their bodily perceptions when making spatial judgments, as late childhood is reached body-visual space relationships become less. This author has noted this same tendency to dissociate body from left-right judgments in space as a function of age in children he has evaluated clinically over the years.

In a thorough survey of the literature on spatial orientation and shape recognition and reproduction by Howard and Templeton, it is apparent that young children are first able to recognize and to replicate figures without any cognizance of a stable reference point. Only later do they become able to place them in correct positions relative to one another and relative to up-down and left-right dimensions. It might be assumed that some kind of body image training might enhance and hasten this "tying down" of spatial figures to stable reference points.

In a recent study by the author, a high correlation was found between a score obtained in a brief survey test of body image and the subjects' total score in a battery of tests evaluating agility, balance, ball tracking, and similar attributes. In other studies, moderate to high correlations have been found between scores obtained on the Benton Finger Identification Test and tests of manual dexterity (5,24). Although the subjects in both these investigations were atypical children, retarded and neurologically handicapped, it is apparent that body and hand image may have something to do with the ability to move the total body and the hands and fingers. Whether movement experiences heighten children's perceptions of their bodies or whether gaining a heightened awareness of the body aids in its movements is unclear. Perhaps a third factor, brain damage or verbal understanding, may contribute equally to both the ability to move the body and to evidence an awareness of its parts. In any case, these relationships should be investigated more thoroughly to determine causality, if any, and the direction of this causality.

SUMMARY

It is probable that when before birth the infant begins to exert his movement capacities, he starts to form his initial perceptions of his body and its capacities for movement. The body image of the child has been measured in innumerable ways, including direct report, reproduction of drawings, imitation of gestures, verbal identification of body parts, responses to various projective tests, ratings of feelings about the body's performance capacities, parts, and shape, construction of manikins using body parts, as well as by asking the child to select ideal as well as his perceived body shape from a series of drawings. Unfortunately, none of these measures has been applied in a systematic way longitudinally to a group of normal children, so that much of the available information is either incomplete or superficial in nature.

In any case, it appears that a cognitive awareness of various components of the body follows by several years the child's ability to move various body parts, although high relationships have been found between movement capacities and children's ability to verbally identify body parts. At two years, the child can identify various gross body parts, including arms, legs, and hands, his front, and sometimes his back. By the age of three and four, he begins to include his trunk in drawings of children, and by four he can usually identify portions of his hand, his thumb, little finger, and first finger, as well as portions of his body not previously identified, including knees, elbows, and sometimes shoulders. Parts of his face, including eyes, eyebrows, nose, and ears, are usually pointed to by the majority of the four-year-olds polled. By five years, the child learns that there is a left and right to things, and to himself, but cannot usually identify these with accuracy. By six, he begins to do so, but with some indecision; but by seven years of age, the normal child can make accurate left-right judgments about himself, and about visual space, using himself as a reference point. At eight and nine years of age, the child can correctly identify another person's left and right sides and in essence can move into another's reference system.

The individual's perceptions of his body, its shape, and his potential for performance of physical skills continues to become modified into adolescence and through adulthood. As indeed the body itself continues to become structurally changed during these years as a result of hormonal modifications during adolescence and structural fluctuations accompanying these biochemical changes, as well as the disuse of the muscular systems that often accompanies early, middle, and late adulthood.

BIBLIOGRAPHY

1 Adams, N., and W. Caldwell, "The Children's Somatic Apperception Test," *J. Gen. Psych.,* **68** (1963), 43–57.

2 Anderson, H. H., and H. F. Brandt, "Study of Motivation Involving Self-Announced Goals of Fifth Grade Children of the Concept of Level of Aspiration," *J. Soc. Psych.,* **10** (1939), 209–32.

3 Attneave, Fred, and Malcolm D. Arnoult, "The Quantitative Study of Shape and Pattern Perception," *Psych. Bull.,* **53** (1956), 452.

4 Ayres, Jean, "Patterns of Perceptual-Motor Dysfunction in Children: Factor Analytic Study," Monograph Supp. *Percept. Mot. Skills,* **1** (1965), 335–68.

5 Benton, Arthur L., *Right-Left Discrimination and Finger Localization,* New York: Paul Hoeber, 1959, p. 14.

Body Image, Developmental Channels

Years

Years	Verbal Identification of Body Parts	Awareness of Performance Capacities	The Hands
13	Body shape and performance capacity changes perceived	↑	↑
9–10	Can move into another's left-right reference system	Performance estimates extremely accurate	Manual capacities well developed
7–8	Accurately locates left and right on self and in space		
6	Locates left and right, details body parts, trunks appear in figure drawings	Performance estimates made with increased accuracy	Can verbally identify middle and ring finger
5	Learns about left and right but cannot locate properly		
4	Thighs, elbows, shoulders		First and little fingers and thumb identified
3	Planes of the body related to objects	Performance and estimates of performance variable	
2	"Tummy," legs, feet, arms, face parts		Identifies "hand"
1		Aware of own movements	Watches hands
Birth			

6 Bergés, J., and I. Lézine, *The Imitation of Gestures* (translated by Arthur H. Parmelee), London: The Spastics Society Medical Education and Information Unit in Association with William Heinemann (Medical) Books Ltd., 1965.

7 Brengelmann, J. C., "Expressive Movements and Abnormal Behavior" in H. J. Eysenck (ed.), *Handbook of Abnormal Psychology*, New York: Basic Books, Inc., 1961, Chap. 3, pp. 69–75.

8 Cleveland, Sidney, and Seymour Fisher, "Prediction of Small Group Behavior from a Body Schema," *Human Relations*, **10** (1957), 223–33.

9 Cratty, Bryant J., *Perceptual-Motor Attributes of Mentally Retarded Children and Youth*, Los Angeles County Mental Retardation Services Board, 1965 (Monograph).

10 ———, *Developmental Sequences of Perceptual-Motor Tasks*, Baldwin, N.Y.: Educational Activities Inc., 1967.

11 ———, *Social Dimensions of Physical Activity*, Englewood Cliffs, N.J.: Prentice-Hall, Inc., 1967, Chap. 3, "Aspiration Level."

12 ———, and M. Wilner, "The Effects of a Three-Month Training Program upon Children with Moderate Perceptual-Motor Dysfunction," unpublished study, 1967.

13. Davidson, H. P., "A Study of the Confusing Letters, B, D, P, and Q," *J. Genet. Psych.*, **47** (1935), 458–68.

14 Dillon, Donald J., "Measurement of Perceived Body Size," *Percept. Mot. Skills*, **14** (1962), 191–96.

15 Gallifret-Granjon, N., "L'elaboration des rapports spatiaux et al dominance laterale chez les enfants dyslexiques-dysorthographiques," *Bull Soc. Alfred-Binet*, **6** (1959), 452.

16 Goodenough, F. L., *Measurement of Intelligence by Drawings*, Yonkers, N.Y.: World Book, Co., 1926.

17 Hacaen, Henry, and Julian de Ajuriaguerra, *Left-Handedness, Manual Superiority and Cerebral Dominance*, New York: Grune & Stratton, 1964.

18 Hamachek, Don E., *The Self in Growth, Teaching and Learning* (Selected Readings), Englewood Cliffs, N.J.: Prentice-Hall, Inc., 1965.

19 Howard, I. P., and W. B. Templeton, *Human Spatial Orientation*, New York: John Wiley & Sons, 1966.

20 Ilg, Frances L., and Louise B. Ames, *School Readiness*, New York: Harper & Row, 1966.

21 Jersild, A. T., *In Search of Self*, New York: Teachers College Columbia University, Bureau of Publications, 1952.

22 Jones, Mary C., "The Later Careers of Boys Who Were Early or Late Maturers," *Child Dev.*, **28** (1957), 113–18.

23 Kephart, Newell C., *The Slow Learner in the Classroom*, Columbus, Ohio: Charles E. Merrill Books, 1966.

24 Meyers, John, "Relationships of Measures of Finger-Hand Perception to Manual Dexterity," unpublished, Perceptual-Motor Learning Laboratory, University of California, Los Angeles, 1967.

25 Mussen, Paul H., and Mary C. Jones, "Self-Conceptions, Motivations and Interpersonal Attitudes of Late and Early Maturing Boys," *Child Dev.*, **28** (1957), 243–56.

26 Piers, Ellen V., and Dale B. Harris, "Age and Other Correlates on Self Concept in Children," *J. Ed. Psych.*, **55** (1964).

27 Rowe, Allen A., and Willard E. Campbell, "The Somatic Apperception Test," *J. Gen. Psych.*, **68** (1963), 59–69.

28 Schilder, P., *The Image and Appearance of the Human Body*. London: Routledge and Kegan Paul, 1935.

29 Secord, Paul F., and Sidney M. Jourard, "The Appraisal of Body-cathexis: Body-cathexis and the Self," *J. Consult. Psych.*, **17** (1953), 343–47.

30 Sheldon, W. H., *Varieties of Temperament*, New York: Harper & Bros., 1942.

31 Subirana, A., "La droiterie," *Arch Suisses Neurol. Psychiat.*, **69** (1952), 1–2.

32 Swensen, C. H., "Empirical Evaluations of Human Figure Drawings," *Psych. Bull.*, **54** (1957), 431–66.

33 Walters, Etta, "Prediction of Postnatal Development from Fetal Activity," *Child Dev.*, **33** (1965), 801–808.

34 Wapner, Seymour, and Heinz Werner, *Perceptual Development: An Investigation Within the Framework of Sensory-Tonic Field Theory*, Worcester, Mass.: Clark University Press, 1957.

35 Werner, H., and W. Wapner, "Sensory-tonic Field Theory of Perception," *J. Personal.*, **18** (1949), 88–107.

36 Wylie, Ruth C., *The Self Concept*, Lincoln: University of Nebraska Press, 1961.

Manipulative Behaviors 6

Within the first few days of birth an infant becomes aware of objects within his space field. It will be several weeks, however, before he attempts to contact and to manipulate these objects. Researchers, to an increasing degree, are becoming interested in the stages through which infants and children pass as they perceive and attempt to deal with objects within their environment. It will be the purpose of this chapter to focus attention on some of these phases as the infant begins to handle objects, to manipulate them, and to otherwise utilize them.

The infant passes through four general phases when dealing with objects. Initially he becomes attracted by an object and sometime later becomes attracted to his own hand. The second stage involves general motor excitation as he is confronted with an object, with no coordinated attempt made to contact it. The third phase involves contact and manipulation to an increasing degree of sophistication. The fourth stage involves various kinds of exploitation of the object. He may stack blocks, throw balls, and otherwise find many things to do with and do to whatever he is handling. This latter phase evolves into more cognitive operations as he begins to give names to the objects with which he is confronted when speech develops during the latter part of the second year.

As the child matures, when he reaches the age of three and four, he begins to handle objects less and less, as he seems to have incorporated various shapes and surfaces into his consciousness. He does not need to directly handle each new object with which he is confronted to learn about it; he merely needs to glance at it (Fig. 6-1).

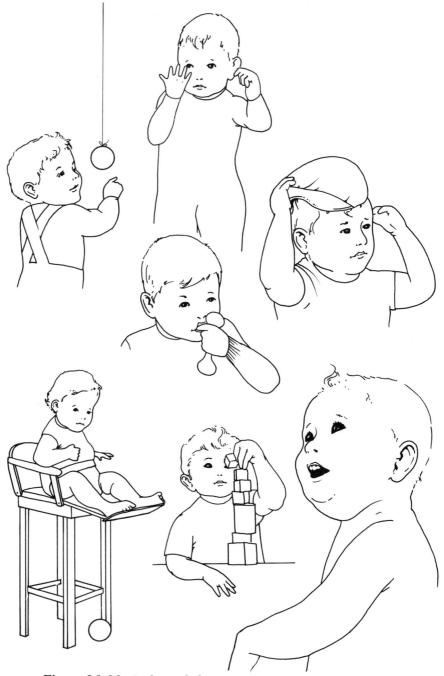

Figure 6-1 Manipulative behaviors take many forms during the first and second year of life.

Studies of the manual behavior of infants carried out during the 1930's and 1940's concentrated on the kind of manipulative behavior evidenced by the child (9). More recent research has focused attention on the basic concepts that may underlie and instigate manipulatory activity and the kind of precepts that seem to be acquired as the infant handles things (11,22). Some experts believe that the first evidence of what might be termed "cognitive behavior" is seen as the infant searches for objects that have temporarily fallen out of sight. This concept of "object permanency" seems to suggest that the child knows something can exist without its constantly being in his view (16).

As with all so-called sequences of emergent behaviors, it must be remembered that several kinds of manipulatory activity may occur within a given time period in the life of an infant. Similarly, an infant's reactions to a given object will vary from day to day, depending on the presence of distracting conditions, the level of arousal present, the nature of the stimuli, and his past experience with the object. Thus the manipulatory behaviors outlined on the following pages are meant to be descriptions of general phases through which the infant passes as he attempts to deal with objects using his hands and guided by his visual apparatus. Vast individual differences within the behavior of a single child as well as between children are usual.

Some investigators have focused their attention on the study of the motor dexterity of children, and others have become interested in various types of manipulatory behaviors because of an interest in the total cognitive-perceptual processes that are evidenced through the manner in which the hands explore objects (8,9,22).

There is evidence that manipulative abilities are accompanied by concomitant changes within the portion of the motor cortex that mediates hand movements. Conel, for example, found that while the initial cortical development in the infant is seen in the anterior central gyrus, which mediates the movements of the shoulder and neck region, by the time the infant is approaching his second year, the change in cortical development is seen in the region of the motor area of the central gyrus, which controls hand movements (2,3).

Important to the emergence of manipulative abilities in the infant is the delivery of the object to the mouth for inspection by tongue, lips, and regions of the inner mouth. Gesell and others have called attention to the importance of "mouthing" behavior, as the infant attempts to form his initial perceptions of size, shape, texture, and the like (7). Some authors suggest that voluntary manipulative behavior emerges from a refinement of the prehensile reflex. However, the most reliable evidence suggests that after the prehensile reflex terminates, the child may tend to hold things placed in his hand but will usually not attempt to manipulate them. Only later will be begin to make conscious efforts to contact and to manually examine objects.

HAND AND OBJECT REGARD

Prior to manipulating anything the child must organize, fixate, and attend to two important components of the processes: an object and his own hand. These two components seem to be initially organized independently of one another (24). Stages in orienting behavior have been identified in rabbits and in children by Polikanina and Probotova (17) and by Degtyar (4). The latter researcher investigated the reactions of 35 newborn children to visual and auditory stimuli during the first 80 days of life. It was found that bright lights elicited adaptive reactions in the eye. Pupil constriction occurred immediately after birth, and fixation of the gaze on a bright object, which was assumed to be the first rudimentary component of the orientation reaction, occurred at about five days in five of the children, at ten days in half the children, and in all 35 children by the fifteenth day. By the fourteenth day one half the children were also following a moving light, and by the fourth week all the children were able to track moving lights. A turning toward the source of sound emerged somewhat later, during the second month of life in one half the children, according to these Russian researchers (4).

It has been suggested that three phases may be identified in the early orienting behavior of infants: (1) From the first to the twenty-fifth day, automatic reactions are seen with the stimuli tending to elicit feeding behaviors, i.e., salivation and sucking. (2) From the twentieth to fortieth day the infant may exhibit some signs of "biological caution," i.e., attempting to shield himself from too strong a stimulus. (3) From 45 days onward, normal orienting reactions to moderate stimuli, or active aggressive or defensive reactions to stronger stimuli, are seen.

Another component of the situation, the hand, seems to be perceived at a somewhat later period in the life of the infant. Usually it is found that the infant begins to look at the reflexive clenchings of his own hand at some time between the fortieth and fiftieth days (24). The use of the hand can only come about, apparently, after the child has engaged in rudimentary visually guided hand-arm movement, prior to any kind of accurate or direct contact with an object or a plane surface. To illustrate this point, some investigators, raised infant macaques from birth in an apparatus that prevented them from seeing their body parts (11). During the thirty-fifth day they were permitted to see one of their hands. Although most monkeys of this type exhibit good visually guided manipulative behavior before one month of age, monkeys under these experimental conditions, although able to watch moving objects prior to the exposure of their hand (i.e., bottles approaching their mouths), became immediately fascinated with the movements of their own hand and exhibited intense hand-watching behavior described by Piaget and others (16). They spent more time watching their hands after they were exposed than they did watching movement in space, as they had done prior to finding out that things on their body also moved, and that they themselves seemed capable of moving these fascinating appendages.

In an investigation with human infants, White and Held attempted to determine whether the onset of such visual-motor behaviors as hand regard could be significantly altered by the imposition of various child-rearing conditions (24). Although, as might be expected, the "handled" group was visually more attentive during this period, the appearance of sustained hand regard was delayed by about one week (day 58), and the controls began to regard their hands (perhaps because they had little else to look at) about one week earlier (day 50). Another group of infants in this same investigation was afforded an even more enriched visual environment. This latter group evidenced less frequent hand regard as compared to the controls and usually first noticed their hands as they contacted portions of the experimental stabile. This latter group evidenced a considerably greater amount of prehensile activity. (These findings are discussed in Chap. 7.) It is important to note here, however, that the hand regard on the part of this second experimental group of 19 subjects was delayed by about two weeks. Thus in both groups it appears that the insertion of extra opportunities to see things, other than the infant's own body parts, may delay the *beginnings* of manipulative behavior from one to two weeks.

CONTACTING OBJECTS

Several concomitant behaviors then emerge. Depending on the youngster, the nature of the object, his previous experience with it, and the level at which the youngster is aroused, he may evidence general excitation when he perceives an object, or he may begin to engage in simple "swiping" and "corraling" behavior.

If he becomes generally excited, the motor activity he may evidence will sometimes consist of vertical arm movements, alternately moving the arms up and down, either in unison, one at a time, or only one. This is usually seen some time between the second and fourth months (24).

During the latter portion of this period the child may begin to make crude, and then increasingly accurate, attempts to contact objects. Initially in his arm wavings he may accidentally touch an object, and then he will begin to "swipe" at mobiles and at other objects that come into his view. Initially, the contacts usually occur by chance. If the object is left on a surface in front of him, his first attempts to contact it will come in the form of corraling movements, in which he reaches out with his entire arm-hand and sweeps the arm toward his body attempting to bring the object into a more advantageous position for viewing.

Following these rather inexact efforts the child seems to slow himself down during the latter part of the third month and the beginning of the fourth month. He begins to evidence behavior described by Piaget and others, in which he slowly moves his hand toward the desired object, alternately glancing from the object to his hand in the process, until contact is made (17). This initial unilateral behavior is often made with alternate hands, but Gesell and others have indicated that initial hand preference is often seen as early as the fourth month (6). Usually, this hand preference is not predominantly right-handed, as it seems later. Often hand preference seen in infants this age will tend to "blur" as he reaches the age of two and begins to focus his attention on his feet, which seem to need all the visual monitoring they can get in order to properly perform their locomotive function.

During this period a certain amount of two-handed reaching and grasping will be noted. At other times the child will initially reach and grasp an object with one hand, bring the other hand to it also, and then bring the object to be dealt with toward the midpoint of the body, just in front of his eyes.

From the second to the sixth month, the infant's manipulative behavior evidences two trends. He begins to examine in more detail each object he contacts. Simple palmar grasp evolves into finite tactile manipulation using the tips of the fingers and the first finger in opposition to the thumb and to the rest of the fingers (9,22). Also, the child begins to exploit objects in many ways. He begins to stack blocks, he may throw objects against surfaces to make noise, he may shake objects for a similar reason, and in other ways he figures out innumerable activities to carry out with the things he touches (7).

During the fifth and eighth months he usually evidences simple grasp with the palms of the hand and the thumb and fingers on the same side of the object, and a month later (the sixth month if he begins to evidence palmar grasp during the fifth month) the infant will begin to exploit objects with his fingers (9).

It is during these months that the child may be making "motor copies" of objects, as advanced in a theory by Solokov (20). Just as novel visual stimuli result in selective attention at an earlier age, objects whose shapes and/or colors are different will also elicit more of his time as he manipulates them. This tendency has been noted on the part of primates in studies carried out in the 1950's as well as in more recent studies using human infants (23,24).

This "motor-copy" theory is based on a cortical neuronal model, involving the tendency of the orienting reflex and manipulatory drive to be elicited by novel stimuli. A cortical cell assembly, it is suggested, preserves information about the characteristics of a stimulus against which stimuli subsequently explored, either visually and/or manually, are compared (20). When there is a lack of concordance between a present object and a previously acquired "perceptual-motor copy," it has been postulated that increased exploratory activity occurs owing to the generation of a cortical discharge to the nonspecific core brain. Continued presentation of an object stimulus, it is further assumed, results in feedback inhibition, which blocks input to this core system and thus inhibits additional visual-motor inspection of the object.

Dunsing and Kephart have proposed that there is another important function of early manipulatory efforts on the part of normal and atypical children (5). They suggest that the child learns about near and distant space as he manipulates objects in near space. The child, it is stated, learns about size-distance relationships by pairing the visual-motor information he obtains as he handles objects and places them various distances from his eyes. Other perceptual-motor data involving interposition and the like, according to these authors, are also explored by the child in the near-space field and transpose themselves to similar perceptual experiences in distant space (5). The child, it is thus hypothesized, extrapolates this sensory-motor near-space information to distant space in which he has no direct contact. Dunsing and Kephart conclude that early and accurate exploratory experiences involving the hand-eye action systems are imperative to the total perceptual organization of the child, and conversely, deficits in hand-eye coordination during these formative months may seriously blunt the child's ability to organize the components of his total visual spatial world.

Their theory is rather a simplistic one, particularly when consulting factorial studies of perception by Coan (1), Smith (19), and other researchers, which suggest the multifactor nature of visual space perception. Its tenets, however, are intriguing and offer hypotheses that might be further explored under well-controlled experimental conditions.

As the child contacts objects with his hand, he passes through three general phases: (1) simple contact, (2) crude palmar grasp and inspection, and (3) the forming of exact "motor copies" of objects through exact tactual inspection. Relative to this latter stage, Gibson has identified many of the perceptions obtained as one manually inspects objects. These include the *rigidity* of the object (how yielding the surface is to the touch); the *unity* of the object (the general configuration obtained from synthesizing the number of discrete sensations obtained from the exploring fingers); the stability of the object (the tendency of an object to assume a stable position in space despite the manner in which the fingers move over its surfaces); the object's weight, as well as texture, shape, and thickness (8).

THE EXPLOITATION OF OBJECTS

During and following the sixth month of life the child begins to evidence numerous cognitive and social processes as he uses objects in various ways. A detailed classification of these schemata was recently developed by Uzgiris (22). It was found that the initial way in which the child deals with objects is to shake them and to hit them against surfaces and against each other at about the sixth month of age. This shaking behavior usually takes the form of back-and-forth movements in a horizontal plane and is not continued for a very long period of time, nor is it appropriate for all types of objects.

The infant, according to Uzgiris, then begins to examine objects, to turn them over. This examination phase, according to this researcher, soon evolves into many differentiated schemata. After the sixth month, behavior in which tearing, pulling, crumpling, squeezing, rubbing, sliding, pushing, and similar activities are carried out concurrently, or in close temporal proximity to one another, is often observed.

The "letting-go" schema is also seen during these months, Uzgiris writes. The infant drops and throws objects, which permits him to pair auditory with visual cues, to explore the manner in which things rebound from various surfaces, to learn the sounds they make on impact, and to form similar perceptual impressions. Kephart suggests that this type of "motor generalization," in which he also includes the receipt (catching of objects), is an imperative one for the initial perceptions of velocity and the like (5).

Following this rather thorough exploitation of objects, the infant may be noted, at about the eleventh month, to use objects to instigate social contact with another individual. Uzgiris has termed this type of behavior the "showing" schema. When presented with the object, the infant will often hold it out to another person during this period, to get his reaction and to perhaps initiate some kind of simple social contact and interaction. If the other individual attempts to take the object, the infant usually withholds it; so apparently all he is striving for is a rather passive reaction on the part of another person, rather than a direct interaction, which he will seek after the age of two years.

The final schema identified by Uzgiris has been termed "naming." This behavior, of course, is dependent on the emergence of verbal behavior and usually is seen at about the eighteenth to the twenty-fourth month. The classification of objects as a basic intellectual process has been alluded to by more than one scholar interested in cognition. Thus one is able to identify a trend by examining the previously discussed schemata, from simple manipulatory activities to more conceptual ones, from the motor through the perceptual to the cognitive.

MANUAL DEXTERITY IN MIDDLE AND LATE CHILDHOOD

After a child becomes able to manipulate objects and to control his hands with reasonable efficiency, he will generally seek to perform a variety of tasks. Although it is probable that his attribute pattern, like that explored within other channels of perceptual-motor development, tends to become diffuse, I am unaware of any major factor analyses identifying the factors of manual dexterity in children that may have been carried out. Thus the pages that follow will discuss the findings from the few available investigations in which performance in manipulative tasks as a function of age has been explored. The Oseretsky test contains several measures of manual dexterity, some of which have been employed by other experimenters. Keogh, for example, used the maze tracing task in which the child must draw a continuous line between two maze pathways with his left and then with his right hand. Scoring criterion for success is the ability of the child to complete the pattern without crossing the lines. The findings in this study indicated that the preferred hand was most proficient, with the boys and girls performing equally well with their preferred hand (13). The girls, however, were somewhat better with the nonpreferred hand (67 per cent of girls passing versus 47 per cent of boys passing) at age six, and also at age seven (with 83 per cent of the girls passing and only 63 per cent of the boys successful). At ages eight and nine the boys and girls evidenced equal proficiency with either hand, and the sex differences were minimal.

FINGER OPPOSITION

A frequently used test in clinical evaluations of neurological functioning involves asking the child to rapidly touch each finger, in turn, to his thumb (Fig. 6-2). In general, when this test is administered to children, five-year-olds do reasonably well but usually perform slowly and need to watch the finger movements carefully. Additionally this age group may evidence "spillover" (i.e., twitchings in the hand not being tested).

By the age of seven and eight years most normal children can perform this type of task quite well. A scoring method developed by Stott for the objectification of this task has been employed by Holbrook, Keogh, Sloan, and others (12,13,18,21). The scoring

Figure 6-2 Finger opposition is evaluated by how fast and accurately a child can touch each finger, in turn, to his thumb. A five-year-old child will have to watch his hand, and often residual tension will be seen in the opposite hand.

criteria involve both time and touch errors (touching a finger out of order, touching two fingers together, or missing a finger).

In general, there is a marked improvement in the children in passing this type of task from the age of six to seven. Girls are usually found to be significantly better than boys. For example, in one investigation 70 per cent of the six- and seven-year-old girls surveyed passed the test, but only 47 per cent of the boys could perform successfully. The most common "touch" errors involved skipping or repeating a touch. In this task, speed increases markedly between the ages of six and seven, and between seven and eight. For example, at age six, Holbrook discovered, 65 per cent of the children she tested completed the task under five seconds; at age seven, 85 per cent could do so. Sloan found that 60 per cent of the children he tested performed rapidly (under five seconds at age seven), and at eight years, 80 per cent could perform rapidly. Keogh also found an increase between the same ages in the data he collected in 1963 (i.e., from 73 per cent at age seven to 92 per cent at age eight).

SPOOL WINDING

A spool-winding task involving the speed with which a child can wind a string around a spool using one or two hands has been used by several researchers. Although the fact that children may tend to get the string tangled has made the task difficult to administer, Holbrook, Keogh, and others have employed it to obtain age norms. In general, children of both five and six years usually take slightly over 20 seconds to complete the task with light sex differences in favor of the boys.

DROPPING OBJECTS INTO SMALL HOLES

Marble-dropping tasks are traditionally used in psychology tests evaluating the influence of a variety of variables on the performance of younger children. The task is easy for the children to understand, reasonably reliable data can be obtained, and the expected learning curves are produced. This type of task, however, is not usually employed specifically to evaluate manual aptitudes; however, a similar "penny bank" task has been used for this purpose. The task requires a child to drop 12 pennies, one at a time, into a bank. It is usually scored for both the left and right hands, in units of time. In general, the differences in mean scores between the ages of five and six are negligible, with the boys slightly superior to the girls (13). Holbrook scored a similar task in which 20 coins were placed in an open box and found that while 30 per cent of her subjects could accomplish the task under 16 seconds at age five (using their preferred hand), by the age of seven, 80 per cent of her subjects could successfully complete the task under the specified time (12).

THREADING BEADS

The common task of bead threading has been employed by Keogh, from the test developed by Stott, to assess manual competence in children. The task involves threading eight cubes onto a metal-tipped lace, with time to the nearest second used as a scoring criterion (21).

By Stott's criterion for passing (completion under 20 seconds), about 80 per cent of Keogh's subjects passed this test at age eight, and 88 per cent passed it at age nine. No other ages were sampled in this portion of his investigation using this task.

MATCHSTICKS

The Oseretsky test contains a task in which matchsticks must be placed in a box. A similar task has been employed by Keogh

(13). Five matchsticks placed on each side of a box must be placed inside the box, and the time to the nearest tenth of a second is taken as the scoring criterion.

Keogh found that the boys were significantly slower than the girls at the age of five. Holbrook, using ten pairs of matchsticks in a similar task (passing mark of 16 seconds), found that 25 per cent of her children passed at age five; 70 per cent passed at age eight.

PREFERENCES FOR MANIPULATIVE ACTIVITIES

In a recent survey compiled in our laboratory at the University of California at Los Angeles a number of game preferences were assessed in children using a short form of the Sutton-Smith test. Among these preferences were certain manipulative activities. The data from this investigation are graphed in Figure 6-3 and are based on the responses of 16 girls and 132 boys.

As can be seen, in the eighth year a large percentage of the girls reported engaging in sewing and playing jacks, both activities requiring manual dexterity. The similarity of the responses in the two activities is remarkable, as indicated.

It is believed that the findings from a study now in progress, in which over 1,000 children's responses are being collected and summarized, should reveal even more interesting information about childhood preferences for both fine and gross motor activities.

SUMMARY

The data outlining parameters of manual dexterity in children from the ages of 4 to 12 are indeed difficult to evaluate. In general, the available information shows the expected age trends and sex differences, but in no consistent or predictable direction. The manual dexterity of children should be explored via factor analytic methods, similar to the studies carried out by Fleishman and his colleagues who employed adult subjects.

The available research studies merely indicate helpful directions and have begun to uncover tasks that one might reasonably expect children to complete. Until more definitive data are available, it is extremely difficult to formulate guidelines to help understand or improve the manual ability of children.

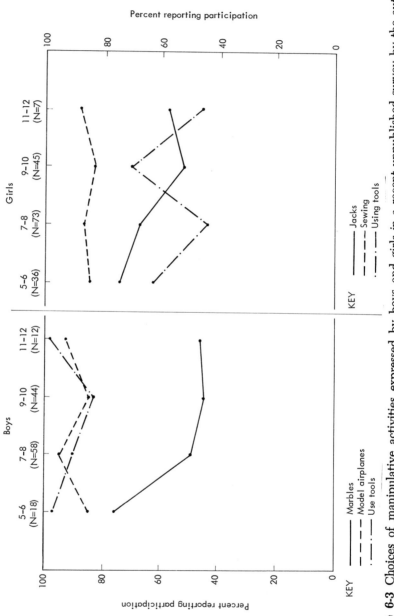

Figure 6-3 Choices of manipulative activities expressed by boys and girls in a recent unpublished survey by the author.

Selected Behaviors	Time During Which It Is Seen in Majority of Infants
1. Separate looking at objects	1–3 months
2. One- and two-arm control	2–4 months
3. Looking at objects, i.e., arm waving and other signs of excitement	2–4 months
4. Alternates his glance from object to hand	1–4 months
5. "Corrals" objects, swipes at objects	2–4 months
6. Both hands brought to the front of his body	2–4 months
7. Gradually brings his hand to an object	3–5 months
8. Hand preference emerges	4–12 months
9. Mouths objects	4–12 months
10. Grasps object with palm	5–8 months
11. Grasps with fingers	6–9 months
12. Grasps with fingers, examines objects, makes "motor copies"	6 months plus
13. Exploits objects, shakes, hits, etc.	6 months plus
14. "Letting-go" behavior, drops and throws	6 months plus
15. Loses sight of object and searches; object permanence concept	6 months plus
16. Showing: the beginning of social behavior by using objects	11 months plus
17. Naming objects: classification concept	18 months plus

BIBLIOGRAPHY

1 Coan, Richard W., "Factors in Movement Perception," *J. Consult. Psych.,* **28** (1964), 394–402.

2 Conel, J. L., *The Postnatal Development of Human Cerebral Cortex. Vol. I. The Cortex of the New Born,* Cambridge: Harvard University Press, 1939.

3 ——, *The Postnatal Development of the Human Cerebral Cortex. Vol. II. The Cortex of the One-month Infant,* Cambridge: Harvard University Press, 1941.

4 Degtyar, E. N., "Conditions Required for the Formation of a CR System at Various Functional Levels of Children's Nervous Activity," *Zhur. Vysshei Nerv. Deiatel.,* **13** (1963), 631–37.

5 Dunsing, Jack, and N. C. Kephart, "Motor Generalizations in Space and Time," in *Learning Disorders Vol. I,* Bernie Straub and Jerome Hellmuth (eds.), Seattle: Special Child Publications, Seattle Seguine School, 1966, pp. 77–121.

6 Gesell, A., "The Ontogenesis of Infant Behavior," in *Manual of Child Psychology,* 2nd ed., L. Carmichael (ed.), New York: John Wiley & Sons, Inc., 1954.

7 ——, and Frances L. Ilg, *Child Development,* New York: Harper & Bros., 1949.

8 Gibson, J. J., "The Useful Dimensions of Sensitivity," *Amer. Psych.,* **18** (1963), 178–95.

9 Halverson, H. M., "An Experimental Study of Prehension in Infants by Means of Systematic Cinema Records," *Gent. Psychol. Monogr.,* **10** (1931), 107–286.

10 Harris, Laurren, "The Effects of Relative Novelty on Children's Choice Behavior," *J. Exp. Child Psych.,* **2** (1965), 297–305.

11 Held, Richard, and J. A. Bauer, "Visually Guided Reaching in Infant Monkeys After Restricted Rearing," *Science,* **155** (1967), 718–20.

12 Holbrook, S. F., *A Study of the Development of Motor Abilities Between the Ages of Four and Twelve, Using a Modification of the Oseretsky Scale,* Doctoral dissertation, University of Minnesota, 1945.

13 Keogh, J. F., "Analysis of Individual Tasks in the Stott Test of Motor Impairment," Technical Report 2-68 (USPHS Grant HD 01059), Department of Physical Education, University of California, Los Angeles, 1968.

14 Lynn, R., *Attention, Arousal and the Orientation Reaction,* New York: Pergamon Press, 1966.

15 Peiper, Albrecht, *Cerebral Function in Infancy and Childhood,* New York: Consultants Bureau, 1963.

16 Piaget, J., *The Origins of Intelligence in Children,* New York: International Universities Press, 1952, pp. 103–107.

17 Polikanina, R. I., and L. E. Probotova, "On the Question of Identifying the Orientation Reaction in Premature Babies," *The Orientation Reaction and Orienting-Investigating Activity,* Moscow: Acad. Pedag. Sciences, 1958, R.S.F.S.R.

18 Sloan W., "The Lincoln-Oseretsky Motor Development Scale," *Gen. Psych. Mono.,* **51** (1955), 183–252.

19 Smith, Olin W., "Developmental Studies of Spatial Judgments by Children and Adults," *Percept. Mot. Skills,* **22** (1966), 3–73, Monograph Supplement I-V22.

20 Solokov, E. N., "Neuronal Models and the Orienting Reflex," in *The Central Nervous System and Behavior,* ed., M. A. Brazier, New York: J. Macy, 1960.

21 Stott, D. H., "A General Test of Motor Impairment for Children," *Dev. Med. Child Neurol.,* **8** (1966), 523–31.

22 Uzgiris, Ina C., "Ordinality in the Development of Schemas for Relating to Objects," in *Exceptional Infant,* Vol. 1, ed., Jerome Hellmuth, Washington: Special Child Publications, 1967, pp. 315–34.

23 Welker, W. I., "Some Determinants of Play and Exploration in Chimpanzees," *J. Comp. Physiol. Psych.,* **49** (1956), 84–90.

24 White, Burton L., and Richard Held, "Plasticity of Sensorimotor Development in the Human Infant," in *The Causes of Behavior: Readings in Child Development and Educational Psychology,* Judy F. Rosenblith and Wesley Allinsmith (eds.), Boston: Allyn and Bacon, Inc., 1966.

Scribbling and Drawing **7**

At birth the infant is attracted for short periods of time to movement occurring in his space field. By about the third month he begins to watch the movements of his own hand, and within a few days he begins to manipulate objects in space with varying degrees of competence.

By about the eighteenth month he has begun to exploit objects manually. He may accidentally throw a block, he may hit the table in front of him with sticks, and he may shake rattles for the satisfying noisy reinforcement they provide. During this period of exploitation the infant is likely to grasp something that, when touched to another surface, makes a mark. If he is lucky and the implements are available, he soon realizes that there are classifications of things, such as crayons, pens, pencils, and the like, that are meant for marking. He will then proceed with vigor to mark every surface in sight in various ways, including the walls, the dining room table, and other handy surfaces.

The stages through which a child passes when scribbling and learning to draw and to write are generally as follows:

1. One child may simply attend to a writing implement by holding it; another child may use this implement to make marks on paper and on other surfaces.

2. Crude scribbling is engaged in and random marks are made seemingly without any plan and without producing any coherent designs.

3. The child reacts to some kinds of stimuli on the writing surfaces. He may draw lines and squares, and he may balance out a figure on one side of a piece of paper with a spiral of scribbling on the other side of that piece of paper.

4. Simple geometrical figures are drawn, usually consisting first of crude crosses and simple spirals.*

5. More exact geometrical figures are drawn; figures are placed in combinations of two and more; and pictures are colored with increasing accuracy.

6. More complex designs are made; drawings are made of people, of houses, and of other objects familiar to the child.

7. Block printing and cursive writing are taught in school and are learned by the child.

8. With proper training and/or interest, pictures and figure drawings of three dimensions and involving increased complexity are drawn.

Although it does not often seem so, the scribbling behavior of the infant from 15 months to two and one-half years and older proceeds within reasonably discernible stages. These sequences become apparent, however, if the efforts of a large number of children are analyzed and classified. One of the several scholars interested in this facet of a child's perceptual-motor behavior is Rhoda Kellogg, who during a period of 20 years collected and classified over 1,000,000 drawings and paintings by infants and children (6).

Kellogg lists four steps in the acquisition of hand-eye control seen in drawing and writing. These include the scribbling stage; the combine stage, during which diagrams and combinations of two diagrams are drawn; the aggregate stage, during which three or more geometrical figures in combination are drawn; and the pictorial stage, during which pictures are made with increasing accuracy.

Within the initial scribbling stage about 20 substeps are identified by Kellogg. Despite these classification systems, it is difficult to obtain exact developmental norms for the acquisition of various degrees of drawing and scribbling competency because of the influence of a number of variables on children's efforts. It is obvious that a child who observes others writing and drawing within the home and who has pencils and other implements available to him will acquire competency before a child who has no opportunities to observe and to practice drawing skills. The reader

---

* In general it has been found that the higher primates (gorillas and chimpanzees) are able to accomplish steps 1, 2, and 3 and can often make simple crosses on a page, such as one short line crossing another short line (8).

should keep in mind, therefore, that, perhaps more so than other skills, scribbling, drawing, and writing are shaped to a large degree by conditions within the home environment.*

RANDOM AND REPETITIVE ACTIONS

The initial stages of scribbling may emerge by accident as a child makes a mark on one object with another object. The visual cue becomes reinforcing and other marks are made. The first marks are usually done hesitatingly, and with practice these marks become bolder and more repetitive.

Some authorities claim that horizontal movements are made prior to vertical ones, but others claim that the opposite is true (3,5). In general the literature suggests that the child may make unrelated marks in a number of directions during the early stages of scribbling.

As courage is gained these marks become repetitive and may either be horizontal or vertical or form a radiating pattern (Fig. 7-1).

Figure 7-1

During these early months, as the child scribbles on a page he may begin to react to visual forms. If the form is a small one, he may attempt to obliterate it with his efforts (Fig. 7-2).

* This amazingly well-detailed text contains an important chapter evaluating "Children's Art as a Mental Test," in which the author poses important questions for those attempting to evaluate mental and emotional attributes through children's efforts at drawing geometrical designs and representational figures, i.e., the human figure. I believe that her evaluation of these tests is among the most lucid I have encountered, and I recommend it to the readers of this book.

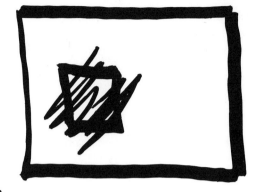

Figure 7-2

On the other hand, the child may try to "balance" a form on a page with his efforts on the opposite side (Fig. 7-3).

Figure 7-3

If the form is large, the child may begin to evidence a desire to stay within its boundaries (Fig. 7-4).

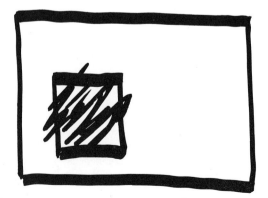

Figure 7-4

ENCLOSING SPACE

As more control is gained, the child will slow down his movements and begin to attempt to guide them with his eyes during the early and middle parts of his second year of life. His first efforts within this second phase seem to evidence a need to enclose space (Fig. 7-5).

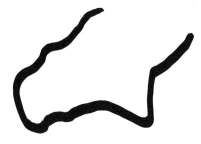

Figure 7-5

These lines may rove and contain a loop or two (Fig. 7-6).

Figure 7-6

Waving lines, usually horizontal but at times either vertical or lateral, may appear shortly after the child begins to enclose space in a restricted area on the page (Fig. 7-7).

Figure 7-7

Prior to the emergence of the often seen "curly-haired" loop is the single loop, which is followed by a repetitious loop (Fig. 7-8).

A   B

Figure 7-8 *A.* Single loop. *B.* Multiple loop.

After the child finds that he can travel with his repetitive loops, he then discovers that he may make a spiral within a smaller amount of space (Fig. 7-9).

Figure 7-9

With practice he may produce an overlaid circle, and then gradually a circle will emerge that contains multiple circumferences with a clear center (Fig. 7-10).

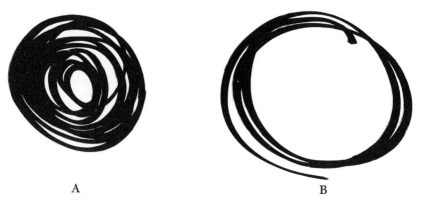

A   B

Figure 7-10 *A.* Overlaid circle. *B.* Circle with several circumferences.

As the circular movement is placed under more strict control, the child begins within the third or fourth years to make imperfect circles consisting of a single circumference (Fig. 7-11).

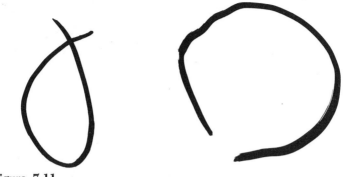

Figure 7-11

At about the same time the child's scribblings evolve to the ability to make a crude circle, his efforts may also lead him toward the drawing of rudimentary squares. His first attempts at replicating geometrical configurations usually take the form of simple crosses, and with practice he makes repetitive crosses with both horizontal and vertical lines (Fig. 7-12).

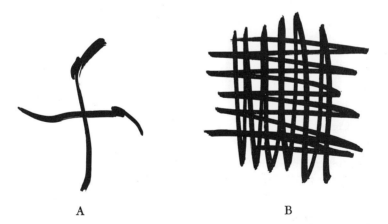

A   B

Figure 7-12 *A.* Simple cross. *B.* Crossing-bar configurations.

Thus by the time the child reaches the middle of his third year he may begin to enter what has been described as the diagram phase.

Squares may begin to emerge in several ways. The child may

begin to leave spaces within his repetitive vertical and horizontal lines (Fig. 7-13).

Figure 7-13

At other times he may begin to "square off" circles (Fig. 7-14).

Figure 7-14

Another child may be seen to copy squares by following sides of his paper with straight lines (Fig. 7-15).

THE DIAGRAM PHASE

Several researchers have been interested in the manner in which children acquire the ability to draw geometrical figures, as well as in the methods they use when drawing these standard configurations (3,5,6,7). In a recently developed test by Vane, using the drawings of geometrical figures, vocabulary, and draw-

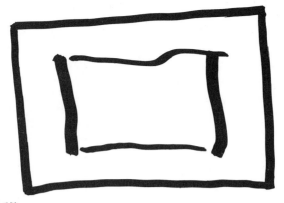

Figure 7-15

a-man subtests, high correlations were found between the total scores and I.Q. (r = .76 with the Binet) and school achievement (r = .6 with the Stanford Achievement Test) (10).

In general, the following characteristics are seen as children begin to draw geometrical shapes during the end of the third year * and during the fourth year. Geometrical shapes begin to resemble houses and other familiar parts of the child's environment. What Kellogg has termed "mandalas" often appear (6). Crude figure drawings, using stick figures, may be tried (Fig. 7-16).

In a study conducted by the author with 170 children from four to eight years of age, the children were asked to copy five geometrical figures including the square, the circle, the rectangle, the triangle, and the diamond (3). The results included the following findings:

1. The younger children of four and five years of age tended to try to draw squares and rectangles one side at a time rather than in a continuous manner.

2. About 50 per cent of the four- and five-year-old children did not close the lines forming their circles.

---

* The accuracy of the drawing depends on several important variables including whether there is a model to copy, whether the child's hand has been just guided through the desired configuration, whether the figure to be copied remains in sight, how long a stimulus figure has been removed from view, and the culture and subculture in which the child is raised. For example, it is unlikely that rectangles and squares will appear very early, if at all, in the drawings of a child reared in the African bush, owing to the absence of these exact configurations within his environment.

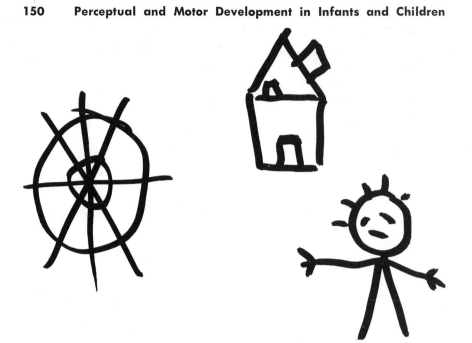

Figure 7-16

3. By the age of five years their drawings of rectangles, circles, and squares were clearly separable.

4. Right-handed children usually began to draw squares and rectangles with the upper left corner of the figures and proceeded in a counterclockwise manner until the figures were complete. Left-handed children usually started with the upper right corner of the figures and proceeded in a clockwise manner.

5. Not until the age of six years did the children draw a triangle with accuracy. Both triangles and diamonds were usually begun in the upper angle.

6. Not until the age of seven years did most children accurately reproduce a diamond.

7. Using the same stimulus figure to copy, the children drew the more difficult geometrical figures smaller; i.e., triangles were drawn smaller than were squares, and diamonds were drawn smaller than were triangles.

8. This tendency to draw the more difficult figure smaller was more marked in older children than in younger children; four- and five-year-old children all drew the figures large and inaccurately.

9. The children generally resisted drawing lateral lines and

often attempted to reproduce triangles by turning the paper when drawing each side of the figure, so that a horizontal and a vertical line were drawn relative to the edge of the table nearest the child.

From 1958 to 1962 Frances Ilg and Louise Ames tested more than 300 different children, assessing their abilities to copy six geometrical forms (Fig. 7-17). Many of the children in this inves-

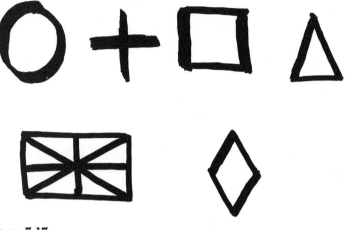

Figure 7-17

tigation were tested more than once, so that a total of 700 examinations were given (5).*

A detailed analysis was made of the manner in which the children drew each of the figures, and the results were presented in percentages. Although the detailed findings are too expansive to be reviewed in detail on these pages, the major findings included the following:

1. The order of difficulty of the figures (from least difficult to most difficult) was the circle, the square, the triangle, the divided rectangle, and the diamond. Generally the three-year-old child was able to execute a complete circle; squares were accomplished by the four-year-old child; the triangle and the cross were drawn by the six-and-one-half-year-old and the seven-year-old child; and the divided rectangle and the diamond were completed by the eight-year-old and the nine-year-old child.

2. As in the previous study, circles were copied from the top downward particularly after the age of five and one-half years, at

* Mean I.Q.'s were 104.8 for the girls and 106 for the boys on WISC from a population containing children from slightly above-average income groups.

which time about half of the children in the sample drew well-proportioned circles in a counterclockwise direction, if they were right-handed, using a single continuous line.

3. Although the four-year-old children could execute a crude cross, it was not perfected until the age of nine years. By age five the right-handed child usually made the vertical line first from top to bottom, and then the horizontal line from left to right. Prior to the age of five years the child often changed hands as he made the horizontal line, drawing from the middle outward in two separate strokes. This latter tendency in children from the age of three and one-half years to five years, the authors suggest, evidences a two-sidedness that is later integrated into a total space field by the more mature subjects.

4. The four-year-old children were able to recognize, to name, and to draw a square. From the age of five to ten years most of the right-handed children drew a square in one continuous line in a counterclockwise direction. Prior to that time the children usually drew two separate horizontal lines, connecting them with two separate vertical lines.

5. Most five-year-old children attempted a triangle with some degree of success, but only about 17 per cent succeeded in drawing one with accuracy. Many left the top open and otherwise distorted the figure. Most seven-year-old children executed a triangle accurately. The most frequent method utilized by the right-handed children was to begin with the top angle and to draw the initial line downward to the left.

6. Similar to the drawing of the single square, the outside of the divided rectangle was drawn in a continuous manner, starting in the upper left corner and proceeding in a counterclockwise direction. The center was often started from a central point with lines radiating outward. This seemed to be a difficult figure to reproduce, and the investigators found inaccuracies even in the drawings of the ten-year-old children.

7. Although the four-and-one-half-year-old and the five-year-old children attempted to draw the diamond, it was executed accurately by the age of seven years.

There was no definite pattern or direction of drawing relative to hand preference in the younger children. However, according to Ilg and Ames, by the ages of six years and seven years most of the left-handed boys and girls drew their figures in a clockwise direction, whereas the right-handed children moved in a counter-clockwise direction around the figures.

COMBINES AND AGGREGATES

The "combine" and "aggregate" stages are developmental levels labeled by Kellogg and occur during and following the years in which children draw single geometrical figures.

The combine stage is marked by the attempt of a child to combine more than one figure at a time into a pattern (Fig. 7-18).

Figure 7-18

The aggregate stage involves the inclusion of three or more figures into various designs (Fig. 7-19).

Figure 7-19

Several clinicians have devised tests that incorporate various combines and aggregates in order to evaluate the perceptual-motor abilities of children. The Bender test is a clinical tool often utilized to assess children suspected of possessing neurological deficiencies and to measure readiness for school (1,7).

In our laboratory we have devised a test that also involves the drawing of an aggregate. The child is required to copy figures, one at a time, attached to the corners of a large square that is copied initially. Through the use of this tool one may obtain a measure of the manner in which the child locates figures relative to one another in space, a measure of the accuracy of a child's figure-drawing attempts, and a measure of distortions of size that may appear in his reproductions (Fig. 7-20) (3).

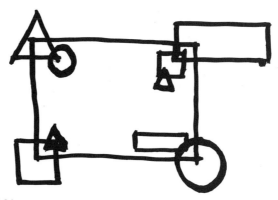

Figure 7-20

In general, on inspection of children's efforts at various age levels, the following are found:

1. The four-year-old child locates and reproduces figures poorly: most of his squares are rounded, and it is unlikely that he will overlap the various figures (perhaps in an attempt to reduce some of the visual confusion that might result were this done) (Fig. 7-21); the triangles, as would be expected, are indistinct, although one can usually differentiate between rectangles, squares, and circles.

2. By five years of age the child will make more exact squares with accurate corners and will overlap one or two of the figures rather than separate them. The triangles are still indistinct although the circles are closed, and the sizes of the reproductions

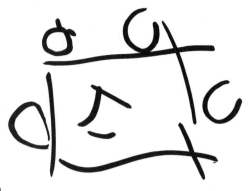

Figure 7-21

are more closely parallel to the stimulus figures he is copying (Fig. 7-22).

Figure 7-22

3. By the age of seven and one-half years the child usually reproduces the complex figure with as much accuracy as is evidenced by the tester.

THE PICTORIAL STAGE

As the child begins to reproduce simple forms in space, it is not infrequent to find that these take the forms of objects within the child's world. Circles are labeled "suns" and "faces," and triangles and squares are sometimes called "houses."

Some of the more important objects within the child's environment are the other people with whom he associates; thus it is not surprising to find that he begins to attempt to reproduce the human form.

As in the case of the aggregates previously discussed, the various forms of the draw-a-person test are utilized to assess a wide range of subtle and obvious attributes in children including emotional stability, intelligence, and social competency. In addition, the accuracy with which a child draws the human figure has been employed by several researchers to assess body image, intelligence, and social adjustment (4,9). Ilg and Ames utilize a test in which an incomplete figure is presented and the child is asked to complete the drawing (Fig. 7-23) (5).

Figure 7-23

Several researchers have traced the manner in which the skill in drawing the human figure evolves in the maturing child. In general, the following sequential steps emerge. Circles with marks in or around them are seen first (Fig. 7-24).

The circles begin to contain marks that represent facial features (Fig. 7-25).

The round face then begins to evidence "stick" arms and legs projecting directly from the circumference (Fig. 7-26).

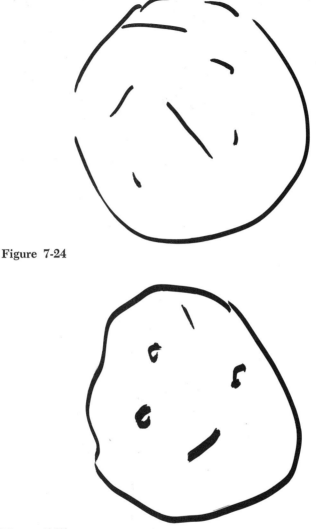

Figure 7-24

Figure 7-25

Fingers and the trunk come next (Fig. 7-27).

The figure becomes increasingly refined; parts of the face appear, including an emphasis on eyes, fingers, feet, and attempts at facial expression (Fig. 7-28).

Finally the limbs and body assume width (Fig. 7-29).

In the most exhaustive treatment of children's drawings to be found in the literature, Kellogg has devoted one chapter to an evaluation of drawing tests that purport to assess a child's mental

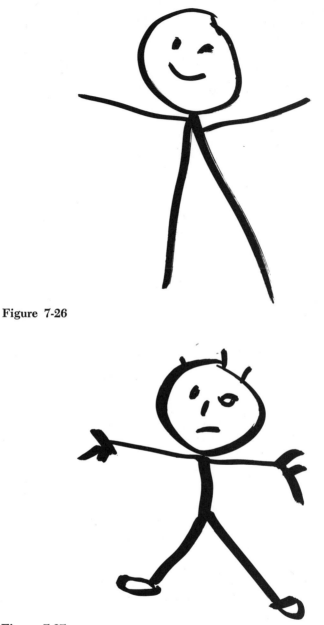

Figure 7-26

Figure 7-27

and/or emotional competencies. At one point she presents five human figures drawn by the same boy within one week (Fig. 7-30).

Figure 7-28

Figure 7-29

I believe this illustrates the rather tenuous nature of the use of this type of task when evaluating anything but the child's ability to draw the human figure! Kellogg states that one third of 2,500 children whose efforts she sampled drew such different

Figure 7-30 Five drawings of the human figure by the same boy within one week (From R. Kellogg and S. O'Dell, *Analyzing Children's Art,* Palo Alto, Calif.: National Press Books, 1969.)

humans on different days that ratings of their intelligence by an expert differed by as much as 50 per cent from drawing to drawing produced by the same child. Kellogg suggests that any ratings of the mental and/or emotional state of a child from inspection of their drawing behavior be carried out only after collecting a large number of drawings from an individual, rather than by observing only one or two efforts. I agree with Kellogg.

PRINTING LETTERS AND NUMBERS

Paralleling efforts at drawing various figures, houses, and the like are attempts on the parts of four-, five-, and six-year-old children to print letters and numbers. When printing letters, the four-year-old child is likely to scatter them on the page, and he has no stable base line for his efforts. Likewise his letters may be placed on their sides and may be slanted to varying degrees.

Many five-year-old children are able to print their first name. And by the age of six years most children can print the alphabet, their first name and their last name, and the numbers from one to ten. By the sixth and seventh years the letters are aligned horizontally, as are the numbers. As children mature, the sizes of their efforts change. The five-year-old child is likely to make his letters and numbers from .5 in. to 1 in. in height, whereas some even utilize 2 in. for their productions. By the age of seven years, however, children utilize only about .25 in. for each number and letter that they attempt.

The five-, six-, and seven-year-old children are likely to have difficulty arranging their figures in an even manner. Uniform spacing of letters and numbers is not achieved until about the age of nine years.

Each child has his own unique way of writing his numbers and letters during the formative years of five and six. The 7, and 8, and the 9 are often executed in two parts using two separate strokes, and the 3, the 4, and the 5 are often written in a continuous manner (Fig. 7-31).

Figure 7-31 (From *School Readiness: Behavior Tests Used at the Gesell Institute* by Frances L. Ilg and Louise Bates Ames. Copyright © 1964, 1965 by Gesell Institute of Child Development, Inc. Reprinted by permission of Harper & Row, Publishers.)

Children of five and six years may reverse numbers and letters in a variety of ways. Individual letters and numbers may be reversed (Fig. 7-32).

Figure 7-32

At times two-digit numbers may be reversed: 10 may be written as 01, and 20 may be written as 02. A lack of rhythm may be seen as a child reverses the order he writes two-digit numbers; yet the number will appear in its final form in the correct order. For example, the child may write the 5 before writing the 1, but the number 15 will appear correctly. According to Ilg and Ames, about 60 per cent of all the five-and-one-half-year-old children reversed letters and numbers, and 52 per cent of the six-year-old boys and 64 per cent of the six-year-old girls reversed their numbers. By the age of seven years, however, only about 12 per cent of the children surveyed evidenced reversals of numbers and letters (5).

THREE-DIMENSIONAL REPRESENTATIONS IN DRAWING

Ilg and Ames tested the ability of children between the ages of five and ten to copy correctly various three-dimensional forms. This kind of task proved considerably more difficult than copying the two-dimensional figures discussed previously (5). Three forms were utilized in their evaluation of this interesting task: a cylinder, a face-on cube, and a point-on cube (Fig. 7-33).

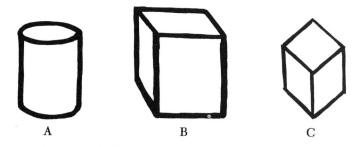

A   B   C

Figure 7-33 *A*. Cylinder. *B*. Face-on cube. *C*. Point-on cube.

The five-year-old child is likely to represent the cylinder with a single circle and will often state that it represents either the bottom or the top of the figure. Until the age of eight years the child will draw a rectangle in response to the cylinder and state that it is the front of the figure. By the age of seven years only about 22 per cent of the boys and about 32 per cent of the girls were able to make a fair replication of the cylinder, but the base was likely to be drawn straight rather than curved. By the age of eight years about 22 per cent of the boys and about 28 per cent of the girls drew a curved base line to their cylinder, and by the age of ten years about 40 per cent of the boys and about 64 per cent of the girls drew a reasonably accurate replication of the cylinder.

Drawing both the point-on and the face-on cubes proved equally difficult for the children tested by Ilg and Ames. Usually between the ages of five and seven years the children gave little indication that they were aware of the three-dimensional characteristics of the two figures, and they often drew single squares or diamonds in response to the stimulus figures. Even at ten years of age most of the children surveyed evidenced difficulty in putting together all the surfaces of the two cubes in the correct perspectives. By the age of ten years the boys were slightly superior to the girls in the drawing of both figures, and the point-on cube proved easier to replicate than did the face-on cube. About 34 per cent of the girls and about 46 per cent of the boys drew a correct point-on cube by the age of ten years, but only 2 per cent of the girls and 20 per cent of the boys could correctly draw the face-on cube at the same age. The researchers note that this is one of the few figure-drawing tasks surveyed in which the performances of the boys were superior to those of the girls.

SUMMARY

Scribbling behavior usually emerges in the child sometime between the fifteenth and the twentieth month. From tentative and irregular markings during the early weeks the child gains confidence and makes repetitive marks with increasing force in horizontal, vertical, and radiating patterns. These patterns will often be drawn on or over figures on a page. As increased control is gained during the second year, he will attempt to enclose space in shaky circular and spiral-shaped patterns. These spirals will then open up and appear as circles, and in several ways he will later begin to draw squares.

During the third and fourth years the child, when given the implements and the opportunity, will engage in various coloring and drawing tasks with increased intensity. By the end of his fourth year he can print various numbers and letters but will arrange them irregularly on a page and make them large in size.

By the age of five the child will usually be able to name various geometrical figures, will begin to draw combinations of squares and circles, and will usually be able to print his first name in an irregular manner. The characteristic counterclockwise direction will be seen in the efforts of the right-handed child to produce circles, squares, and rectangles. He is usually unsuccessful at this age at drawing figures containing lateral lines; triangles are usually open at the top, and diamonds are impossible to master. He cannot draw two-dimensional figures at all.

By the age of six the triangle is becoming recognizable. About half of the six-year-old children can write numbers from 1 to 20 and the letters of the alphabet. The letters are becoming smaller and will evidence fair horizontal alignment on the page. Circles are drawn rounder than they were at age five, and squares and rectangles are likely to be made in one continuous stroke.

The seven-year-old child evidences an increased control of the hand-eye coordination needed to draw well. A good triangle is drawn from the top downward, and a fair diamond may be copied. The seven-year-old child will, however, still have difficulty with the three-dimensional replications of cylinders and cubes, but his renditions of numbers and letters are smaller, usually about .25 in. in size.

By the eighth year the child can draw a diamond, however crude, and will attempt with fair success three-dimensional figures. His efforts at drawing will lack perspective, but his renditions of the human figure often contain arms and legs, which are represented by two parallel lines rather than by the stick figures of the previous years.

By nine years the child can usually copy triangles and cylinders reasonably well and can draw a two-dimensional cylinder with only minor problems. About one half of the children at this age can copy numbers and letters in correct horizontal alignment. Few reversals of numbers and letters will be seen.

By age ten the child can render most two-dimensional geometrical figures correctly and will evidence little tendency to reverse letters and numbers. The latter are written in a uniform manner .25 in. in size. Three-dimensional drawings will still cause problems, but in the research by Ilg and Ames, the ten-year-old child was seen to draw reasonably accurate cylinders.

Years	Selected Behaviors
1	
	Scribbling emerges, repetitive in radial or circular patterns
2	Multiple and single line crossings
	Variety of scribbling patterns, various positions on a page
3	Simple cross may be drawn, using two lines
	Encloses space; a variety of patterns emerge
	Figures placed in simple combinations using two figures
	Aggregates, more than two figures combined
4	"Suns" drawn with extra lines, sometimes forming faces
	Human figures emerge, crudely drawn
	Crude buildings and houses appear
	Human figures contain more detail; trunks usually absent; "stick" arms, legs, and fingers
	Boats and cars crudely drawn
	Circles and squares may be drawn
5	Animals drawn, trees appear in drawings
	Refined buildings and houses
	Better drawings of means of transportation; cars, airplanes, boats, etc.
6	
	Triangles drawn reasonably well
7	
	Diamonds drawn
8	
9	
	Three-dimensional geometrical figures drawn
10	
11	
	Linear perspective seen in drawings
12	

BIBLIOGRAPHY

1 Bender, L., "Psychological Principles of the Visual Motor Gestalt Test," *Tr. N.Y. Acad. Sci.*, **11** (1949), 164–70.

2 Bremer, M. W., and S. Gillman, "Verbal Intelligence, Visuomotor Ability and School Achievement," *Brit. J. Ed. Psych.*, **75** (1967), 132–45.

3 Cratty, B. J., and Sister Margaret Mary Martin, *Perceptual-Motor Efficiency in Children, the Measurement and Improvement of Movement Attributes*, Philadelphia: Lea & Febiger, 1969.

4 Goodenough, F. L., *Measurement of Intelligence by Drawings*, Yonkers, N.Y.: World Book Co., 1926.

5 Ilg, Frances L., and Louise B. Ames, *School Readiness: Behavior Tests Used at the Gesell Institute*, New York, Evanston and London: Harper & Row, 1965.

6 Kellogg, R., and S. O'Dell, *Analyzing Children's Art*, Palo Alto, Calif.: National Press Books, 1969.

7 Koppitz, E. M., "The Bender Test for Children—A Normative Study," *J. Child Psych.*, **16** (1960), 432–35.

8 Morris, D., *The Biology of Art*, New York: Alfred A. Knopf, 1962.

9 Ochs, E., "Changes in Goodenough Drawings Associated with Changes in Social Adjustment," *J. Clin. Psych.*, **6** (1950), 282–84.

10 Vane, Julia R., "The Vane Kindergarten Test," *J. Clin. Psych.*, **24** (1968), 121.

Motor Development **8**
in Children from
Six to Twelve

Children from 6 to 12 years of age improve to a marked degree in the ability to move and to manipulate their environments. Although during this period obvious growth changes occur, the rates of growth begin to subside as children reach their sixth year and do not continue at the rapidity that characterized the first five years of life.

More important than growth and body weight changes in the modification of performance during this period of childhood are a number of experiences and situations in which motor skill is demanded. The boys form teams and the girls begin to interact socially in more individualistic games, and as both groups reach adolescence toward the final years of childhood, they learn to dance.

The motor development of children has been studied from several standpoints by various investigators. Some have come to prefer a single test and have traced the manner in which children improve in its execution as a function of age. The research on the hurdle jump and on similar skills is an example of this approach to measurement.

Other scholars have devised more complex tests by which to evaluate changes in motor competency of children. The Johnson test, containing tumbling as well as locomotor subskills, is typical of this kind of test (37). Vickers and associates have modified the scoring of the Brace test, a stunt-type test, for use in the evaluation of children (59). The Denver Developmental Screening test also offers potentially valid subtests for the evaluation of the perceptual-motor attributes of children (23). The Lincoln Oseretsky is another battery of tests that has been developed for the evaluation of children, and that contains an even greater variety of both fine and gross motor skills to measure (57).

Although some investigators have collected normative data by age in either single tests or in batteries composed of several sub-tests, others have studied more complex aspects of motor development of children. Several helpful factor analyses of the motor attributes of children have been carried out in order to delineate just how motor attribute scores tend to group themselves when they are intercorrelated. Other investigators have explored the relationships between measures of intelligence, of academic performance, and of motor competence of various types. Information as to whether boys and girls are more or less competent in a given test or group of tests is obtained whenever normative data by age have been collected.

In the pages that follow several facets of the motor development of children from 6 to 12 years of age will be covered. Problems and procedures of testing will be discussed. The inter-relationships between motor test scores will also be explored, including a review of the findings of some of the factorial studies carried out within recent years. The manner in which motor proficiencies improve as children grow older will be surveyed, including comparisons of the motor performance scores of boys and girls.

On reviewing the research literature dealing with the various aspects of the motor development of children, one cannot help but notice that a great many more people are anxious to write about children's motor development than are willing to take the trouble to confirm or reject speculations through the collection of "hard" data. Thus it is hoped that, after reviewing the material that follows, some readers may be encouraged to formulate and to carry out their own investigations into this interesting area of inquiry.

MEASUREMENT PROBLEMS

Numerous measurement problems have plagued scholars attempting to evaluate the motor abilities of children. Young children are extremely variable in the manner in which they decide to perform given skills, as they often have not worked out efficient work methods that for them would prove helpful. Thus a researcher may construct what he believes to be a consistent testing instrument and then find that the performance of children who are exposed to this testing instrument is extremely unreliable. The scores he may collect one day from a given group of children may be dissimilar to the scores that he collects on a second day on the same tests by the same children.

Since the early 1950's factorial studies of motor attributes, in which adults and young men have been used as subjects, have revealed attribute patterns and interrelationships of various types of motor skills that offer reasonable guidelines in the construction of valid batteries of tests for this age group. One may, after consulting the factorial work of Fleishman, devise a battery of skill and fitness tests each of which are likely to be evaluating a different attribute (19,20,21,22).

Unfortunately the same extensive program of work has not been carried out utilizing children as subjects. The few factorial analyses of motor attributes of children do not delineate the attribute patterns of children of various ages and of both sexes as clearly as might be hoped. Thus the batteries of tests that have been devised are largely constructed by intuition rather than by recourse to more exact statistical guidelines.

The problem of locating valid norms is also difficult. Groups of children of the same age and tested by two different researchers in the same event, an event such as the standing broad jump, will often obtain highly dissimilar average scores. At the same time some of the work that has been done fails to exactly delineate testing procedures. It is well known that if either instructions or conditions are varied slightly, children will often modify their performances to marked degrees. It is sometimes not clearly specified whether the children on whom the norms were based were tested individually or in groups, despite the fact that the social influences on the effort that children were willing to exert are well known.

Despite these drawbacks conscientious researchers over the years, and particularly during the 1930's and 1940's, outlined the manner in which children of various ages perform skills and how efficiency in various basic movements improves with age. Sex differences in the tests administered have also been delineated with some clarity. In the section that follows information of this nature will be considered.

FACTOR ANALYSES

Several investigators have studied the manner in which scores collected in batteries of motor ability tests tend to cluster into common factors indicative of unique and separate attributes. The early studies were simple correlative investigations. Hartman found that the hurdle jump scores, when compared to other standard measures of motor ability then in use, such as the vertical jump, the standing broad jump, the baseball distance throw, and the 35-yd dash, yielded r's ranging from .4 to .56 (29).

Other investigators, however, correlated the scores of more extensive batteries of tests and provided information that should lead toward more extensive investigations with an even wider variety of tests similar to those carried out with adult males.

In 1940 Aileen Carpenter, using the Johnson test together with other measures, evaluated the abilities of 530 children and found that three separate factors emerged. These included general agility factors specific to the items on the Johnson test, a strength factor to which the grip strength scores contributed, and a hand-eye coordination factor, evaluated by reference to tests of marble manipulation, ball bouncing, and the like (7).

In 1941 Carpenter investigated various measures of speed in children and found that again three separate factors were isolated. Running-speed tests were related but were independent of tests in which strength was evaluated. Hand-eye coordination was again contributed to by the scores in tasks involving ball handling. In this investigation Carpenter found that improvement in the measures obtained was evidenced as children grew older, but that when correlations between age and ability were computed they were moderate to low (8).

A more comprehensive test battery was utilized in 1957 by Cumbee, in which 92 subjects were tested. Six factors were identified as a result of this investigation (18).

1. Balancing objects, i.e., rod balancing.

2. Speed of change of direction of arms and hands, i.e., block tapping.

3. Body quick change of direction, i.e., the Johnson test items.

4. Body balance, measured in tests of dynamic balance, i.e., walking a balance beam.

5. Vertical body change of direction, i.e., vertical jump and rhythm tests involving hopping.

6. Ball catching and throwing, i.e., basketball throwing, soccer kicking, ball catching, and the like.

The 36-item revised Lincoln-Oseretsky test has also been subjected to factor analysis. Vandenberg, in a study carried out in 1964, obtained data collected using the test and identified several factors including:

1. *Control Precision.* Contributed to by scores on tasks and involves placing coins in boxes, tapping, and line drawing for accuracy.

2. *Alternate Hand and Leg Use.* Alternate foot tapping, inscribing circles with both arms simultaneously, and opening and closing doors with both hands simultaneously.

3. *Balancing.* Both static and dynamic balance scores on tasks.

Other less definitive factors were also isolated in this investigation, including a factor that seemed to combine factors 1 and 2. It would have been helpful if some second-order factors had been extracted by this researcher (58).

It has been suggested by the individuals devising the Oseretsky that the tasks evaluate general static coordinations of the body, manual coordination, speed of movement, the performance of simultaneous movements, and the extent to which children can avoid extraneous movements when performing tasks. Thus Vandenberg's factors isolated statistically were not at marked variance with those advanced by the innovators of the testing using their intuition.

One of the more recent testing programs in which factor analytic techniques have been employed has been carried out by Ismail at Purdue (34). Although his primary intent seemed to be the identification of relationships between mental and motor tests, his findings also reveal much about the factors that contribute to motor ability in children. In previous studies among educationally impaired children Ismail found that different domains of intellectual and motor attributes emerged (35,36).

To summarize, the findings of the factorial studies of the motor attributes of children are far from conclusive. Relatively few studies have been carried out, and those that have often involve either too few tests or an inadequate number of subjects. Although Carpenter (1940) states that there were no sex differences identified in her factor analysis, it is probable that differences do exist (7). Carpenter's study involved children within a narrow range, from seven to nine years; and with a greater number of children in a wider range of ages it is probable that differences in the factor structure of motor ability will appear. Sex differences will also probably be identified when more extensive work is carried out.

A review of the available literature indicates that a great deal more work is needed in the factor analysis of the motor attributes of children. Little information is available in comparing factor changes as a function either of age or of sex. Analyses of this type may be difficult to carry out because of the imposition of contaminating variables such as changing cultural expectations, an increase in intellectual capabilities, and the like. At the same time, until findings from investigations of this nature are available, conclusions about the basic nature of children's motor attributes as well as guidelines for development of meaningful curricula intended to improve the manual and gross motor attributes of children may be made only intuitively.

MENTAL-MOTOR RELATIONSHIPS

A number of approaches have been made in comparisons in children of mental performance measures and motor performance measures. One type of study is generally a predictive one. These investigations summarized by Bloom and others have involved comparing mental and motor scores at various points within a child's lifetime, usually in attempting to determine whether early motor indices are in any way predictive of later intellectual development (5). Still another approach has been to produce correlative data between mental, academic, and motor attributes using children of various types. Ismail's work, reviewed previously, exemplifies this (35,36).

A few investigators have explored whether or not intelligence is in any way predictive of the ability to *learn* motor skills, whereas some additional scholars have concerned themselves with the manner in which participation in various kinds of motor development, physical education, and perceptual-motor training programs exert a causal effect on measures of intelligence. (See Chap. 10.)

Drawing generalizations from the findings of these various investigations is sometimes difficult; the Hawthorne effect, or the influence of the experimenter's personality on the children being tested, often causes more change than the motor activities applied. The placebo effect, or the tendency of the investigators to report positive findings relative to their more cherished theories, is also often apparent in the descriptions of the studies' procedures. The subject populations are often either small or poorly defined. One investigator used eight subjects in his experimental group, and others have utilized atypical children but have seemingly rejected the aid of physical, neurological, and psychological tests, which might have delineated with precision their subjects' characteristics.

Further confusion is found when one compares I.Q. scores gained from children of various ages. It is likely that the type of test given to a four-year-old child contains different types of tasks than does the I.Q. test that is administered to a child of nine years, of 12 years, and of 15 years. Thus the I.Q. test scores themselves are difficult to compare, not to mention relationships between I.Q. and various motor indices collected during life. The I.Q. tests administered during the first 18 months are highly saturated with physical and psychomotor skills, whereas those administered to 17- and 18-year-old children usually measure verbal and cognitive traits. Thus it is important to keep these facts in mind when reviewing the information below.

A number of studies have compared longitudinally intellectual scores in later life to I.Q. and various psychomotor indices of intelligence gathered during the first two years of life. It has been common to find small, nonpredictive relationships between the two scores. Bayley in 1949 compared test scores at ages 10, 11, and 12 months with those collected at 17 and 18 years, and found an r ranging from +.41 to +.55 (3). Studies by Cattel in 1931, by Anderson in 1939, and by Cavanaugh in 1957, however, yielded correlations very nearly approaching zero when early psychomotor indices of intellectual behavior were compared with I.Q. tests obtained after the age of ten years (1,10,11).

It is possible to assess the separate effects of the psychomotor and the intellectual components of intelligence tests given to two- and three-year-old children and to compare the latter scores obtained with later indices of intellectual competency. Guilford and Michaels in 1948 by doing this found that the correlations between early and late indices of the intellect were slightly increased (26).

However, to obtain higher correlations between early indices of the intellect and intelligence test scores collected in late adolescence, one must wait until a child is an age at which he is relatively free from the "contamination" of psychomotor functions and administer a "pure" verbal-intellectual test before one may obtain valid initial scores for comparison.

The contention that early motor indices of efficient behavior are in some way predictive of later intellectual success, as claimed by several authors, is difficult to substantiate with reference to the experimental literature. Although early success in motor endeavors may contribute in a general way to a child's aspiration level and in more specific ways to writing and manipulative as well as to play behaviors, the somewhat inexact suggestion that motor ability somehow forms the basis of the intellect is not substantiated by the research now available.

CORRELATIVE STUDIES

It is common to find in groups of normal children that motor ability test scores and measures of intelligence are slight, but many times these provide insignificant, positive correlations. However, if the complexity of the task is increased, by inserting cognitive elements or sampling behavior in groups of children who are less capable intellectually, higher correlations between mental and motor measures are more likely to be obtained.

These types of findings are likely to occur for several reasons: (1) many so-called intellectual tests designed for retarded children actually are heavily laden with psychomotor elements; (2) simple tasks for a retarded child actually tap an unusual amount of his intellectual efforts for correct performance; (3) some kind of rather extensive brain damage within groups of atypical children may influence both mental and motor attributes; and (4) there are few "pure" motor tasks, in that most take either some kind of decision making relative to the work methods adopted or some kind of serial memory ability similar to the kind of attribute sampled.

PHYSICAL FITNESS AND INTELLIGENCE

In addition to investigating relationships between physical performance, several researchers have explored the relationship between classroom learning and intelligence and physical fitness measures. When simple correlations are computed between such measures, there is generally little or no relationship between the fitness scores and academic achievement.

Statements in the literature persist, however, that suggest that the children who are more fit are likely to sustain their efforts in academic exercises and thus to perform better in school. In an effort to explore this kind of relationship Professor Railo, of the Norwegian College of Physical Education, has carried out a series of interesting studies whose findings, I believe, may have important implications for educators and physical educators.

In a preliminary investigation Railo, using a test of oxygen consumption during work, separated 203 seventh-grade children into high- and low-fitness groups. Both groups were given a standardized intelligence test lasting two hours, and then both were retained in a classroom and given hard mental work for an additional two hours, divided by a ten-minute rest period. Following these two sessions of testing and mental work, a second different test of intelligence was administered that again lasted two hours.*

Contrary to what was hypothesized, it was found that both the boys and girls who were in the high-fitness group performed significantly poorer on the second intelligence test, despite the possibility that some kind of skill at taking intelligence tests might have elicited positive transfer. On the other hand, the children who posted low-fitness scores improved their mean scores significantly on the second test administered.

Railo, in an effort to explain these unexpected findings, suggested that the children with high capacities for movement (and thus probably high *needs* for movement) were frustrated by the prolonged period of confinement in the test-study-test situation devised. They thus experienced extreme discomfort and brought less dynamic energy to the second testing situation, whereas the less fit children (with perhaps less need for activity during the day) evidenced less inhibition within the prolonged test-study-test situation.

These findings are perhaps applicable only to the Norwegian culture; however, this type of investigation should be replicated in the United States and elsewhere, for if results of this nature

---

* The two tests were similar and standardized on the same criterion.

continue to be obtained, they suggest several principles that might be followed to more effectively educate youth.*

1. Fit children should be afforded frequent and vigorous opportunities during the school day to exercise their movement capacities and thus enable them to bring their full attention and intellectual "energy" to their academic work.

2. So-called academic work, for some children, should be integrated with movement activities.

In follow-up investigations by this same researcher, it was found that during the fourth grade, at about the age of ten, the less fit children were the more capable academically, whereas by the fourteenth year, this trend had reversed itself. It was hypothesized that during the early school years more scholarly children achieving success in their initial academic efforts (i.e., reading) spend less time in the vigorous and unstructured games of that period of their life. However, in later childhood, as the games become more codified and contain more complex rules, the more intellectually able children are challenged to participate, thus raising their fitness levels. The less capable child, on the other hand, Railo suggests, may not be able to deal efficiently with the complexity of games in later childhood and therefore participates less, thus lowering his fitness levels.

Other findings within these studies are equally intriguing. For example, it was found that a subpopulation of the high-fitness group who evidenced the highest levels of condition were able to maintain their levels of intellectual functioning in the classroom and thus seemed able to overcome the inhibition caused by classroom "confinement" and still were able to bring "energy" to the second intellectual test with which they were confronted.

In general, these types of investigations suggest that intelligence test scores not only are a measure of basic intellect but are also influenced to a marked degree by the momentary motivational level of the child and his physical fatigue, as well as by experiences occurring just prior to the testing session. Further investigations of this nature should serve to clarify the interesting relationships and trends noted by Railo in these studies carried out in Scandinavia.

---

* The author, of course, rejects the hypothesis that one should be certain children do not become too fit and thus reduce their intellectual attainment!

AGE TRENDS

A survey of the changes in motor ability traits from the ages of 6 to 12 years reveals that, although children of this age range do not change as rapidly as do the children from birth to five years of age, there is invariably a regular improvement with the performance curves usually assuming a rough linear relationship to age. Myelination is usually completed somewhere between the sixth and the eighth years, so that a variety of complex tasks are able to be mastered by older children within this age range. At the same time their needs for activity may remain high, and thus their basic capacities increase as a result of frequent and vigorous participation.

A number of structural changes are evidenced during these years. There are regular increases in long-bone growth, and the muscle quality of both sexes undergoes modification. Increased muscle density and power are evidenced by both boys and girls. The boys begin to move ahead in most tasks involving simple applications of force and power during the early part of this period, and at times the girls catch up and surpass them in late childhood as they become influenced by hormonal changes earlier than do the boys.

Throwing is generally more efficiently carried out by boys between the ages of 6 and 12 years, but the girls are often superior in tasks requiring agility and rhythm. The girls will usually take less time to hop a given distance than will the boys, and the former will hop more accurately. The boys will often excel the girls in measures of running speed.

On the pages that follow a reasonably detailed survey is made of the changes that occur between the ages of 6 and 12 years in a variety of motor tasks. Additionally, some of the graphs presented illustrate sex differences during these years.

The results of various studies are sometimes difficult to compare insofar as the experimenters have employed different methods for administering similar tasks. For example, some researchers have timed running speed by giving the children a running start, and others have employed a standing start. Many have failed to specify exactly how their tasks are administered despite the fact that slightly different evaluative procedures, such as how the hand dynamometer is held, will have a significant influence on the scores obtained.

Invariably the authors of studies of this nature either have failed to survey the particular physiques of their subjects or in some way have demonstrated that they have obtained a representative sampling of body types prior to administering some performance tests. The influence of physique in a variety of motor performance measures has been repeatedly demonstrated; thus unless either this type of information accompanies these types of investigations or an extremely large sample has been obtained, results may be "contaminated" by an excess number of linear or obese children.

Similarly one must consider carefully just what measures are being employed by an investigator when he purportedly evaluates some performance quality. Strength studies of children invariably contain measures of grip strength despite the fact that investigators employing more mature subjects have often demonstrated that grip strength is not highly correlated with other measures of force exerted in other ways by the body. It is probable that children from the ages of 6 to 12 years function in specific ways when performing a number of types of tasks. As an example, some measure of standing broad-jump ability is not likely to correlate with an apparently similar but slightly different task that requires the application of leg power, such as the vertical jump.

There are undoubtedly changes occurring in the motor capacities of children that are caused by differences in the sociocultural conditions that have occurred between the years of 1930 and 1970 (the period during which most of the studies surveyed were carried out). A comparison of the physical abilities of fathers and sons that I carried out some years ago, utilizing data collected at the same time in their lives by the same testers and on the same facilities, demonstrated the decreasing capacities of the sons. Other investigations have produced data that indicate that the size and strength of the present generation are significantly different from those of the previous generations (15).

Within the material that follows attempts have been made at times to control for the influence of many of the variables outlined above, by graphing surveys of data carried out by Metheny (49), Keogh (41), and others. At the same time definitive longitudinal studies of motor ability changes in children, with the exception of the Medford study nearing completion, are difficult to find in the literature (12). Most of the investigations consist of cross-sectional samples obtained at the same time using children of different ages, with the questionable assumption made that they are in some way comparable owing to the fact that everything but their ages is similar.

With the above limitations in mind the survey that follows has been divided into several sections and subsections. Initially, information dealing with what has been termed "basic physical attributes" is presented. This section includes data describing changes in strength, in flexibility, and in balance as a function of age.

The section that follows deals with "locomotor qualities," including jumping tasks of various types, speed runs and agility runs, and similar measures. General data emanating from various tests purporting to evaluate agility comprise the third section.

The final sections of the chapter present information describing the manner in which children from 6 to 12 years of age deal with balls; thus studies of ball-throwing skills, including distance, accuracy, and velocity, of ball-catching skills, of ball-kicking skills, and of ball-batting skills are reviewed.

BASIC PHYSICAL ATTRIBUTES

STRENGTH

Factorial studies of the ability traits of adolescents and young men carried out by Fleishman and his colleagues have identified several highly specific ability traits under the general classification of strength. These consist of static strength (pounds of pressure exerted against a reasonably immobile surface), dynamic strength (force applied through a range of motion in a controlled manner), and explosive strength or ballistic strength (the ability to propel a reasonably heavy object, such as the ability to "put" a medicine ball for distance) (21). Despite the evidence arising from this type of investigation, investigations of strength in children have usually employed very few indices of strength. Although some investigators have used push-ups and similar fitness measures to obtain norms for children and to attempt to delineate general indices of motor ability, the overwhelming number of studies contain data based on measures of grip strength.

Metheny and later Keogh have surveyed this type of evidence, which generally points to the following conclusions (41,49). Little difference is usually found when the pressures exerted by the right and left hands are compared.* Slight sex differences are usually found, with the boys superior to the girls in early childhood and with the girls often catching up to the boys in late childhood. The data from a study by Keogh illustrate the usual trend found when the grip strength of children of both sexes within this age range is surveyed. No significant differences between the left and right grip strength scores were found in this investigation, although the mean left grip score was on the average a pound less than was the same measure collected with the right hand.

A summary of the studies in grip strength was carried out by Metheny in 1941, in which her own data were also included (49) (Fig. 8-1). In general, the same linear relationship is seen between age and strength improvement in both boys and girls, with the boys superior by about 2 lb at each age. It is difficult to determine whether the sex differences found are caused by differences in hand size, by cultural variables concerning the emphasis on physical performance by boys, or by qualitative differences in muscle strength as revealed in the investigation by Rarick and Thompson dealing with leg muscle efficiency in children (53).

It is probable, however, that slight qualitative sex differences exist in children's muscular make-up even during childhood that are reflected in the differences illustrated in these studies of grip strength. I am not aware, however, of investigations that conclusively demonstrate hormonal differences reflected in measures of blood chemistry and existing between boys and girls within this age range. It is apparent nevertheless that grip strength of boys and girls undergoes marked changes between the ages of 6 and 12 years. The average scores of the boys double during these years, and those of the girls increase by more than two and one-half times.

During the past ten years a longitudinal analysis of strength and motor development of the same children has been carried out by H. Harrison Clarke and his students at the University of Oregon (12). The subjects have been from the Medford city schools in Oregon. During this time many data have been collected, and the interactions of a number of variables, including

* Scores from left and right grips are often compared; however, it is seldom that the investigator specifies differences in grip strength occurring between preferred and nonpreferred hands.

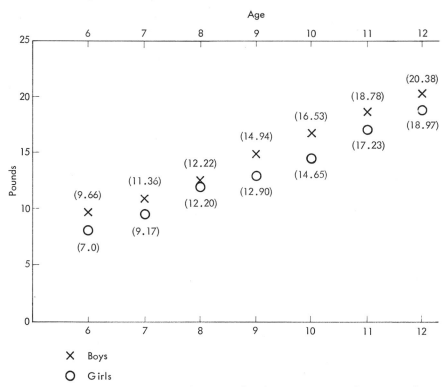

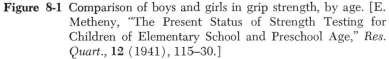

Figure 8-1 Comparison of boys and girls in grip strength, by age. [E. Metheny, "The Present Status of Strength Testing for Children of Elementary School and Preschool Age," *Res. Quart.*, **12** (1941), 115–30.]

skeletal maturation and motor abilities, have been studied and compared.

One portion of this larger study was devoted to assessing strength changes in boys from seven to nine years of age. The findings from this analysis have important implications for programs of physical education and for the study of muscle strength in children.

Overall it has been found that there are only low to moderate correlations between strength measures obtained in various parts of the body. Elbow flexion strength correlated only from +.3 to +.5 to measures of trunk extension strength. Furthermore, it was found that as children mature, the increase in muscle strength in various portions of the body proceeds at uneven rates. Shoulder flexion strength was found to accelerate to the age of eight; back lift strength improved through early childhood and then tended to become less pronounced at 12 years of age; and ankle flexion strength continued to improve regularly at all ages in childhood.

At the present time the investigation is nearing its completion. The total data from this important and comprehensive ten-year investigation should soon be available in book form.

FLEXIBILITY

Relatively few investigations have been carried out that deal with the muscular flexibility of children in elementary school. The findings that are available, however, point to the same specificity of function as was described in the studies of adolescent strength. Hupprich and Sigerseth, for example, found that flexibility of girls was due to specific factors because low intercorrelations were obtained between the various scores, indicating a range of joint motion (33). The experimenters' findings revealed that, contrary to the common hypothesis, as girls grow older they do not always evidence decreases in flexibility. Although decreases in measures reflecting flexibility of the knees, the thighs, and the shoulder joints were recorded, the scores obtained suggested that girls may have increased trunk flexibility, wrist flexion, and leg abduction.

A summary of some of the measures of Hupprich and Sigerseth obtained from girls of 6, 9, and 12 years of age is found in Figure 8-2. The data indicate the complex manner in which flexibility changes during childhood, as described above. I am unaware of a similar study in which boys have been utilized as subjects.

REACTION TIME

Another basic attribute that plays an important role in the modification of motor performance and learning among young children is the speed with which they initiate a response when confronted with stimuli of various types. Although in common parlance "reaction time" is sometimes used to denote the speed with which a child or adult moves, a more correct definition of reaction time is the time taken between the initiation of a stimulus to be reacted to (i.e., seeing the ball moving from the hand of the thrower) and the *initiation* of the response (i.e., catching). Thus reaction time is a function of the facility with which the

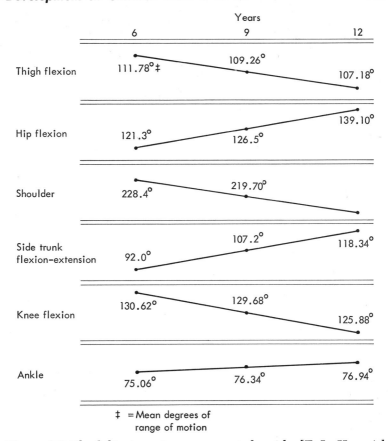

Figure 8-2 Flexibility in various movements by girls. [F. L. Hupprich and P. O. Sigerseth, "The Specificity of Flexibility in Girls," *Res. Quart.*, **21** (1950), 25–33.]

stimulus is integrated with the response within the central nervous system, as well as the speed with which the incoming and outgoing impulses travel on the nerve pathways involved.

Numerous studies have been carried out in which the reaction time of adults has been studied. Generally the results indicated that a number of factors either speed up or slow down reaction time. For example, adults usually react faster if they know a simple response has to be made to some light or sound cue than if the light or sound is to be followed by a complex response. To a point, the more intense the stimulus (i.e., the louder the sound), the more quickly the action will be initiated. However, if the sound is made too loudly, reaction time may be slowed down. Similarly, if there is some kind of forewarning that a stimulus to be reacted to is to appear, the subsequent reaction will be quicker than if no warning is given to the subject. Reaction times in various parts of the body (i.e., the hands) have been found to be more rapid than in other parts (i.e., the legs). In general, adult humans react more quickly to a sound than to a light cue. The dominant hand will usually react quicker than the nondominant hand, and practice in a reaction time situation will usually elicit only slight improvement on the part of the subject (about 10 per cent in many studies, depending on the complexity of the response to be made).

The measurement of reaction time in young children has not been studied in any large range of tasks. The information that is available, however, indicates that in simple reaction time problems, the reaction time of five-year-olds is twice as long as is found at adulthood. At the same time, there is a marked improvement of about 43 per cent from the ages of three to five years of age. These findings indicate that a large amount of the motor ineptitude apparent in young children may be caused by the inability to rapidly start a movement itself. For example, as Whiting points out, if a five-year-old is expected to catch a ball from a distance of 10 ft, which is traveling only 15 ft per second, he must initiate his response as soon as the ball has left the thrower's hand (61). Thus in some measure ineptitude in this type of task might be attributable to slow reaction time, rather than to the inability to correctly place the body and hands when catching the ball.

Complicating the study of reaction time in young children is the fact that reaction time may be added to as the child hesitates and *thinks* about the movement to be made. Thus, many times in both adults and children, it is difficult to separate judgment time from reaction time, and, indeed, in investigations in which adult subjects have been employed, it has been ascertained that about ten times more time may be taken to make the decision within the central nervous system than is taken for the nerve impulse to travel from the sensory end organ (i.e., the eyes) and out again to the muscles.

BALANCE

Balance may be defined as the ability to maintain the equilibrium in the presence of disrupting conditions. Balance is a

basic and, at the same time, a complex attribute. Balance under-
lies a number of performance tasks, and if it is deficient, it will
probably negatively influence efforts involving locomotor activity,
hopping, skipping, and the like, as well as the ability to throw
balls with accuracy. Balance is mediated to some degree by the
vestibular apparatus, but it is primarily influenced by the subtle
interactions of the visual and muscular systems working together.

Balance qualities seem to have attracted the attention of a
number of investigators during the past 30 years. A variety of
methods have been devised to get at this elusive performance
quality, including walking beams of various widths, posturing on
one foot either on the floor or on a narrow edge with the body
and/or arms in various positions, hopping with alternate feet
from circle to circle placed irregularly on the floor, as well as
attempting to maintain some position indicative of static equilibrium with the eyes closed (Fig. 8-3).

Investigations of balance have revealed that the measures obtained tend to be highly specific. At least two definitive categories
usually emerge when measures of children's balance are compared: one is static balance, which involves posturing on one
foot; the other is dynamic balance, which involves moving down
a balance beam. It is probable that other factors will emerge when
more sophisticated studies are carried out, including the quality
needed in surfing and skate boarding, as well as some closed-eyes
balance abilities that have been identified in investigations in
which older subjects have been used (2,25).

When beam-walking tests are utilized, it is usually found that
most six-year-olds can walk a beam that is 2 in. wide, but many
fail to walk a beam that is only 1 in. wide. The scores obtained
from these tasks are the distance walked (before falling) on a
beam of a given width and/or the number of steps taken prior to
losing balance. Static balance measures are usually the number
of seconds the child is able to posture in a specified position.
Surveys carried out delineating changes in the ability to balance
during the elementary school years generally indicate both that
the attribute matures slightly earlier in the life of a child than
do some other attributes, such as strength and endurance, and
that there are usually two or more significant improvements in
mean balance scores evidenced during childhood. Typical of the
trends in the data between the ages of 6 and 12 years are the
scores graphed from the work carried out by Seashore (Fig. 8-4)

A

B

Figure 8-3 Static balance may be evaluated in the ways shown: *A.*
By standing parallel to or across beams of various widths,
or by assuming a heel-to-toe position, or by requiring
one-foot balances of various durations, or with various
stresses imposed, e.g., the arms folded and/or eyes closed
as shown in *B.*

(55). In general, sex differences are not usually marked; however,
Keogh and others have demonstrated that girls between seven
and nine years of age are often superior to boys in dynamic balance abilities (41).

When trends in the scores from balance studies are considered

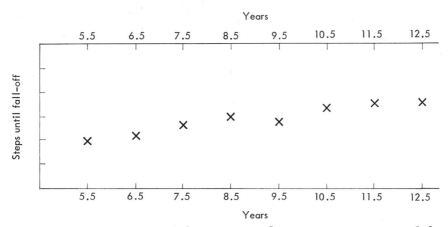

Figure 8-4 Dynamic balance, measured at various ages, using a balance beam–walking test [H. G. Seashore, "The Development of a Beam Walking Test and Its Use in Measuring Development of Balance in Children," *Res. Quart.*, **18** (1949), 246–59.]

separately by sex, it is sometimes seen that boys tend to improve most between the ages of seven and nine years and again by age ten. The girls, on the other hand, often evidence more marked improvement between the ages of six and seven years and later between the ages of 10 and 11 years (41).

Ismail has reported a moderate correlation between balance scores, I.Q., and school achievement measures (35). I have also obtained similar correlations in a study conducted in our laboratory in 1968 (16). These low and nonpredictive correlations, however, do not indicate any causal relationship between some component of intelligence and balance, and probably simply reflect some slight common influence of ocular control on both academic functioning and balance ability.*

In studies I have carried out employing a series of tests of static balance, similar age trends have been noted. These tests have been made increasingly difficult by requiring the child to fold his arms across his chest and to close his eyes to earn a higher score; then to perform in the same manner on his nonpreferred foot (16).

In general, it was found that the average children of both sexes

* Goetzinger obtained no correlation between measures of dynamic balance using the Heath rail-walking test and I.Q. scores obtained from the draw-a-person test (25).

at five years of age cannot posture on one foot with their eyes closed but can maintain control in this position from four to six seconds with their eyes open and arms folded across their chests. By seven years of age childen can usually maintain a closed-eyes balance on the floor in an immobile position, while using their arms to maintain equilibrium.

In this test of static balance it was found that during the sixth and seventh years the boys performed better than the girls, but after those years the performance means of the two sexes were similar (Fig. 8-5). Significant improvment in the girls' ability was seen between the efforts recorded by each age group between five, six, seven, and eight years, but the boys' scores tended to reach a plateau between the ages of six through eight and one-half years. A comparison of the scores of boys at eight and one-half years and those of boys from 9½ through 11½ years elicited a significant difference. When comparing trends seen in tests of static and dynamic balance and when consulting either correlative or factorial studies contrasting these two measures, it is apparent that they are indeed independent measures.

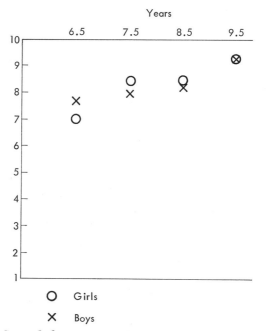

Figure 8-5 Static balance scores, by age, in boys and girls. (Bryant J. Cratty and M. M. Martin, *Perceptual-Motor Efficiency in Children,* Philadelphia: Lea & Febiger, 1969.)

A child's balance ability thus may be assessed in a number of ways, and the test used may be one of several possible measures available. Balance abilities are seen to reach a plateau earlier in life than do other basic attributes. In general, it appears that sex differences not marked in dynamic tests of balance may be more distinct when scores obtained from static tests of balance are compared. Furthermore, it is apparent that although balance improves markedly during the years from 6 to 12, there may be one or more plateaus that are caused by factors in the child's ability to balance that are not easily identified at this time. It might be assumed, however, that integrative processes, similar to those outlined for drawing, for ball interception, and for similar complex attributes (Chap. 11), are similar to the processes by which the child organizes the input from his muscular system and visual cues as he attempts to maintain stable relationships between himself and the force of gravity.

LOCOMOTOR ATTRIBUTES

By the age of six years normal children can run well, evidencing well-coordinated arm and leg actions. They can jump vertically and horizontally reasonably well with take-offs of two feet. Sometimes their jumping is accompanied by arm action, and sometimes this arm action is absent.

In addition to simple forward and lateral movements, six-year-old children are beginning to experiment with numerous variations of locomotor patterns; they can skip, and some can hop rhythmically from one foot to the other foot while in place. Numerous experimenters have devised a variety of running tasks that require for their successful executions what might be termed "locomotor agility." These have included requiring the children to jump and hop accurately into squares on a grid, to hop from disk to disk placed in a line, to execute zigzag agility runs around obstacles, and perform similar tasks (8,16,37,41).

Additionally various tests of speed of locomotor function have been given to children during the elementary school years. Running speed has been measured by several researchers, as has the speed at which children can hop a specified distance. In the following sections the material has been divided into two sections: (1) one dealing with the development of jumping abilities in which the scores are influenced by bodily coordinations, including the vertical jump, the standing broad jump, and the hurdle jump; and (2) the other dealing with jumping tasks in which accuracy and timing are required, such as rhythmical hopping.

Vertical Jump

A frequently used test with an older child and with an adolescent requires that the child first stand flat-footed and reach above his head with his hands, and then see how far above that height he can touch when he jumps (Fig. 8-6). Successful per-

Figure 8-6 Vertical jump is evaluated by first asking children to reach and then to determine how far above the standing reach they can jump and touch. This is a measure of leg power and of arm-leg coordination while jumping.

formance is probably dependent on leg power and on proper jumping mechanics.*

* I know of no factor analyses that have been carried out exactly delineating the qualities contributing to these and to other similar tasks in children.

As can be seen in Figure 8-7, the boys excel the girls in this type of vigorous movement after the age of seven years. At seven

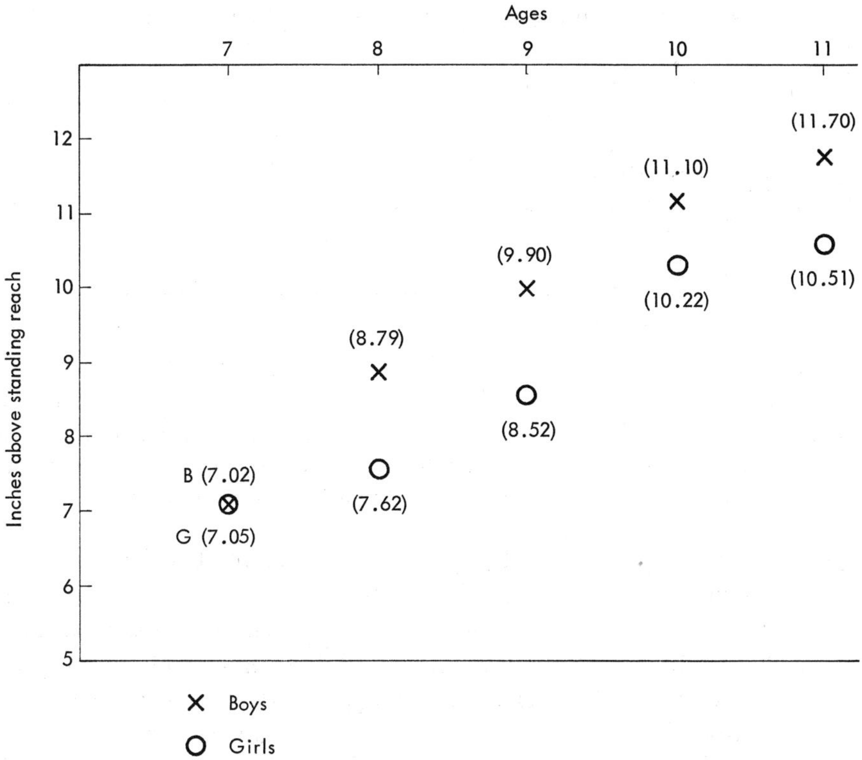

Figure 8-7 Vertical jump performance by age and sex. [R. D. Johnson, "Measurements of Achievement in Fundamental Skills of Elementary School Children," *Res. Quart.*, **33** (1962), 94–103.]

years, both female and male children can jump about 7 in. in the air straight upward, and following that age the sex differences are apparent. After that age there is about a 1-in. mean difference in this attribute between the boys and girls. The girls are seen to improve most between the ages of nine and ten years, and the boys' mean improvement is more marked between the ages of seven and eight. The boys improved about 66 per cent, and the girls during this same age range evidenced improvement of about 50 per cent.

Standing Broad Jump

A broad-jump test requires the child to broad jump forward as far as he is able from a standing position, using a two-foot take-off and landing (Fig. 8-8). Although success in this is ap-

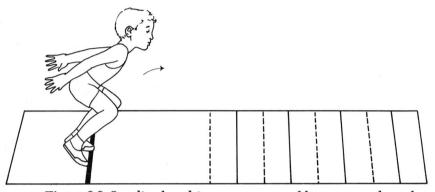

Figure 8-8 Standing broad jump, a measure of leg power and arm-leg integration while moving in a horizontal plane.

parently an index of leg power, it is probable that arm involvement, the coordination of leg extension, and arm throw upward and forward all contribute to the performance of this skill. Zimmerman and others have analyzed the manner of jumping of children who are successful jumpers and of children who are unsuccessful jumpers and have found significant differences in the manner in which they moved. The better jumpers utilized their arms through a greater range of motion and, at the same time, evidenced a more pronounced knee bend (64).

As in many measures of power, boys are usually slightly more successful than are girls in the performance of this task. As can be seen from Figure 8-9 the performance of children in this type of task improved in a linear fashion during the six years surveyed. At the same time, about 20 in. are added on the boys' scores from the sixth to the eleventh years, and the girls evidence only slightly less improvement. Contrary to performance measures that require precise locomotor activity, this measure of leg power suggests that the boys' superiority in leg strength becomes increasingly manifested in the later years of childhood.

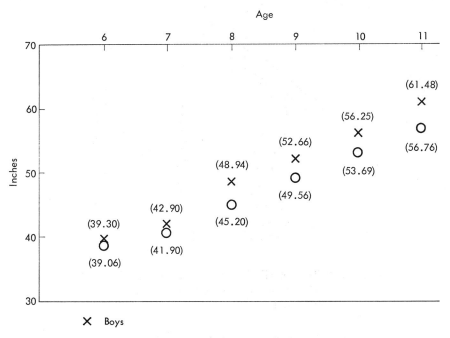

Figure 8-9 Standing broad-jump performance by age and sex. (J. F. Keogh, *Motor Performance of Elementary School Children*, Monograph, University of California, Los Angeles, Physical Education Dept., 1965.)

Hurdle Jump

Another way in which vertical jumping ability is evaluated is through the use of a hurdle jump test. The execution of this task requires a two-foot take-off over a wooden bar placed at various heights and a two-foot landing (Fig. 8-10). Thus the child must execute a jump covering a short distance and, at the same time, must coordinate the height of the jump with the height of the bar.

In common with the previous jumping tasks evaluated, data from an investigation of the hurdle jump indicate that the mean score improves at about the rate of 1.25 in. at each year of age, with the exception of the change from the eighth to the ninth years, which amounted to about 3.75 in. on the average. At five years of age the child can usually jump over a hurdle that is slightly more than 10 in. high. In general, the girls excel the boys in this until about the age of seven and one-half years, at which

Figure 8-10 The hurdle jump was a frequently used test in the 1930's and 1940's. A two-foot take-off and landing were required.

time the boys' means evidence slight superiority (29). Cowan and Pratt found no correlation between the scores obtained from the hurdle jump test and either body height or body weight (13). The data from this investigation, based on the combined mean scores of both the boys and the girls, are found in Figure 8-11.

Carey (6), using this same task, found mean scores in children of 10 and 11 years of age that were from 5 to 6 in. higher than those mean scores from the population tested by Cowan and Pratt (13). It is difficult to determine the cause of this kind of difference, which is not infrequently found between data obtained in different studies that are based on performance of apparently similar measures of motor ability.

HOPPING AND JUMPING INTO GRIDS

Parts of the Johnson test developed in the early 1930's are used together with investigations of more recent years. Keogh and I have employed grids containing squares into which children are required to jump and to hop with accuracy (Fig. 8-12) (16,37, 41).

In the research I have carried out it is generally found that not until about the age of six years can children perform hop-

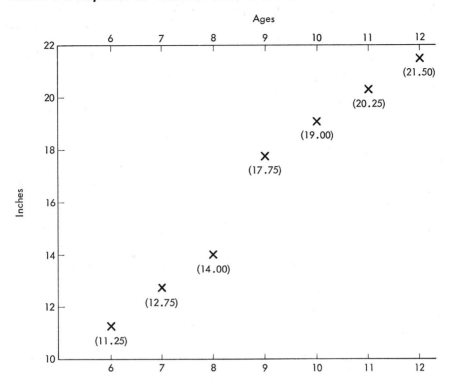

Figure 8-11 Hurdle-jumping ability by age. [E. Cowan and B. Pratt,
"The Hurdle Jump as a Developmental and Diagnostic
Test," *Child Dev.*, **5** (1934), 107–21.]

ping and jumping movements with the precision necessary to
place either one or both feet into squares that are 1 ft by 1 ft in
area. In general, the girls excel the boys in the performance of
this type of task. The most marked improvement is seen when
the mean scores of the six and one-half-year old children are
compared with those of children one year older, and when the
mean scores of the seven and one-half-year old children are contrasted with those of children one year older. At about the age
of nine years the scores in this type of task tend to reach a plateau.

Keogh has found similar results when comparing the mean
scores he obtained from children between the ages of six and
nine years, which he divided by sex. At all ages the girls excelled
the boys. As can be seen from Figure 8-13, the most marked
changes occur between the same ages as was described in the
previous investigations (41, 42).

Figure 8-12 Jumping and hopping in squares in various orders, either forward or backward, have been used by several researchers to test locomotor competencies. The score is usually determined by the number of successful trips down the mat without errors or with a given number of errors.

Rhythmic Hopping, Alternating Legs

Clinicians concerned with the motor development of atypical children have often referred to the inability to hop rhythmically while alternating feet to be a sign of some kind of difficulty in motor coordination. In order to test this hypothesis, Keogh and his colleagues recently obtained norms delineating the accuracy that can be expected in this task by children of both sexes and at various ages. The results of this investigation, some of which are graphed below, indicate that this kind of task poses a rather difficult problem to most children in the early years of elementary school, especially if the rhythm is uneven, such as executing two hops on one foot followed by three hops on the other foot (42,44, 45).

As can be seen in Figure 8-13, girls are generally superior to boys in this task through middle childhood, as they usually are superior in other tasks that require precise movements of the feet. Additionally, it can be ascertained from inspection of the chart that not until the age of eight years can more than 50 per cent of the children of both sexes be expected to hop rhythmically using a two-two rhythm, such as two times on one foot and then

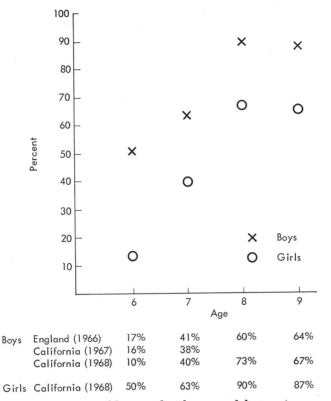

Figure 8-13 Percentage of boys and girls successful at various ages in an alternate hopping task—two hops on one foot with an immediate transfer to the other foot for two hops. Comparative data are shown in other studies by Keogh. (J. F. Keogh, "A Rhythmical Hopping Task as an Assessment of Motor Deficiency," Paper reported at the 2nd International Congress of Sports Psychology, Washington, D.C., 1968.)

two times on the other foot, without breaking cadence. These data further reveal that condemning a male child as evidencing motor deficits at the age of five years because he cannot hop rhythmically, changing feet, is less than a sound practice, for about 85 per cent of the males at this age cannot be expected to do so.

Previous studies by Keogh have examined the ability to perform other hopping patterns: two-three, or two hops on one foot and then immediately three hops on the other foot; and three-three, or three hops on one foot and then immediately three hops on the other foot. Generally, the findings of these investigations are similar to the findings presented in the previous paragraphs.

The more difficult hopping patterns were those in which an un-
equal number of hops were performed on each foot, such as a
two-three pattern. Not until about the age of eight years can
most children master this pattern successfully.

In a detailed analysis of the reasons that children have difficulty with this type of task, Keogh found that more than one half
evidenced an inability to recognize when their limbs had moved
a given number of times and had similar difficulty when they attempted to reproduce alternate tapping movements with the
upper limbs.

The 50-Ft Hop

A third type of hopping task involves the speed with which a
child can hop a given distance while remaining on one foot. As
Figure 8-14 indicates, the girls' mean scores slightly exceed those
of the boys at seven and eight years of age, but before and after
these ages their abilities are very similar. The greatest improvement in the ability to execute this task is seen between the ages
of six and seven years in girls, and between the ages of seven and
eight years and nine and ten years in boys.

It has also been found in the various studies that more than 10
per cent of boys at six years of age and about 2 per cent of girls
at the same age cannot perform this type of task successfully;
that is, they cannot remain on one foot for a distance of 50 ft. By
the age of seven years it is usually found that the percentages of
failures among boys and girls are roughly similar, and this remains so through the eighth and ninth years. In the studies of this
attribute all ten-year-old children who were tested could hop
successfully a distance of 50 ft (43).

In summary the data from these investigations of simple and
complex locomotor attributes suggest that, to the extent to which
the task seems to require relatively simple straightforward or
upward manifestations of leg strength and power, the boys between the ages of 6 and 12 years excel the girls. The girls, on the
other hand, seem better than the boys in jumping and hopping
tasks that require precision and accuracy. In part these differences
in the simple tasks probably reflect superiority in the leg power
and strength of the boys, whereas the girls excel in the more
complex tasks because their visual-motor coordinations necessary
to execute these activities are more mature at earlier ages and

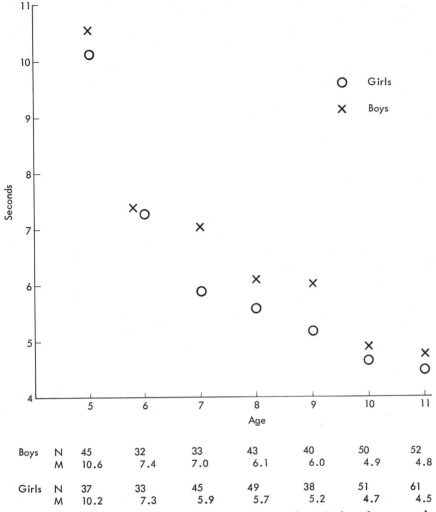

Figure 8-14 Speed with which children can hop 50 feet, by sex and age. (J. F. Keogh, *Motor Performance of Elementary School Children,* Monograph, University of California, Los Angeles, Physical Education Dept., 1965.)

Boys	N	45	32	33	43	40	50	52
	M	10.6	7.4	7.0	6.1	6.0	4.9	4.8
Girls	N	37	33	45	49	38	51	61
	M	10.2	7.3	5.9	5.7	5.2	4.7	4.5

because they more frequently engage in this type of task (hopscotch) in the American culture.

RUNNING SPEED AND AGILITY

In addition to employing locomotor tasks in which the child is not required to cover a great deal of space, numerous experimenters have used tasks involving running speed and agility measures requiring changes of direction while running.

It is probable that the two types of running tests measure separate attributes in children of elementary school age. Carpenter has found, for example, that running-speed test scores cluster in a factor separate from those of strength scores and ball-handling scores (8). Cumbee also has found that tests evaluating quick changes of direction while running are independent of other measures of motor performance in children (17).

RUNNING SPEED

As with the simple measures of leg power in children, the boys excel the girls between the ages of 6 and 12 years. Comparisons of the data collected from the various studies, however, are made difficult because of the differences in distances run and in the ways in which subjects were started. Some employed running starts, and others started their subjects from standing and crouching positions.

As Figure 8-15 indicates, both boys and girls run about 1 ft per second faster each year from the ages of 6 to 11 years. In general, the girls run about 1 ft per second slower than do the boys of comparable age toward the latter end of the age continuum under consideration.

AGILITY RUNS

Various agility runs have been frequently employed in batteries of tests purporting to identify some kind of general motor ability by researchers interested in only this single component of children's performance. Interstudy comparisons of the scores collected in agility runs are impossible owing to the wide variations in the manner in which the scores were obtained: in the sizes of the courses and in the nature of the obstacles employed. Some of the testers required their subjects to pick up and to replace hand-held objects as they traveled between points in a run. Some of the courses were laid out in a zigzag conformation, and others were shuttle runs in which the subjects moved back and forth executing 180-degree turns after each leg of their journeys. The American Association of Health, Physical Education, and Recreation has standardized the manner in which a shuttle run may be executed,

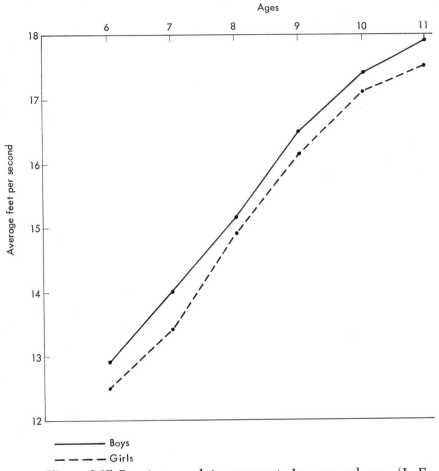

Figure 8-15 Running speed improvement, by age and sex. (J. F.
Keogh, *Motor Performance of Elementary School Chil-
dren*, Monograph, University of California, Los Angeles,
Physical Education Dept., 1965.)

but at the same time the studies by Latchaw (47) and Johnson
(38) have employed different types of courses.

The data indicate that the boys improve substantially until
between the ages of eight and nine years, at which time mean
performance increases become less marked. The girls, on the other
hand, improve a great deal between the ages of six and seven
years, with smaller yearly increases occurring after this time. The
boys in most of the studies are from 0.3 second to 0.7 second
faster when running 30 yd than are the girls of similar age.

In summary, the available evidence suggests that boys during elementary school years are slightly superior to girls in tests of running speed and when running is evaluated in various agility run tests. The performances of children in these tasks evidence a regular increase with age, with the greatest improvement occurring between the beginning and the end of the age range under study.

AGILITY

A number of tasks have been employed in various batteries, and complete batteries of tests have been formulated that consist of skills intended to evaluate some elusive quality termed "agility." In general, agility may be defined as the ability to integrate the larger movements of the body into efficient manners. Agility has been evaluated in tasks resembling tumbling movements in what has been termed a "cable jump," in which a short cable must be jumped over while the jumper holds it in front of his body with both hands. Additionally, in my laboratory we have attempted to evaluate what we have termed "gross agility," by scoring how fast children of various ages can arise from a back-lying position when asked to do so, and the efficiency with which children can descend to both knees and, with one knee at a time, regain their original standing positions in a similar manner.

These more complex tasks are probably influenced by a number of factors, including explosive power of the trunk muscles (arising from a black-lying position), balance (the kneel-and-stand test), courage (the cable jump test), jumping ability and flexibility (cable jump and tumbling movements), and other attributes involving balances of various types and visual-motor coordinations.

CABLE JUMP

Keogh utilized a measure obtained from the cable jump test (Fig. 8-16) with children in a recent study and found that 69 per cent of the boys and 51 per cent of the girls at six years of age either could not or would not jump the held obstacle (43). By the age of nine years, however, about 62 per cent of the boys and about 71 per cent of the girls could correctly execute this difficult task on six to eight attempts. In general, the girls seemed to master the task by the age of seven years, as 86 per cent were found to be able to execute three successful trials, and the boys

Figure 8-16 Child engaged in cable-jumping task.

seemed to master the task by the age of eight years, as 85 per cent were able to master a similar number of trials. In general, the scoring method for the test needs some revision, as the test-retest reliabilities were not found to be high (from +.60 to +.51).

INTEGRATION OF LIMB MOVEMENTS

A preliminary study has explored various arm-leg coordination tasks as possible indices of motor competency among 300 children from five through nine years of age. The tasks consisted of seated hand-clapping, knee-clapping tests executed in various combinations and in various rhythms, as well as tasks that are variations of the familiar jumping-jack task.* Thirty boys and 30 girls were tested at each age level by a well-trained group of research assistants. Each child was tested on 61 separate items on a pass-fail basis within several categories of limb coordination tasks, including: tapping while seated, clapping while seated, the use of hands while seated, foot and arm movements while standing, and hopping movements both in place and while moving forward. A passing score was recorded if a child was able to repeat five cycles of each task without interruption.

In a test-retest to determine reliability the children almost invariably improved their scores, by from 10 to 25 per cent, and test-retest agreement ranged from 60 to 90 per cent. The greatest changes in performance were seen when the scores of the five-

* Keogh's study was exploratory in nature, and with further refinement tasks of this nature should prove helpful in the assessment of the motor competencies of children in middle childhood.

and six-year-olds were compared, and in general the girls were superior to the boys, by about slightly over one year. For example, an overall passing score of the six-year-old girls reached 82 per cent and that of the boys of a similar age was only 67 per cent. More marked differences were obtained when the scores of the five-year-olds were obtained (girls 60 per cent passing, while the average passing score for the five-year-old boys was only 30 per cent).

SKILL IN THE USE OF BALLS

Children between the ages of 6 and 12 years usually spend a great deal of time playing ball. In general, by the latter part of the sixth year a reasonably mature throwing pattern will usually emerge in boys, and a weight shift accompanied by a step with the foot opposite to the throwing arm will be evidenced. The girls will often evidence a weight shift by the age of six years when throwing but will sometimes step with the foot on the same side as the throwing arm.

Intercepting balls seems to be a more difficult task for children than throwing balls, and accuracy in the former usually lags several years behind the ability to impart velocity and accuracy to hand-held missiles. The integration of visual cues supplied by the ball in flight with movements of the total body and of the hands as the child stands and attempts to catch a ball thrown from a distance is usually not performed well until late childhood. By the age of six years most children can catch a large playground ball bounced waist-high from a distance of about 15 ft (16).

In addition to being thrown and caught, a ball may be struck with a bat, kicked with a foot, and dealt with in many other ways. The findings of studies of these skills are summarized in the following paragraphs.

THROWING

Throwing behavior in children is said by some to be derived from a natural protective mechanism inherited from our early ancestors, and others suggest that throwing merely emerges when the infant suddenly and accidentally swings his hand while holding an object that is dislodged by the resultant centrifugal force.

In any case, the normal six-year-old child can throw with force and with reasonable accuracy. The studies of throwing by children have usually focused on one or more of three subskills in throwing: (1) throwing distance, (2) throwing velocity, (3) throwing accuracy in hitting targets placed in the horizontal and vertical planes.

Throwing Distance

Using a standing throw for distance, Keogh's data reflect sex differences in a study completed several years ago (41). It appears as if the boys are throwing farther than the girls at every age tested, with their superiority more marked in the later years of childhood, at 10 and 11 years of age (Fig. 8-17) (41).

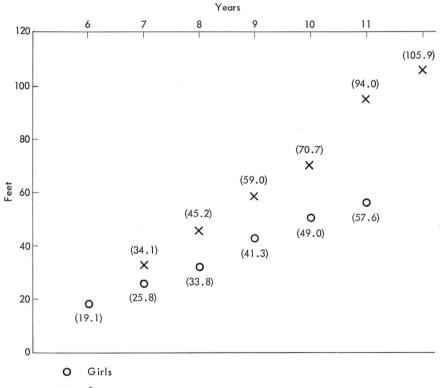

Figure 8-17 Throwing distance by age and sex. (J. F. Keogh, *Motor Performance of Elementary School Children*, Monograph, University of California, Los Angeles, Physical Education Dept., 1965.)

As can be seen in Keogh's data, the most marked improvement in the throwing distances for boys and girls occurs between the tenth and eleventh years. Although an improvement of from 9 ft to more than 20 ft is seen each year in the boys' mean scores, a lesser improvement of from 7 to 9 ft is seen in the mean scores of the girls during these same years.

Keogh found that both boys and girls between the ages of seven and ten years were throwing balls about two times farther than they could at six years of age, whereas the scores posted at six years tripled by 12 years of age. It is probable that the boys' frequent exposure to throwing tasks coupled with superior arm-shoulder strength contributes to their superiority over the girls in the ability to throw for distance.

As would be expected, smaller balls are thrown farther. Studies that have employed tennis balls, as contrasted with softballs, produce data indicating that the former can be thrown about 10 ft farther than the latter by children in each age group.

Throwing Velocity

Glassow and Kruse evaluated throwing velocities, using girls from the ages of 6 to 12 years, and found that improvement occurred in a linear relationship with age (Fig. 8-18) (24). In gen-

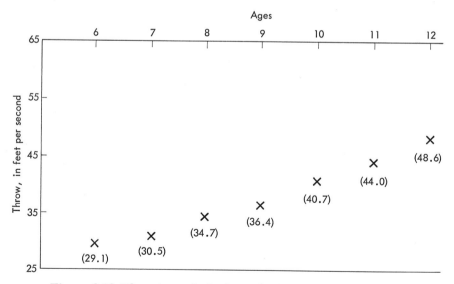

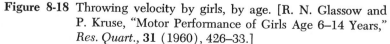

Figure 8-18 Throwing velocity by girls, by age. [R. N. Glassow and P. Kruse, "Motor Performance of Girls Age 6–14 Years," *Res. Quart.*, **31** (1960), 426–33.]

eral, the average improvement at each age was about 2 ft per second, with the exception of the scores at nine and ten years of age when slightly more improvement was noted. It appears from these data that the throwing velocity of girls improves about 67 per cent between the ages of 6 and 12 years.

Throwing Accuracy

Comparisons of data by various investigators reflecting throwing accuracy are difficult because of the many different methods employed by each. Keogh varied the distance that each age group was placed from a target, thus making even interage comparisons of mean scores within the same study a somewhat tenuous undertaking (41).

It is almost a ubiquitous finding, however, that boys throw more accurately than do girls of comparable ages. Particularly when testing younger children, investigators have had trouble obtaining reliable data owing to the variety of ways in which children may choose to let go of the ball from trial to trial. In a study carried out in our laboratory, girls were seen to exhibit regular improvement between the ages of six, seven, eight, and nine years; however, after those ages their accuracy tended to reach a plateau. Boys' accuracy will often reach a plateau somewhat later at the eleventh and twelfth years (16).

CATCHING

Catching is generally more difficult for children to master than is throwing, depending on the way in which the child is required to intercept the missile, the type and size of the missile, and the distance from which it is projected. The initial rudimentary "catching" skill usually involves merely trapping a large ball placed conveniently in the child's arms by his interested parent. More difficulty, of course, is encountered if the ball must be caught "on the fly" rather than being bounced to the child, and small balls thrown from a distance will invariably prove even more difficult to intercept than will larger ones projected from shorter distances.

Failure to catch well can prove socially traumatic for the maturing male child in the American society. For example, one of the ten-year-old children in a remedial program I administer was elated last year to have had the experience of catching his first ball. One can only imagine the social censure he must have incurred from his peers as he continued to drop balls for a period of ten years.

An investigation completed in our laboratory in 1968 contained a task that required that the child intercept with a direct forward movement of his first finger a ball on a string swinging through a 180-degree arc before the ball completed its third swing. The string was held by the tester in such a way that the ball swung an arm's distance from the child and directly in front of him. The ball was restarted by the tester after each attempt made by the child to intercept it (16).

The six-year-old children could usually touch the ball one time in five trials; the seven-year-old children could usually touch the ball two times in five trials; and the eight-year-old children could usually touch the ball three times in five trials. From the ages of 8½ to 11 years the scores on this task plateaued at about four interceptions in five trials.

All normal children between the ages of 6 and 12 years were able to catch a large playground ball bounced to them by a tester standing 15 ft away so that the ball arrived at chest height (16).

In a study by Williams an evaluation was made of the manner in which children judge the terminal point of a ball projected so that they were unable to observe the final part of the trajectory. The children stood under a long flat roof so that the ball would land over their heads, and so that they could observe the ball projected at the end. The subjects stood on switches attached to the ball-throwing machine so that reaction time (time between the projection of the ball and the child's leaving the switches) could be recorded. The task facing the children was to indicate where they thought the ball would arrive, by running to the point under the roof (62). The findings of this investigation were previously discussed in Chapter 6. It was found that not until the age of ten years could children move quickly and accurately to the correct terminus of the arc. Between the ages of six and eight years the children proved quick but inaccurate, misestimating the distance by about 22 ft on the average. At the age of nine years the children's judgment speed (reaction time) slowed down, but they became more accurate. During the final three years of elementary school the average error evidenced by both the boys and girls was about 2 ft.

Contrary to what might be expected on reviewing the previously discussed findings of throwing speed and distance, Williams found no sex differences in her data.

Developmental studies of ball-throwing behavior and of throwing and catching accuracy are not well standardized, and thus data emanating from these are difficult to compare. Investigations of the accuracy with which children judge movement in space and can intercept balls as a function of age are virtually absent from the literature.

KICKING AND BATTING BALLS

Relatively few investigations have assessed kicking accuracy and batting accuracy, and I am not aware of any surveys of kicking distances in children from the ages of 6 to 12 years. The sparse information that is available suggests that boys are generally superior to girls in kicking at horizontal targets at the ages of eight, nine, and ten years (7). There is improvement in kicking accuracy with age to the ninth year, and after this time there is a tendency to plateau.

Boys are also found to be superior to girls in their ability to bat a ball. It is probable that experience and cultural expectations for boys relative to the batting and kicking of balls influence the intersex comparisons of the mean scores in these tasks.

GAME CHOICES OF CHILDREN

In a recent unpublished investigation carried out in our laboratory at U.C.L.A., a revised version of the Sutton-Smith Games Choices was employed to survey the percentage of children (132 boys and 161 girls) who indicated that they engaged in various games. As can be seen in Figures 8-19 and 8-20, the "peak" years seem to be between the ninth and tenth years, after which there is a decline in the choices of the games surveyed. In later years children become highly selective in the games they report playing.

The graphs also reveal the similarity in the percentages of the children of various ages who play hopscotch and jump rope in the case of the girls and who play wall dodge ball and bowling in the case of the boys. It can also be seen in these data that about three times as many girls reported playing these vigorous games at the age of eight years as reported playing the same games at the ages of six and seven years, and after the age of nine years

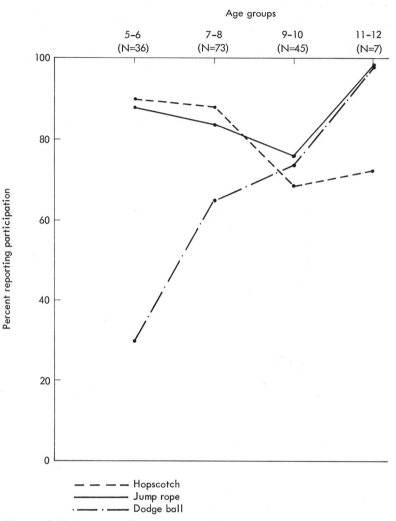

Figure 8-19 Game preferences voiced by girls at various ages in an unpublished study by the author.

a decline was noted. A similar, although less marked, trend is noted in the graphs of the boys' responses to this same questionnaire. More valid data should be forthcoming soon when the responses of more than 1,000 children are computed.

SUMMARY

A survey of the scores elicited in tasks through which the motor proficiencies of boys and girls between the ages of 6 and 12 years have been assessed led to the following generalizations.

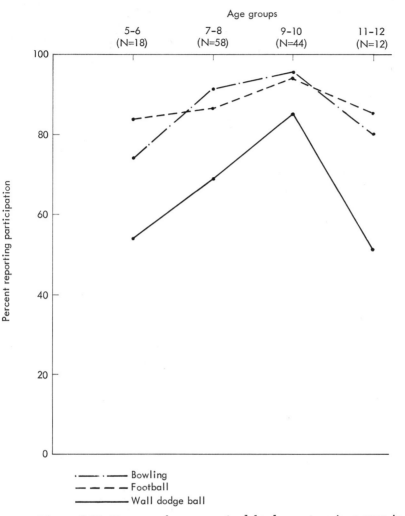

Figure 8-20 Game preferences voiced by boys at various ages in an unpublished study by the author.

1. As children mature in these years, they usually evidence regular increases in the ability to do most motor tasks. With some exceptions there is usually a linear relationship between age and mean scores, reflecting improvement in reasonably complex tasks.

2. Boys are stronger than girls in both the shoulder girdle and hip region during these years, and their scores exceed the scores of the girls in tasks involving forceful and direct acts of the hands (grip strength), acts of the arms (throwing speed), and acts of the feet and legs (vertical jump and standing broad jump).

3. The girls often excel the boys in tasks involving rhythmic

and accurate locomotor activities, including alternate hopping tasks, agility tasks, hopscotch, and similar tasks.

4. Measures of flexibility in children are highly specific, and as a child moves from his sixth year to his twelfth year, he may grow less flexible in some body regions and more flexible in other body regions.

5. Balance seems to mature toward the end of the twelfth year in most children.

6. Sex differences in throwing, running, and strength tasks seem to become greater as late childhood is reached, with the boys superior to the girls.

Age	Selected Behaviors
6 years	Girls superior in movement accuracy; boys superior in forceful, less complex acts
	Skipping acquired
	Throwing with proper weight shift and step
7 years	One-footed balancing without vision becomes possible
	Can walk 2-in.-wide balance beams
	Can hop and jump accurately into small squares
	Can execute accurate jumping-jack exercise
8 years	12 lb pressure on grip strength by both sexes
	The number of games participated in by both sexes is greatest at this age
	Can engage in alternate rhythmical hopping in 2-2, 2-3, or 3-3 pattern
9 years	Girls can throw a small ball 40 ft
	Girls can vertical jump 8½ in. and boys 10 in. over their standing height-plus-reach
	Boys can run 16½ ft per second
10 years	Boys can throw a small ball 70 ft
	Can judge and intercept pathways of small balls thrown from a distance
	Girls can run 17 ft per second

11 years	Standing broad jump of 5 ft possible for boys, 6 in. less for girls
12 years	Standing high jump of 3 ft possible

BIBLIOGRAPHY

1 Anderson, J. E., "The Limitations of Infant and Preschool Tests in the Measurement of Intelligence," *J. Psych.*, **8** (1939), 351–79.

2 Bass, R., "An Analysis of the Components of Tests of Semicircular Canal Functions, and of Static and Dynamic Balance," *Res. Quart.*, **10** (1939), 33–52.

3 Bayley, Nancy, "Consistency and Variability in the Growth of Intelligence from Birth to Eighteen Years," *J. Gen. Psych.*, **75** (1949), 165–96.

4 ———, "Behavioral Correlates of Mental Growth—Birth to Thirty-Six Years," *Amer. Psych.*, **23** (1968), 1–17.

5 Bloom, Benjamin S., *Stability and Change in Human Characteristics*, New York: John Wiley & Sons, 1964.

6 Carey, R. A., "A Comparison of the Lincoln Revision of the Oseretsky Tests of Motor Proficiency with Selected Motor Ability Tests on Boys at Elementary Level," unpublished doctoral dissertation, Indiana University, 1954.

7 Carpenter, Aileen, "Tests of Motor Educability for the First Three Grades," *Child Dev.*, **1** (1940), 293, 299.

8 ———, "The Differential Measurement of Speed in Primary School Children, *Child Dev.*, **12** (1941), 1–7.

9 ———, "Strength in Testing in the First Three Grades," *Res. Quart*, **13** (1942), 328–32.

10 Cattel, P., "Constant Changes in the Stanford-Binet I.Q.," *J. Ed. Psych.*, **22** (1931), 544–50.

11 Cavanaugh, M. C., *et al.*, "Prediction from the Cattel Infant Intelligence Scale," *J. Consult. Psych.*, **21** (1957), 33–37.

12 Clarke, H. Harrison, and D. B. Jordan, "Longitudinal Analysis of Strength and Motor Development of Boys Ages Seven Through Twelve Years," Unpublished paper, based upon dissertation of second author, 1966.

13 Cowan, E., and B. Pratt, "The Hurdle Jump as a Developmental and Diagnostic Test," *Child Dev.*, **5** (1934), 107–21.

14 Cratty, Bryant J., "Athletic and Physical Experiences of Fathers and Sons Who Participated in Physical Fitness Testing at Pomona College, 1925–1959," *Calif. J. Ed. Res.,* **10** (1959), 207–11.

15 ———, "A Comparison of Fathers and Sons in Physical Ability," *Res. Quart.,* **31** (1960), 12–15.

16 ———, and M. M. Martin, *Perceptual-Motor Efficiency in Children,* Philadelphia: Lea & Febiger, 1969.

17 Cumbee, F. Z., "A Factorial Analysis of Motor Coordination," *Res. Quart.,* **25** (1954), 412–28.

18 ———, Margaret Meyer, and G. Peterson, "Factorial Analysis of Motor Coordination Variables for Third and Fourth Grade Girls," *Res. Quart.,* **28** (1957), 100–108.

19 Fleishman, E., "Factorial Analysis of Complex Psychomotor Performance and Related Skills," *J. Appl. Psych.,* **40** (1956), 2.

20 ———, and Gaylord Ellison, "Factor Analysis of Fine Manipulative Tests," *J. Appl. Psych.,* **46** (1962), 96–105.

21 ———, E. J. Kremer, and G. W. Shoup, "The Dimensions of Physical Fitness: A Factor Analysis of Strength Tests," Report No. 2, Office of Naval Research, 1961.

22 ———, P. Thomas, and P. Munroe, "The Dimensions of Physical Fitness: Factor Analysis of Speed, Flexibility, Balance and Coordination Tests," Report No. 3, Office of Naval Research, 1961.

23 Frankenberg, W. K., and J. B. Dodds, "The Denver Developmental Screening Test," *J. Pediat.,* **71** (1967), 181–91.

24 Glassow, R. N., and P. Kruse, "Motor Performance of Girls Age 6–14 Years," *Res. Quart,* **31** (1960), 426–33.

25 Goetzinger, C. P., "A Reevaluation of the Heath Railwalking Test," *J. Educ. Res.,* **54** (1961), 187–91.

26 Guilford, J. P., and W. B. Michaels, "Approaches to Univocal Factors," *Psychometrika,* **13** (1948), 1–22.

27 Gutteridge, Mary V., "A Study of Motor Achievements of Young Children," *Arch. Psych.,* **244** (1939), 34.

28 Harrison, J. C. E., "The Relationships Between Selected Physical and Motor Factors and the Skeletal Maturity of 9, 12, and 15 Year Old Boys," Microcard doctoral dissertation, University of Oregon, 1959.

29 Hartman, Doris M., "The Hurdle Jump as a Measure of the Motor Proficiency of Young Children," *Child Dev.,* **23** (1943), 201–11.

30 Heath, S. R., "The Rail Walking Test: Preliminary Maturational Norms for Boys and Girls," *Motor Skills Res. Exchg.,* **1** (1949), 34–36.

31 Hindmarch, R. G., "Significance of Physique, Maturational, Body Size, Strength, Motor Ability and Reaction Time Characteristics of Eight Year Old Boys," Microcard doctoral dissertation, University of Oregon, 1962.

32 Honzik, M. P., J. W. MacFarlane, and L. Allen, "The Stability of Mental Test Performance Between Two and Eighteen Years," *J. Exp. Ed.,* **17** (1948), 309–24.

33 Hupprich, F. L., and P. O. Sigerseth, "The Specificity of Flexibility in Girls," *Res. Quart.,* **21** (1950), 25–33.

34 Ismail, A. H., and C. C. Cowell, "Factor Analysis of Motor Aptitude of Preadolescent Boys," *Res. Quart.,* **32** (1961), 507–13.

35 ———, and J. J. Gruber, *Motor Aptitude and Intellectual Performance,* Columbus, Ohio: Charles E. Merrill Books, 1967.

36 ———, and D. R. Kirkendall, "Relationships Among Three Domains of Development," paper presented at 2nd International Congress of Sports Psychology, Washington, D.C., 1968.

37 Johnson, G. B., "Physical Skills Test for Selecting Classes into Homogeneous Units," *Res. Quart.,* **3** (1932), 128–36.

38 Johnson, R. D., "Measurements of Achievement in Fundamental Skills of Elementary School Children," *Res. Quart.,* **33** (1962), 94–103.

39 Jones, H. E., "Sex Differences in Motor Abilities," *Hum. Biol.,* **19** (1947), 12–24.

40 Kane, R. J., and H. V. Meredith, "Ability in the Standing Broadjump of School Children, 7, 9 and 11 Years of Age," *Res. Quart.,* **23** (1952), 198–208.

41 Keogh, J. F., *Motor Performance of Elementary School Children,* Monograph, University of California, Los Angeles, Physical Education Dept., 1965.

42 ———, "Physical Performance Test Data for English Boys, Ages 6–9," *Phys. Ed.,* **5** (1966), 65–69.

43 ———, *Analysis of Individual Tasks on the Stott Test of Motor Impairment,* Monograph Technical Report 2–68 (USPHS Grant HD 01059), University of California, Los Angeles, Physical Education Dept., October, 1968.

44 ———, "Developmental Evaluation of Limb Movement Task," Technical Report 1–68 (USPHS Grant HD 01059), Department of Physical Education, University of California, Los Angeles, Monograph, 1968.

45 ———, "A Rhythmical Hopping Task as an Assessment of Motor Deficiency," Paper reported at the 2nd International Congress of Sports Psychology, Washington, D.C., 1968.

46 ———, and P. W. Pedigo, "An Evaluation of Performance on Rhythmical Hopping Patterns," Unpublished Report, University of California, Los Angeles, Physical Education Dept., 1967.

47 Latchaw, Marjorie, "Measuring Selected Motor Skills in Fourth, Fifth and Sixth Grades," *Res. Quart.*, **25** (1954), 439–49.

48 Meredith, H. V., "The Rhythm of Physical Growth, A Study of 18 Anthropometric Measures in Iowa City Males Ranging in Age Between Birth and 18 Years," University of Iowa Study, *Child Welfare*, **3** (1935), 11.

49 Metheny, E., "The Present Status of Strength Testing for Children of Elementary School and Preschool Age," *Res. Quart.*, **12** (1941), 115–30.

50 Railo, Willi S., "Physical and Mental Endurance," and "Physical Fitness and Intellectual Achievement," unpublished reports, Norwegian College of Physical Education and Sport, Oslo, Norway, 1968.

51 Rarick, G. L., *Motor Development During Infancy and Childhood*, Monograph, Madison, Wis.: College Printing and Typing Co., 1961.

52 ———, and R. McKee, "A Study of Twenty Third Grade Children Exhibiting Extreme Levels of Achievement on Tests of Motor Proficiency," *Res. Quart.*, **20** (1949), 142–50.

53 ———, and J. A. Thompson, "Roentgenographic Measures of Leg Muscle Size and Ankle Extensor Strength of Seven-Year-Old Children," *Res. Quart.*, **27** (1956), 321–22.

54 Roach, E. G., and N. C. Kephart, *The Purdue Perceptual-Motor Survey*, Columbus, Ohio: Charles E. Merrill Books, 1966.

55 Seashore, H. G., "The Development of a Beam Walking Test and Its Use in Measuring Development of Balance in Children," *Res. Quart.*, **18** (1949), 246–59.

56 Seils, L. G., "The Relationship Between Measures of Physical Growth and Gross Motor Performance of Primary-Grade School Children," *Res. Quart.,* **22** (1951), 244–60.

57 Sloan, W., "Lincoln-Osteretsky Motor Development Scale," *Genet. Psych. Monogr.,* **51** (1955), 183–252.

58 Vandenberg, S. G., "Factor Analytic Studies of the Lincoln-Osteretsky Test of Motor Proficiency," *Percept. Mot. Skills,* **19** (1964), 23–41.

59 Vickers, V., L. Poyntz, and M. Baum, "The Brace Scale Used with Young Children," *Res. Quart.,* **13** (1942), 299–308.

60 Watt, Norman, "Maturity, Structural, Strength, and Motor Convergence Growth Analysis of Boys Seven through Seventeen Years of Age," Microcard doctoral dissertation, University of Oregon, 1963.

61 Whiting, H. T. A., *Acquiring Ball Skill, a Psychological Interpretation,* London: G. Bell and Sons, Ltd., 1969.

62 Williams, H. G., "The Perception of Moving Objects by Children," unpublished study, Perceptual-Motor Learning Laboratory, University of California, Los Angeles, 1967.

63 Yarmolenko, A., "The Motor Sphere of School Age Children," *J. Genet. Psych.,* **42** (1933), 298–318.

64 Zimmerman, Helen J., "Characteristic Likenesses and Differences Between Skilled and Non-Skilled Performance of Standing Broad Jump," *Res. Quart.,* **27** (1956), 352–62.

Social Development 9

At birth, a child emerges into a world in which various social forces begin immediately to impinge upon him, to mold his behavior in direct and subtle ways, and to reward and punish him for his proficiencies and ineptitudes. As a result of these social variables, the child's perceptual-motor behaviors are shaped, and while he is engaged in various movement activities, the social behavior of the child, in turn, is modified.

A number of workers have studied various relationships between sociality and perceptual-motor functioning (57). Among the facets of this complex problem area that have been dealt with are: (1) the evolving social characteristics of infants and children while at play, and (2) the manner in which various social factors influence the performance and movement patterns of children at various ages. Within the first category, one may find studies concerned with the development of leadership and cooperative behaviors in children at play, the manner in which children organize themselves into groups while playing, and investigations of similar problems. Researchers interested in the second problem area have studied the influence of verbal reinforcement, the presence or absence of peers and parents, and similar conditions on measurable physical performance.

Other subproblems that have been covered in the literature include the gaining of status and friends as a function of physical proficiency, relationships between success in athletics and social skill, sex differences in social behavior at play, and the influence of various subcultures on the individual's efforts in vigorous activities. The subcultures often dealt with include the peer group, the family, and siblings.

It is interesting to note that within the several scales that have been developed to assess the social behavior of children are contained many measures that are primarily indices of the child's motor competencies. The Vineland Scale of Social Maturity, for example, contains a preponderance of motor ability items, particularly at levels designed to evaluate the social competence of younger children (24). It thus seems that a child's perceptual-motor and social development during the first year or two of life are difficult to separate.

Research concerned with the social development of children at play, and with the influence of various social variables on the physical output of children, is at times spotty and lacks cohesiveness. There is a dearth of investigations, for example, that have followed the social growth of a subject population for a number of years. Exceptions are the investigations by Kagan and Moss (45) and the study in progress in Medford, Oregon, by Harrison Clarke (18).

Frequently data undergirding the research that is available have been derived from rather inexact "behavioral samplings" gained from observing children at play, or from the even more unreliable parental questionnaire. The findings on which the discussion that follows is based must therefore be considered tentative until comprehensive longitudinal programs of research on these problems are initiated.

INFANCY

Infantile gestures and facial expressions are influenced very early in life by various social stimuli. Not until about the second year of life, however, are the infant's more exact performance attributes influenced by the social clime.

The literature suggests that imitative smiling usually occurs sometime between the fifth week and fifth month of age in family-reared infants and at about eight months of age in institution-reared infants (25,41). Usually smiles are more likely to be elicited by familiar persons, and not until after the first year is smiling seemingly caused in the absence of some direct stimuli, i.e., "deferred imitation" (41,72,79).

Other writers have suggested that the gesture patterns of infants as early as two years of age and their manner of posturing are imitations of the adult behaviors to which they are exposed (10). Very early in life, at about the ages of three to four years, definite sex differences are seen in the throwing patterns of children (80).

Other than this kind of imitative behavior, however, little direct social interaction is seen during the first two years between children who are in close proximity. Usually at about the age of two years "parallel play" is seen in which two children may do the same thing at the same time, but not in direct contact or relationship to one another (19,59). Most of the play activities of infancy, however, are rather egocentric in nature, and other than the simplest rivalry seen by Bühler when two infants are placed next to a desired object, their activities tend to center around their own limb and hand movements in connection with objects in close proximity (16).

EARLY FAMILIAL INFLUENCES

Parents exert an early and profound influence on the behavior of their children. In addition to supplying some of the stimulation eliciting emotional expressions of pleasure and gesture and posturing patterns, they provide models of action and inaction that the child begins to copy. Bender and Rappaport, for example, on analyzing children's drawings of animals, suggest that children's animal fantasies reflect not only a fear of the parental figure but also admiration of the strength and agility of their parents (8).

Loving, accepting parents elicit different kinds of behavior in their children than do cold and rejecting ones. Children scoring high in measures of self-acceptance, for example, have been found to have parents who could be classified as loving (33,70,72).

Soon after birth, rage is largely nonspecific, but at about the first year the child begins to strike at people, and by the second year, aggressive acts may consist of dropping and spilling things in order to control authority figures within close proximity (70). Aggression in children is sometimes related to parental confusion about child-rearing practices and dissatisfaction on the part of parents with their mate and the current situation in the family (71). And although parents usually demand moderate aggression from their children against other children when it is required, they are far less tolerant of aggression directed toward themselves and toward the other children within the family. Early hostile behavior is, many times, a direct reflection of attitudes about child rearing on the part of parents.

Hostile acts are more likely to be punished directly when carried out by boys. Paradoxically, however, boys are more likely to be encouraged to express themselves in acts of direct aggression than are their sisters (72).

The amount of physical control exerted by the parents appears influential of the acquisition of movement attributes on the part of children between the ages of two and six years. The amount of physical mobility permitted by mothers, as well as how often the child is "checked" while at play, varies markedly between parents. Sears, in a study of this component of child rearing, found that about 50 per cent of the mothers studied restricted children of five and six years to their immediate neighborhood, and 11 per cent restricted their children to the yard. Only 1 per cent of the parents surveyed admitted imposing no restrictions on their child's geographical play areas (72).

This same investigation polled mothers concerning the frequency with which they located their children while at play. It was found that about 36 per cent of the parents monitored them occasionally, if they had not heard their voice for an hour; 25 per cent checked fairly often at one- to one-half-hour intervals; 8 per cent constantly oversaw their children; and only 10 per cent practically never became concerned about their children's whereabouts.

Sears also evaluated the amount of physical restriction imposed on the child's actions within the home. About half the parents did not permit the children to jump from furniture or engage in other vigorous activity within the home; however, 30 per cent of the parents reported permitting their children to exercise their physical capacities in a moderate fashion within certain restricted areas.

Zunich, studying relationships between child behavior and parental attitudes, obtained positive correlations between parental approval of activity and the amount of social interaction seen at play by the children within his sampling (83). Both Zunich and Bishop (11) found that irritability and strictness on the part of parents elicited indices of anxiety and noncooperative behavior on the part of children.

It seems apparent on consideration of the previous information that the parents exert early and direct influences that mold the child's inclinations for action and the amount of vigorous activity they consistently express, as well as the child's emotional expressions as they engage in various structured and unstructured play situations. As Sears points out, the child's personality is "the cluster of potentialities for action," and among the primary determiners of a child's personality are the dimensions of his parents' personalities (72).

GENDER IDENTIFICATION

By the age of three years, children of either sex are seen to evidence preference for different amounts and various types of physical output. Bridges, for example, surveying a sampling of three-year-olds, found that the boys tended to prefer larger movements requiring a greater energy output than did the girls, who preferred to move in a more constricted manner (13).

Kagan and Moss, in their longitudinal study of 89 children from "birth to maturity," found that passive boys during the preschool years selected different adult occupations and evidenced more aggressive masculine behaviors in early adulthood than did boys who played vigorously between the ages of three and four years. Thus, it would seem that within the masculine and feminine categories, children can be classified early according to the extent to which they evidence motor attributes consistent with those expected of their sex (45).

It is interesting to note that one of the most frequently used measures purporting to evaluate masculinity and femininity in children is carried out by assessing their games choice (68), and the earlier tests by Brown and others also allude to children's choices of games to evaluate feminine and masculine components within the child's personality (15,77).

These measures suggest that boys show an early preference for a masculine role (68) but may have trouble achieving that role owing to the discrepancy between the time a male versus a female "model" is available within the home (33). Boys and girls tend to imitate the like parents, but girls seem to exceed the boys at an early age at this type of sex-linked imitative behavior (9,33).

By the first grade, children's sex role preference becomes apparent to teachers and parents alike. Masculine boys have been found to perform better academically, are rated higher by teachers in social virtues, perform more proficiently in motor activities, are more mature, and engage in more constructive play during their initial year at school (61). Inappropriate gender identification in children can become a serious problem to both the parents and the children involved, and if it is observed, remedial action is usually called for. This should probably take the form of direct help in assuming appropriate masculine and feminine gesture patterns and play habits by exposure for additional periods of time to an appropriate male or female "model," as well as indirect help through the services of a psychiatrist or psychologist.*

By the age of eight years, clear-cut sex differences are seen in normally developing children with regard to game choice and their tendency to draw masculine and feminine figures (68). By middle childhood, the children are seen to give their emotional allegiance to one of their parents, after both female and male children initially identify with their ever-present mothers during the preschool years.

The boys switch to their father as he becomes a chief source of rewards, but if the father is absent from the home, the boy is likely to be delayed from adopting appropriate sexual behavior patterns. A further impediment to the assumption of appropriate gender identification in boys, it has been postulated, is the presence of a domineering mother within the family, and the presence of older sisters also may inhibit the assumption of masculine characteristics in boys.

By adolescence, boys who have had rewarding relationships with their fathers are strongly sex-typed (50). They are interested in masculine things and engage in male activities. Boys high in masculinity, Musson asserts (54), are more stable emotionally and are better adjusted socially than are boys low in masculinity.

Although measures of femininity in girls are at times more variable than the same measures among boys, girls' tendency to assume gesture patterns characteristic of their mothers is seen as early as age three, and their responses to various projective tests normally indicate a strong sex link by the age of six years (9). The problem of inappropriate gender identification among girls

---

* The author in a previous text presents information relative to the relationship between the assumption of an appropriate and/or inappropriate sex role as related to physical activity (22).

is not usually as traumatic for the family as is inappropriate gender identification among boys. At the same time, girls who begin to exhibit markedly inappropriate sex-linked behavior in middle and late childhood should also be given proper counseling. Analysis of the responses of girls to the games preference test over a period of years reveals a trend indicative of the fact that girls in our culture are beginning to show more preference for the more vigorous physical occupations than was true several years ago (75). However, the extent to which this preference may be approved by the society is probably specific to various sections of the country.

In any case, game preference as indicative of gender identification of girls and boys is a critical variable in assessing normal and abnormal development. Failure to note the manner in which growing children move in both unstructured and structured tasks is an important omission from a total assessment of developmental trends in individuals and in groups of maturing youngsters.

PARENTAL ATTITUDES AND PERFORMANCE ATTRIBUTES OF THEIR CHILDREN

Parents mold the behavior of their children in obvious and in subtle ways. As has previously been pointed out, the child's early social competencies are reflected in the imitated smile. Relatively little data, however, are available concerning how parental attitudes about physical activity interact with the physical attributes and attitudes of their children. The assessment of attitude is always a somewhat tenuous undertaking. At the same time it is difficult to separate attitudes of success from the attributes that elicit success in physical activities. For example, what is the relative influence of a father's attitude toward physical activity on his child's performance as opposed to the heredity factors (i.e., physique) that are likely to influence the performance capacities of both the father and son, and thus their mutual attitudes toward physical activity?

Data I have collected revealed that by the age of 18 performance differences may be obtained between students whose parents place a high value on physical education versus students whose parents are not as favorably inclined toward motor activities (22). There is relatively little information, however, on this same relationship on the part of younger children.

Heathers published an interesting study in 1955 in which dependency behavior was evaluated in a stressful performance situation (34). Children aged 6 to 12 years were blindfolded and asked to walk an unstable, narrow plank 8 in. above the ground. The experimenter offered help to all the children. It was noted who accepted and who rejected help. It was found that children who accepted help tended to have parents who had encouraged them to depend on others rather than themselves.

Rarick and McKee published a study in 1950 that explored differences in children exhibiting extremes in motor performance (66). Among the data collected were indices of parental participation in physical activity. In general it was found, as would be expected, that the parents of the superior children were active in sports, whereas very few parents of children in the inferior group participated in any type of vigorous physical activity. Additionally, the parents of the inferior group did not participate with their children, whereas 80 per cent of the children in the superior group had their parents sometimes accompany them in play.

A comprehensive study of relationships between parental attitudes toward physical education and the performance capacities of their children (111 children were studied) was recently completed in my laboratory by Zeller (81). The index of parental attitude used was the inventory prepared by Wear, and the measure of motor performance was a six-category test evaluating agility, balance, ball-handling skills, and body image. In general her findings reflected moderate to high positive correlations between the physical performance of the children and parental attitudes and between the attitudes of the two parents evaluated separately. When the children were separated into high- and low-ability groupings, the measures of parental attitudes were significantly different, with those having children in the low-ability group evidencing negative attitudes toward physical education, whereas the reverse was true on the part of the parents whose children performed well in the test battery.

The overall correlation between father and mother attitude scores was +.69, and the correlation between these measures using the scores from parents whose children were in the low-ability grouping was even higher (+.77). It was thus apparent that the attitudes of the parents (collected separately) were remarkably similar.

The correlations between parental attitude scores and children's performances were also statistically significant and moderately high. The correlation was +.67 when the scores of the girls were compared with the attitude indices of their parents, and the same measure utilizing the boys' scores was +.73.

When measures of parental participation were compared with the performance scores of their children, a similar trend was seen in the data. The participation by the mothers correlated higher than +.6 with both the boys' and girls' scores, and the same measure obtained from the father was also positive and high (ranging from +.59 when contrasted with their daughters' scores and even higher, +.74, when their sons' performance scores were employed in the comparison).

Data of this nature, of course, do not indicate that parental attitudes *cause* performance fluctuations in their children, but they are highly suggestive. In summary, this investigation revealed not only high concordance between parents concerning the value of physical education, but also a high correlation between their feelings and how their children actually perform.

Further investigations, in which data are collected longitudinally, should illuminate the factors that influence these high correlations. For example, successful performance by a child may engender more positive attitudes toward physical activity or, conversely, positive attitudes by parents may lead them to encourage their children at early ages to become physically active. This, in turn, is likely to elicit good performance. The enigma still needs to be "unraveled" whether parental physiques, attitudes toward activity, or success, which is probably influenced by physique and performance capacities, is more important in the molding of the offspring's physical performance.

PHYSICAL MATURITY AND PERFORMANCE AS PREDICTIVE OF SOCIAL SUCCESS

It is a common assumption that children, particularly males, who perform well physically enjoy more status among their peers than do underdeveloped, poorly functioning youngsters. Studies among schoolchildren affirm the findings derived from older populations that social success is related to the ability of some people to distinguish themselves in desirable ways from the group (2). And as physical performance is valued to varying degrees by maturing children of both sexes, distinguishing oneself in this area of competence may lead to increased social acceptance. According to innumerable studies, friendships are usually formed by people who are in close physical proximity for prolonged periods of time and who perceive themselves to be similar in various attributes. The same finding is echoed in the literature dealing with child development. Similarities of physical maturity, along with I.Q., are found to be more important indices of affiliation among youngsters than are more subtle personality traits (5,17,43,64).

Status is usually conferred on children who perform above accepted group norms in various physical tasks (20,27). In a number of studies by Mary Jones and her colleagues at Berkeley, it was found that physically accelerated boys are more accepted and treated more favorably by both peers and adults. This status leads to positions of leadership in the school community and persists in measurements of personality traits made during adulthood (44). Hardy also found that the best-liked pupils were superior to other pupils in tests of physical achievement, with 70 per cent of them scoring above the group mean. The effects of motor ability, as might be expected, are more marked on the social acceptability of boys than girls (32). Similarly, as boys progress from elementary school years through secondary schools, social status increases as a function of athletic ability (2,38,55,65). At the same time, with increased association, the effects of athletic ability on social status may be diminished, as boys perhaps begin to look for less obvious personality qualities on which to base their friendships (23,43,65).

Outlining trends relative to the assumption of social success as a function of age and sex, however, is a somewhat tenuous undertaking, upon review of the available data. At the same time, for the sociologist, educator, and psychologist to ignore the marked influence that game success has on the social acceptance of children and adolescents is to ignore an important dimension of the value system with which youngsters are surrounded.

At the same time, it is difficult to separate the effects, particularly among boys, of early maturity versus athletic proficiency on social acceptance and positive personality traits. As indeed maturity begets superior physical performance, and thus early maturing boys appear to form a base of success at play upon which to rest a positive self-concept. At the same time, early physical maturity on the part of males results in a physique that is more attractive to adults and peers with whom the child comes in contact. Thus, drawing direct causal relationships between sociality and physical proficiency during infancy, childhood, and adolescence becomes an even more difficult undertaking.

SOCIAL CHARACTERISTICS OF CHILDREN AT PLAY

Several variables have been assessed on observing children of various ages at play. The complexity of the group in which the children choose to play, its size, leadership patterns, and the nature and vigor of the efforts they expend have all been subjects of various amounts of experimental attention. Usually such measures are collected via a technique whereby an individual child is observed for a period of time at regular intervals, and notations are made relative to his methods of gaining group recognition, leadership attempts, vigor of activity, the influence of various play materials on play characteristics, and similar assessments (26).

Using such a technique, for example, it is usually noted that as children grow older, they tend to form more complex and larger social systems when at play (19,39,59). At the same time, the nature of the leadership patterns seen in these groups becomes more complex and more directly related to group goals. Sex differences in the vigor of activity, as well as in the nature of the social attributes evidenced, also seem related to age when children are observed in systematic ways while at play.

During the preschool years, children stimulate each other in indirect ways by their very presence. More vigor as well as more expressions of joy while at play is usually seen when more than one child is present in a play situation (59). The nature of this mutual stimulation during the nursery school years, however, is relatively nonspecific in nature. And the typical play patterns include either solitary participation or what has been termed parallel play. In this latter pattern of participation, children engage in similar tasks but are not directly interacting with one another (Fig. 9-1). They seem to be affecting one another by indirect imitation, rather than by direct physical and/or verbal interactions (19,39,48,69). Sex differences in play characteristics have been noted by several observers of preschoolchildren. Girls are seen to engage in less vigorous activities during these years and to engage more in verbal social interactions than in contacts involving some overt physical output (13,30).

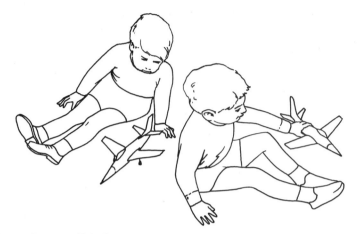

Figure 9-1 Parallel play in which each child is working independently but at similar tasks. Each is apparently receiving social stimulation from the other.

The usual size of the group in which children two to three years of age will form when playing consists of two individuals, containing playmates of the same sex (39,69). The presence or absence of play materials at this age will apparently exert a significant influence on the amount of social contact the child will evidence (48,76). Deprivation of play materials will result in a child's paying more attention to himself, than to others, according to research by Cockrell (19). The presence of play materials, as might be expected, will generally encourage a wider variety of play behaviors in preschoolchildren.

At about the age of four years, however, children seem to begin to seek the direct companionship of at least one other child while at play, and if such a friend is lacking, they will tend to make up imaginary friends to fulfill their apparent need for social interaction. As children grow older, they tend to watch less and participate more, to engage in imitative activity less and more in group play.

Rudimentary attempts at leadership may emerge at the age of four, as some children through direct and indirect means are seen attempting to manipulate the actions of others. These attempts at gaining leadership at play have proved to be highly correlated with a child's general social competence (32,58).

As children enter grade school at about the age of five, they begin to seek more and more companions to play with at one time and will more often seek members of the opposite sex with whom to associate, although still preferring members of their own sex when engaging in various play activities (19). The range of activities decreases, particularly in the case of boys, in which children of five and older participate, perhaps as various cultural sanctions as to what kinds of activities are given value become more exactly known by the participants (4).

During middle childhood, various aspects of the subculture in which the child resides begin to exert a more marked influence on the modes of play as well as the type of activities selected. For example, rural boys of from eight to ten years were found by Lehman to engage in fewer activities than town boys of the same age. Boys in a city environment, Lehman hypothesized, are more suppressed by their environment in their selection of play interests than are boys who grow up on farms (48).

The influence of the type and number of siblings begins to exert itself on play characteristics in middle childhood. Children tend to prefer either older or younger playmates according to whether they have older or younger brothers and sisters at home (22).

As adolescence is reached, more marked sex differences are, of course, discernible. The boys participate within strict codified rules and within strict cultural sanctions as to what are appropriate levels and types of participation.

LEADERSHIP AT PLAY

Within the past 30 years, several workers have focused their attention on the emergence of leadership in children at play. Although their findings do not point to definitive developmental trends, at the same time inferences from these investigations may lead toward future investigations that do survey the evolution of leadership traits and behaviors in children as a function of age more precisely.

According to Pigors (63), leadership does not appear in any kind of structured form in children until the ages of two to three years. This writer suggests that several conditions have to be present to elicit leadership, including the awareness on the part of the child that other playmates are individuals and have personalities, the development of some kind of self-discipline on the part of the child, an increased span of attention and memory enabling the pursuit of long-range goals, and the recognition of social ideals.

A child's role in the play group may vary from time to time, relative to the degree of leadership he asserts (58). For example, he may neither follow nor direct another effort, he may both direct and follow at the same time, he may simply follow another's instructions, or a child may engage only in leadership behavior and assume a primary role in directing group efforts.

Parten has defined two types of leadership patterns emerging in childhood as reflected in behavior of the ascendant members of play groups. On one hand are those who artfully and by indirect suggestion control a large number of children, the "diplomat." On the other hand is the child who may be classified as a "bully," who simply employs brute force and bosses the small group he has decided to master. Domination, being simpler, usually appears at younger ages in children's play groups (58).

Generally, childhood leaders are a little more intelligent than those who follow (67), and according to a study by Reaney, leadership at play rests on the ability to play games well, as might be expected (67). The effects of age and sex differences during the early school years on the assumption of leadership seem negligible (14,58,63). As a school year progresses, leadership patterns emerged more markedly in groups of children who have been surveyed (67).

Leadership patterns in older children's groups, as is the case with adult groups, may be evaluated rather reliably. For example, Parten, using four observers, found a high consistency when comparing their observations of leadership behavior in children's play groups; 87 per cent of the leadership indices recorded were agreed upon by the four observers (58). The results of this and other studies suggest that structured leadership of children's groups composed of both sexes usually is not seen until the age of nine or ten, although before that time the leadership characteristics discussed above are sometimes noted.

In groups of children of mixed socioeconomic status, the leadership usually falls to those who reside within the more favored social groups, according to Parten (58). However, as adolescence is approached, early maturing youngsters of less advantaged social and racial groups frequently attain leadership roles as a result of their athletic proficiency.

Several attempts have been made to experimentally induce

leadership behavior in children at play. Jack, for example (40), surveyed play groups of children and selected from them those who exhibited a lack of leadership (i.e., low "ascendant" scores). These children were then given individual training by the experimenter in using specific types of play materials including mosaic blocks, in assembling picture puzzles, and in learning a story in a book. The subjects were then placed in groups and their interactions were again recorded. Evidence of their feelings of ascendance in the new groups was forthcoming to a significant degree. For example, the children trained in this manner exhibited impatience at the mistakes of their companions. A "control" group within this investigation who received no practice in ascendant behavior exhibited no comparable changes in behavior.

It would seem, therefore, that children may learn their leadership behaviors as a result of group esteem as well as by an outcome of their own perceived proficiencies within the play situation. On learning of their potential for leadership, they may then begin acting as leaders, assuming a role that reflects a constellation of ascendant behavior including gesture patterns (38) and verbal behaviors, as well as specific and general leadership skills (38).

As adolescence is reached and youngsters play within codified rules, leadership may be bestowed for different reasons than was apparent during childhood. Early maturing males tend to elicit leadership, owing to their proficiency at games because of the acquisition of strength, speed, and power, as a result of earlier biochemical changes (42). Thus the age, size, skill in play, and expertise as a fighter will tend to gain a boy leadership, particularly in street gang situations (55,65).

Adolescent boys who are more accepted and who gain leadership are those who tend to carry impulses into action (63) and who desire to lead (65). Leaders of adolescent teams have been found to be more interested in people and to be aware of others' needs for social recognition. They are talkative and expressive socially, adventurous, and relatively impervious to social criticism (55).

Nelson, who studied the personality traits and social attributes of captains of basketball teams, found that leadership of these teams was not always attained by the best-liked boys. Boys who became captains of these teams were often rated as selfish by their peers, but at the same time the student leaders' proficiencies and social adroitness had somehow gained them the grudging respect of their teammates (55).

COOPERATION AND COMPETITION

A frequently researched facet of childhood play has concerned the extent to which cooperative and competitive behavior is evidenced, as well as the conditions that encourage or inhibit this facet of group interaction (62). It has been suggested that awareness of others and the social facilitation arising out of this awareness precede competitive behavior, and competition in children occurs before cooperation (22,29,31).

An interesting study carried out in 1927 dealt with competition during infancy. Bühler placed babies of from 4 to 22 months together in pairs in the presence of a single toy and then recorded their interactions. During the first six months, there was no rivalry, as indeed the children possessed no behavior that was highly developed enough to elicit rivalry. By the second one-half year, however, despotism and rivalry appeared at a vigorous level, as grasping behavior became fully developed in the children. During the first few months of age the children were able only to look at the objects and at each other; however, when their behavioral development enabled them to evidence competitive behavior, they did so (16).

Bühler found that the relationship in age between the two children influenced the extent to which they competed. Unless the children were of approximately the same age, i.e., within two and one-half months, vigorous rivalry was not evidenced, and the older child was usually the despot.

As children reach the ages of three and four, cooperative behavior begins to appear. Cooperative children, according to Graves, are characterized by imitativeness and the seeking of approval. At the same time, this researcher asserts that the incidence of competitive and cooperative behaviors in children is unrelated to sex (29).

Structured competition between children also seems to increase with age according to Greenberg and depends largely on the child's familiarity with the material or objects that may be competed for. Children who perform well are more likely to compete than those who do not, according to Greenberg, as the latter seem prompted by the desire to excel sometimes at the expense of another child. Criteria for eliciting competitive impulses, according to this researcher, thus include understanding the problem, interest in the task, a competitive attitude toward another child, and perceived competencies, as well as other variables within the situation. The extent to which the child has been reinforced for competitive responses by his parents, and when working with other children, is also believed to be important in the development of competitive behavior, according to Greenberg (31).

Using a block-building task, Greenberg scored the percentage of children at various ages who evidenced competition. This percentage was positively related to age; for example, none of the children between two and three years who were surveyed evidenced definite competitive behavior, whereas after the age of three, about 43 per cent did so. By the age of four, almost 70 per cent of the children competed while building blocks, and by the age of five years, 75 per cent were seen to compete within the situation described. Between the ages of six and seven, all but about 5 per cent of the children Greenberg studied evidenced at least a moderate amount of competitive behavior. Although the number of subjects within this investigation, particularly within various age groups, was limited, the findings point to a reasonably definite developmental trend, which might be validated by a more comprehensive study. It would be interesting to survey the incidence of competitive behavior as a function of age within play situations other than block building.

Competition in children seems a relatively natural and expected component of their personality; however, it is usually desirable to induce varying degrees of cooperative behavior into their temperament. Two researchers have attempted to study how cooperation might be taught to children of various ages, and both were reasonably successful in their efforts. Azrin and Lindsley (6) utilized operant conditioning methods, i.e., giving jelly beans to children on opposite sides of a screen when they exhibited cooperative reactions. The task was to place a stylus in holes at the same time. This reward pattern was effective, and in the absence of specific instructions concerning cooperation, it was found that children developed and maintained cooperative behavior, with one child usually assuming a leadership role and the other becoming the follower (6).

Heise found that specific instruction in principles of effective group interaction also elicited cooperative behavior by children.

The children were taught, for example, the nature of group conflicts and how they might be resolved. Following this type of
training, the children exhibited behavior toward each other that
was restrained and was marked by a definite feeling for group
unity (35).

The study of competitive and cooperative behavior in children
involves many variables: the nature of the task, the age of the
children, as well as their personalities and past successes and
failures in cooperative and competitive situations (28). Usually
children both cooperate and compete at the same time when
engaged in group play, as they cooperate with teammates while
competing with their rivals on the other team. Thus, definitive
investigations of childhood competition and cooperation as a function of age should seek to control other social variables that
impinge upon the primary behaviors under consideration.

At the present time, the evidence upon which to construct developmental trends of childhood play patterns is extremely scant,
as can be discerned from the previous discussion. The available
findings do, however, point to constructive directions that more
sophisticated contemporary researchers might follow.

SOCIAL REINFORCEMENT

Several developmental trends can be discerned in the literature
relative to the influence of various kinds of social reinforcement
on the motor performance of infants and children (46,53,78).
For example, during the early years of life, prior to the age of
four, children, when confronted by verbal encouragement from
another, or by the presence of an audience, seem to become generally excited and aroused. But this increase in activation does
not usually translate itself into improved performance scores
(37,51).

Missiuro, for example, studying the effects of social reinforcement on several motor tasks, concluded that before the age of
six general tension was increased in children because of social
stimulation, but rarely were performance scores improved (51).
Philip, in a similar study in which the effects of strangers and
friends utilized as competitors were studied as affective of kinder-
gartener's performance, also concluded that the type of pairing
did not influence the mean efficiency at a marble-dropping task,

but it did affect the quality of the response. "Strange" pairs resulted in relatively unexcited, quiet performance on the part of the five-year-olds studied, and "preference" pairs elicited noisy and excited performance from the youngsters (62). Even though children at an early age become aware of the presence of onlookers, their performance is not affected positively by this kind of social stimulation until about the age of six, judging from the available research evidence.

Patterson also found that with increased age children became more responsive to various social reinforcers. Using a marble placement task, this researcher found more marked changes in older subjects when they were reinforced for their efforts by friends than was true when younger children were exposed to the same experimental situation, despite the fact that children at early ages become aware of and perform more vigorously for friends than for a neutral peer (60).

The period of childhood during which verbal encouragement and various other kinds of social stimulation appear to affect performance most is between six and about 10 or 11 years. After this time, children seem to become relatively sophisticated and tend at times to block off various kinds of social reinforcers, becoming more sensitive to the difficulty and intrinsic interest of the task itself (53). For example, in a study by Lewis and others, it was found that, in a level pressing task, social reinforcement, i.e., the experimenter's directly indicating a correct response, was more motivating to first-graders than to sixth-graders and more motivating than indirect correction of the response (49). Allen also found that younger children (five years of age) remained longer under conditions of social approval in sorting, drawing, and puzzle tasks than was true when children of ten were asked to perform under the same circumstances. It was found by Allen that when adults' comments differed from the childrens' evaluation of their performance, they would remain longer on the task, tending to "cast off" this kind of verbal reinforcement. Similarly, the children in this investigation tended to evidence less effects of social reinforcement as the tasks became more difficult (1).

The effects of social stimulation in children, similar to the findings of studies with adult subjects, tend to vary as functions of the complexity of the task and the personality of the child. Arousal-producing conditions, as might be expected, will tend to elicit faster responses but may block the production of accurate responses in children (47). Similarly, the state of habitual arousal in the child, his anxiety level, may interact with various social reinforcers in the modification of his performance in various motor tasks. Again, using a marble-dropping task, Cox found that boys evaluated as evidencing low levels of anxiety improved more in the presence of their mothers, a peer, teachers, and a strange female, whereas boys with high levels of anxiety already present in their personality trait complex performed best when only the experimenter was present in the testing situation (21). In a similar context, Latane and Arrowwood found that emotionally arousing a teen-age girl, by berating her verbally, did not influence her ability to execute a simple task, but did tend to disrupt her responses on a complex task, i.e., pushing buttons to light cues (47).

Another important variable is the sex of the onlookers as compared to the sex of the performer (36). For example, Stevenson found in children the same "cross-sex effect" sometimes seen in studies of adults (74). Testing by a member of the opposite sex, Stevenson concludes, increases competitiveness, anxiety, and desire to please, and this effect is more marked when male experimenters are dealing with female subjects.

Children perform motor tasks better, on the whole, when in groups with both obvious and subtle social stimulation present than when performing alone. Mukerji suggests that this effect is more marked in the case of boys than girls (52). The direction and influence of the presence of other people on performance scores are functions of the number and the social proximity of the onlookers (82) and whether they heap praise or blame on the performing child, as well as the complexity of the task (56).

As children enter school at about the age of five and six, their reactions to various social reinforcers become more specific and reflect inexact performance scores, whereas, prior to that time, the presence of encouraging, discouraging, or neutral onlookers seems simply to excite them. After late childhood is reached, however, the more sophisticated child does not merely base his performance on the amount and quality of social reinforcement present in the situation but also evaluates carefully the interest and difficulty of the task prior to deciding on the quality and quantity of effort he will expend.

SUMMARY

The early social development of infants and children is closely linked with the manner in which they deal with play materials and with each other when playing. The scales upon which infant and childhood sociality is based are composed primarily of motor ability items at the primary levels.

The child's initial social contacts are the parents, who seem to elicit early expressions of emotions and in other ways transmit gesture patterns, posturing, and other forms of movement behavior that are incorporated into the child's manner of dealing with his world.

Infant interactions at play initially take the form of "parallel play," although studies carried out using infants six months old indicate that two youngsters will evidence simple rivalry for an object as soon as grasping behavior has developed. By the age of two, children will many times begin to play in unisexual pairings. And simple leadership patterns will be evidenced. By the age of four, the groups will tend to become larger, and more structured competition will begin to emerge within and between groups.

As middle childhood is reached, innumerable facets of the environment will influence childhood play, including the social and economic conditions, the play materials, and the siblings available to play with, as well as the opportunity to receive instructions from another. Children from the ages of six to ten begin to evidence marked sexual differences at play, the boys preferring more vigorous activities, and the girls tending to prefer more passive expressions of the play instinct. Rules become codified and leadership reaches higher levels of competency as the structure of the groups assumes more complexity. By the age of seven, most children engage in competitive behaviors.

The adolescent period is marked by increased differentiation between the sexes at play and by the increased acquisition of status for physical prowess by the boys, owing to early maturity and/or the acquisition of forceful and accurate movement capacities on their part. The chart that follows summarizes the primary trends relating social to motor development, seen in the rather limited literature available.

Social-Motor Development, Developmental Channels

Years   *Behavioral Components*

Years	Complexity of Group Organization	Competition	Leadership	Influences of Reinforcement
16 plus	↑	↑	↑	↑
13–15	Status gained by boys in athletics			
11–12	Sex differences alloted for in group organizations			Simple social reinforcement loses some of its impact; child evaluates task outcomes
9–10	Large teams are seen, codified rules	Competition and cooperation highly developed	Structured leadership evidenced in team efforts	Effect of individual differences emerge, i.e., anxiety, etc.
7–8	More complex rules are used; larger groups containing both sexes at times	Competitive behaviors evidenced by most		
5–6	Three or more in groups, simple rules	Cooperative behaviors emerge	Simple leadership patterns seen of small groups	Social stimuli may aid per formance
3–4	Unisexual groups of two	Unstructured competition seen at times	The bully and diplomat emerge	
2	Parallel play			Child excited by social stimuli
1	Egocentric world	Simple rivalry for objects by two infants		
Birth				Parental influences seen

BIBLIOGRAPHY

1 Allen, Sara, "The Effects of Verbal Reinforcement on Children's Performance as a Function of Type of Task," *J. Exp. Child. Psych.*, **13** (1965), 57–73.

2 Anastasiow, Nicholas J., "Success in School and Boys' Sex Role Patterns," *Child Dev.*, **33** (1965), 1053–66.

3 Anderson, Harold H., and H. F. Brandt, "Study of Motivation Involving Self-Announced Goals of Fifth Grade Children and the Concept of Level of Aspiration," *J. Soc. Psych.*, **10** (1939), 2–9, 232.

4 Arrington, R. E., "Interrelations in the Behavior of Young Children," *Child Dev. Monogr.*, **8** (1932), 174.

5 Austin, Mary C., and George G. Thompson, "Children's Friendships: A Study of the Bases on which Children Select and Reject Their Best Friends," *J. Ed. Psych.*, **39** (1948), 101–16.

6 Azrin, Nathan J., and Ogden R. Lindsley, "The Reinforcement of Cooperation Between Children," *J. Abnorm. Soc. Psych.*, **52** (1956), 100–102.

7 Baldwin, A. L., and Harry Levin, "Effects of Public and Private Success on Children's Repetitive Motor Behaviors," *Child Dev.*, **29** (1958), 263–73.

8 Bender, Lauretta, and Jack Rappaport, "Animal Drawings of Children," *Amer. J. Orthopsych.*, **14** (1944), 521–27.

9 Bielianskos, Vytantas, "Recent Advances in the Psychology of Masculinity and Femininity," *J. Psych.*, **60** (1965), 255–63.

10 Birdwhistell, R. L., "Kinetics and Communications," in *Explorations in Communications*, Edmund Carpenter and Marshall McLuhan (eds.), Boston: Beacon Press, 1960.

11 Bishop, Barbara M., "Mother-Child Interaction and the Social Behavior of Children," *Psych. Monogr.*, **65** (Whole No. 328), 1951.

12 Brackett, C., "Laughing and Crying of Preschool Children," *Child Dev.*, Monogr. No. 14, 1934.

13 Bridges, K. M. B., "Occupational Interest of Three Year Old Children," *Ped. Sen. J. Genet. Psych.*, **34** (1928), 413–23.

14 ———, *The Social and Emotional Development of the Pre-School Child*, London: Kegan Paul, 1931, p. 277.

15 Brown, D. G., "Masculinity-Femininity Development in Children," *J. Consult. Psych.*, **21** (1957), 197–202.

16 Bühler, C., "Die Ersten Socialen Verhaltungsweisen des Kindes. in Sociologische und Psychologische Studien Ueber das Erste Lebensjahr," *Quell. u. Stud. Z. Jugendk.* pp. 1–102, No. 5, Jena: Fischer, 1927.

17 Challman, Robt., "Factors Influencing Friendships Among Pre-School Children," *Child Dev.*, 3 (1932), 146–58.

18 Clarke, Harrison, and D. B. Jordan, "Longitudinal Analysis of Strength and Motor Development of Boys Ages Seven Through Twelve Years," unpublished report, based upon Doctoral Dissertation of second author, 1966.

19 Cockrell, D. L., "A Study of the Play of Children of Pre-School Age by an Unobserved Observer," *Genet. Psych. Monog.*, 17 (1935), 372–469.

20 Cowell, C. C., and A. H. Ismail, "Relationships Between Selected Social and Physical Factors," *Res. Quart.*, 33 (1962), 40–43.

21 Cox, F. N., "Some Effects of Test Anxiety and Presence or Absence of Other Persons on Boys' Performance on a Repetitive Motor Task," *J. Exp. Child. Psych.*, 3 (1965), 100–12.

22 Cratty, Bryant J., *Social Dimensions of Physical Activity*, Chap. 6, Englewood Cliffs, N.J.: Prentice Hall, 1967.

23 Davitz, J. R., "Social Perception and Sociometric Choice of Children," *J. Abnorm. Soc. Psych.*, 50 (1955), 173–76.

24 Doll, E. A., *The Measurement of Social Competence: A Manual for the Vineland Social Maturity Scale*, Minneapolis: Educational Testing Bureau, 1953.

25 Goldfarb, W., "The Effects of Early Institutional Care on Adolescent Personality," *J. Exp. Ed.*, 12 (1943), 106–29.

26 Goodenough, F. L., "Measuring Behavior Traits by Means of Repeated Short Samples," *J. Juv. Res.*, 12 (1928), 230–35.

27 ———, "Inter-Relationships in the Behavior of Young Children," *Child Dev.*, 1 (1930), 29–48.

28 Graves, E. A., "The Effect of Competition and Reward on the Motor Performance of Pre-School Children," Master's thesis, University of Minnesota Library, 1934.

29 ———, "A Study of Competitive and Cooperative Behavior by the Short Sample Technique," *J. Abnorm. Soc. Psych.*, 32 (1937), 343–61.

30 Green, Elise H., "Group Play and Quarreling Among Pre-School Children," *Child Dev.*, 4 (1933), 302–308.

31 Greenberg, P. J., "Competition in Children: An Experimental Study," *Amer. J. Psych.*, **44** (1932), 221–48.

32 Hardy, Martha C., "Social Recognition at the Elementary School Age," *J. Soc. Psych.*, **8** (1937), 365–84.

33 Hartup, Willard, "Some Correlates of Parental Imitation in Young Children," *Child Dev.*, **33** (1962), 85.

34 Heathers, G., "Emotional Dependence and Independence in Nursery School Play," *J. Genet. Psych.*, **87** (1955), 37–57.

35 Heise, Bryan, *Effects of Instruction in Cooperation on the Attitudes and Conduct of Children*, Ann Arbor, Mich.: University of Michigan Press, 1942.

36 Hill, Kennedy T., and Harold W. Stevenson, "The Effects of Social Reinforcement vs. Nonreinforcement and Sex of E on the Performance of Adolescent Girls," *J. Person.*, **33** (1965), 30–45.

37 Horowitz, F. D., "Incentive Value of Social Stimuli for the Pre-School Children," *Child Dev.*, **33** (1962), 111–16.

38 Hunt, J. McV., and R. L. Solomon, "The Stability and Some Correlates of Group Status in a Summer-Camp Group of Young Boys," *Amer. J. Psych.*, **55** (1942), 33–45.

39 Hurlock, E. B., "Experimental Investigations of Childhood Play," *Psych. Bull.*, **31** (1934), 47–66.

40 Jack, Lois M., "An Experimental Study of Ascendant Behavior in Preschool Children," in *Behavior of the Preschool Child*, pp. 7–65, Vol. IX, No. 3., Ames, Iowa: University of Iowa Studies in Child Welfare, 1934.

41 Jesild, A. T., and G. F. Ding, "A Study of the Laughing and Smiling of Pre-School Children," *J. Genet. Psych.*, **40** (1932), 452–72.

42 Jones, H. E., *Motor Performance and Growth*, Berkeley: University of California Press, 1949.

43 Jones, Mary C., "Adolescent Friendships," *Amer. Psych.*, **3** (1948), 352.

44 ———, and Nancy Bayley, "Physical Maturing Among Boys as Related to Behavior," *J. Educ. Psych.*, **41** (1950), 129–48.

45 Kagan, Jerome, and H. A. Moss, *Birth to Maturity: A Study in Psychological Development*, New York: John Wiley & Sons, 1962.

46 Keiley, Richard, and M. W. Stephens, "Comparison of Different Patterns of Social Reinforcement in Children's Operant Learning," *J. Comp. Physiol. Psych.*, **57** (1964), 294–96.

47 Latane, B., and A. John Arrowwood, "Emotional Arousal and Task Performance," *J. Appl. Psych.*, **47** (1963), 324–27.

48 Lehman, H. C., and P. A. Witty, *The Psychology of Play Activities*, New York: A. S. Barnes and Company, 1927.

49 Lewis, Michael, M. Wall, and J. Aronfreed, "Developmental Change in the Relative Values of Social and Non-Social Reinforcements," *J. Exp. Psych.*, **66** (1963), 133–37.

50 Medinnus, G. R., "Adolescents' Self-Acceptance and Perceptions of their Parents," *J. Consult. Psych.*, **29** (1965), 150–54.

51 Missiuro, W., "The Development of Reflex Activity in Children," in *International Research in Sport and Physical Education*, E. Jokl and E. Simon (eds.), Springfield, Ill.: Charles C Thomas, 1964, pp. 372–83.

52 Mukerji, N. P., "An Investigation of Ability to Work in Groups and in Isolation," *Brit. J. Psych.*, **30** (1940), 352–56.

53 Murphy, L. B., and G. Murphy, "The Influence of Social Situations Upon the Behavior of Children," in *Handbook of Social Psychology*, Carl Murchison (ed.), Worcester, Mass.: Clark University Press, 1935, Chap. 22.

54 Mussen, Paul, "Some Antecedents and Consequences of Masculine Sex-Typing in Adolescent Boys," *Psych. Mono.*, **75** (Whole No. 506), 1961.

55 Nelson, Dale O., "Leadership in Sports," *Res. Quart.*, **37** (1966), 268–75.

56 Noer, David, and James Whittaker, "Effects of Masculine-Feminine Ego Involvement on the Acquisition of a Mirror-Tracing Skill," *J. Psych.*, **56** (1963), 15–17.

57 Palermo, D. S., and L. P. Lipsitt, *Research Readings in Child Psychology*, New York, Chicago: Holt, Rinehart and Winston, 1967.

58 Parten, Mildred B., "Leadership Among Preschool Children," *J. Abnorm. Soc. Psych.*, **27** (1933), 430–40.

59 ———, "Social Play Among Preschool Children," *J. Abnorm. Soc. Psych.*, **28** (1933), 136–47.

60 Patterson, G. R., and D. Anderson, "Peers as Social Reinforcers," *Child Dev.*, **35** (1964), 951–60.

61 Payne, D. E., and P. H. Mussen, "Parent-Child Relations and Father Identification Among Adolescent Boys," *J. Abnorm. Soc. Psych.*, **52** (1956), 358–62.

62 Philip, Alice J., "Strangers and Friends as Competitors and Cooperators," *J. Genet. Psych.*, **57** (1940), 249–58.

63 Pigors, P., "Leadership and Domination Among Children," *Sociologus*, **9** (1933), 140–57.

64 Pintney, R., F. Forlands, and H. Freedman, "Personality and Attitudinal Similarity Among Classmates," *J. Appl. Psych.*, **21** (1937), 48–65.

65 Puffer, J. A., "Boys' Gangs," *Ped. Sem.*, **12** (1905), 175–212.

66 Rarick, G. L., and L. McKee, "A Study of Twenty Third Grade Children Exhibiting Extreme Levels of Achievements on Tests of Motor Proficiency," *Res. Quart.*, **20** (1950), 142–50.

67 Reaney, M. J., "The Correlation Between General Intelligence and Play Abilities as Shown in Organized Group Games," *Brit. J. Psych.*, **7** (1914), 227–52.

68 Rosenberg, B. G., and B. Sutton-Smith, "The Measurement of Masculinity and Femininity in Children: An Extension and Revalidation," *J. Genet. Psych.*, **96** (1960), 165–70.

69 Sadusky, A. S., "Collective Behavior of Children of a Pre-School Age," *J. Soc. Psych.*, **1** (1930), 367–78.

70 Schaefer, E. S., "Converging Conceptual Models for Maternal Behavior and for Child Behavior," in *Parental Attitudes and Child Behavior*, J. C. Glidewell (ed.), Springfield, Ill.: Charles C Thomas, 1961.

71 ———, and R. Q. Bell, "Patterns of Attitudes Toward Child Rearing and the Family," *J. Abnorm. Soc. Psych.*, **54** (1957), 391–95.

72 Sears, Robert R., E. C. Maccoby, and H. Levin, *Patterns of Child Rearing*, Evanston, Ill.: Row, Peterson and Company, 1957.

73 Spitz, R. A., and K. M. Wolf, "The Smiling Response: A Contribution to the Ontogenesis of Social Relations," *J. Genet. Psych. Monogr.*, **34** (1946), 57–156.

74 Stevenson, H. W., "Social Reinforcement with Children as a Function of CA, Sex of E, and Sex of S," *J. Abnorm. Soc. Psych.*, **63** (1961), 147–54.

75 Sutton-Smith, B., and B. Rosenberg, "Sixty Years of Historical Changes in the Game Preferences of American Children," *J. Amer. Folkl.*, **74** (1961), 17–46.

76 Updegraff, Ruth, and E. K. Herbet, "An Experimental Study of the Social Behavior Stimulated in Young Children by Certain Play Materials," *J. Genet Psych.*, **42** (1933), 372–91.

77 Walker, Richard N., "Measuring Masculinity and Femininity by Children's Games Choices," *Child Dev.*, **35** (1964), 961–71.

78 Wardweel, Elinor, "Children's Reactions to Being Watched During Success and Failures," Unpublished doctoral dissertation, Cornell University, 1960.

79 Washburn, R. W., "A Study of the Smiling and Laughing of Infants in the First Year of Life," *Genet. Psych. Monogr.,* **21** (1929), 113–26.

80 Wild, Monica R., "The Behavior Pattern of Throwing and Some Observations Concerning Its Course of Development in Children," *Res. Quart.,* **9** (1938), 20–24.

81 Zeller, Janet, "The Relationship Between Parental Attitude Toward Physical Education and the Physical Performance of the Child," Unpublished Master's thesis, University of California, Los Angeles, 1968.

82 Zigler, Edward, and Paul Kanzer, "The Effectiveness of Two Classes of Reinforcers on the Performance of Middle and Lower Class Children," *J. Person.,* **30** (1962), 155–63.

83 Zunich, Michael, "Child Behavior and Parental Attitudes," *J. Psych.,* **62** (1966), 41–46.

Evaluation and Discussion **10**
of Selected Perceptual-Motor
Programs Purporting to
Enhance Academic Functions

Within the last 12 years, and particularly during the last five or six years, a number of theories outlining ways in which various types of motor activities may aid children to improve a wide variety of attributes have received widespread exposure in the popular press. One theory suggests that motor activities, properly applied, will prepare children for spelling, reading, and similar intellectual endeavors during the first grade. Other theories imply that severe sensory and motor disturbances that reflect pronounced brain damage can be remedied by recapitulating the stages of motor development through which a child passes as he learns to walk.

These pronouncements have had various effects on parents, educators, and clinicians concerned about normal and atypical children. Some have overreacted and have instituted programs of movement activities into elementary school programs in which all the normal children participate. Other parents and clinicians have imposed on atypical children demanding programs of hourly applied motor therapy, sometimes enlisting the help weekly of as many as 200 friends and neighbors.

Other more skeptical and perhaps more sophisticated school administrators either have proceeded with caution by attempting to identify for remedial help only children with movement problems within their school populations or have totally rejected the rather extravagant claims made for these theories, excluding any kind of special motor training from their curricula.

The primary detrimental effect of these theories has arisen from the expansive promises offered for participation in motor activities. Although it is true that a normal growing child learns much by moving, it is also true that the human animal does more than move. He is also a thinker, possessing a brain, a large portion of which permits the storage and association of ideas and abstractions relatively independent of the ability to move and to see.

The theories, however, have had some positive effects on educational practices. Statements emanating from them have prompted many to take a longer and deeper look at the *obvious* things a child can or cannot do rather than dwelling on only the subtle, and sometimes elusive, emotional and intellectual components of his behavior. If a child cannot play well and cannot move his hands accurately when writing his thoughts on paper, he will usually experience social problems on the playground and academic difficulties in the classroom. These problems will many times result in emotional maladjustments of a mild or severe nature.

Many well-informed educators, however, are beginning to evidence a type of backlash reaction sometimes seen in the political arena. When the mention of perceptual-motor or sensory-motor training arises, they are quick to enumerate the poorly supported claims of some of the movement medicine men as the reason for totally rejecting attempts to evaluate and to provide remediation for children under their supervision who may evidence movement problems that interfere with efficient and total school performance. This type of reaction, the author believes, is to be avoided.

This chapter will attempt to put the claims and consequent practices of three of the more prominent perceptual-motor theories into perspective by examining basic research evidence that either supports or negates the claims made within each. Also discussed are the results of studies in which the practices advanced have been applied in educational programs.

The writer believes that motor activities may indeed play a more important role in the education of more children. However, the nature of this role can and should be outlined in a scholarly and positive way by consulting sound research data.

PERCEPTUAL-MOTOR TRAINING

Newell C. Kephart is a clinical psychologist formerly of Purdue University who, in several books, a series of 19 one-hour films, and several articles, has outlined a theory that proposes motor learning is the basis of all learning. Proceeding from this basic premise, he outlines motor activities that he purports will positively influence academic readiness, school achievement, and reading. In his theory, Kephart deals with perception and learning more than with the neurological underpinnings of movement-cognitive relationships, although, at one point in his 1956 text, he suggested that since balance is controlled by the cerebellum, a child's deficit in balance (thus having a malfunction in his cerebellum) will tend to be "short-circuiting" thoughts descending from the cortex. In one of his films, he spends a considerable amount of time explaining that the malfunctioning of one neuron will probably negatively influence the functioning of a vast network of neurons. The lessons he suggests we draw from both these illustrations are, of course, that balance training will aid cognition by eliminating possible cortical "short circuits" and that remedial help that positively influences a single neuron is likely to clear up a number of problems.

Kephart states that, similar to Getman's levels of visual-perceptual development, one must aid a child to establish what are termed "motor generalizations." These include:

POSTURE AND BALANCE

Kephart places great emphasis on the importance of balance in the belief that a child who cannot orient his body well to the "only constant in the universe" (gravity) by balancing well cannot be expected to make accurate perceptual judgments owing to the unstable base from which his spatial judgments are made (i.e., his body).

LOCOMOTION

Locomotor activity aids the child to better learn about the dynamics of his relationships to objects and things, it is hypothesized. Thus, a child who evidences a clumsy gait pattern may be spending too much time watching his feet, thereby not effectively organizing the world around him and thus becoming perceptually handicapped, according to Kephart.

CONTACT

Similar to Getman's second visual-perceptual level (special movement patterns), Kephart also suggests that deficits in manipulative skills preclude the child's becoming aware of objects, shapes, and textures. Furthermore, Kephart states that as a child becomes aware of near space via manipulative activity, he extrapolates this visual-motor "data" to distant space. He thus suggests that manipulative problems will also be reflected in problems resulting from the child's attempts to organize more distant space.

RECEIPT AND PROPULSION

This fourth generalization is derived from the child's experiences when throwing and catching balls. It is through this type of activity that a child learns about velocities, sizes, and distances in distant space, Kephart writes.

MOTOR GENERALIZATIONS

Besides the four enumerated, Kephart also mentions other generalizations including body image and laterality in his film series.

The body image is a rather all-encompassing group of perceptions formed as the child moves his body in various ways and in various media, according to Kephart, and the "laterality generalization" involves the child's ability to coordinate one side of his body with the other and cognitively to discriminate between one side of his body and the other. A deficiency in this second area, Kephart asserts, will result in problems involving directionality in space reflected in letter reversal (strephosymbolia) and in the incorrect placement of letters in words. Laterality then, suggests Kephart, is related to directionality as the child must project his body image and its left-right dimensions to space when forming left-right judgments. Stemming from this hypothesis is the suggestion that body-image training will correct problems of letter reversal when reading and printing.

Further, Kephart suggests that it is imperative that these motor generalizations be well established for they provide the basis from which the child organizes his world perceptually, which, in turn, makes possible sound intellectual functioning. Conversely, a deficiency in motor coordination is thus likely to produce a child who is perceptually disorganized and therefore intellectually incapable, according to this theoretician.

Kephart's theory may be examined indirectly or by reviewing research dealing with the effects of his program on reading and other perceptual-motor attributes. Data collected in our laboratory and in a study by Ayres indicated that measures of directionality in children with perceptual-motor deficits are not related to their ability to correctly identify their left and right body parts (4). Moreover, if a child *is* seen to reverse letters, it may not be critical. Some research findings, for example, suggested that reversal problems contribute to poor reading on the part of only from 2 to 4 per cent of all children with reading deficits. Further, the work of Olin Smith (61) results in the identification of five unrelated visual-perceptual attributes, whereas the studies of Fleishman and others (18) through the years have pointed to the specificity of motor performance. Thus, the suggestion that motor learning influences perceptual processes is at best imprecise, and at worst misleading. Additionally, studies summarized by Bloom (7) have pointed out the difficulty of predicting later intelligence by evaluating the perceptual-motor attributes of young children. Bayley, who recently published a longitudinal study of 54 individuals from birth to 36 years of age, has found that an infant's abilities can be factored into six separate attributes by the age of five months, including visual following, social responsiveness, perceptual interest, manual dexterities, vocalizations, and object relations. Furthermore, she found that only the quality of a child's early vocalizations correlate with later I.Q., whereas, indeed, boy babies who are active and rapid before 15 months of age tend to have I.Q.'s that are lower than those of the calmer, less active infants. The early motor responsiveness of girls, according to Bayley, was not correlated in any way with I.Q. Not until a child is about eight years of age was it possible to predict I.Q. in later childhood and early adolescence with any degree of accuracy (5). Thus, Kephart's assertion that the quality of early motor abilities is predictive of and influences later intellectual development is at odds with the findings from a number of research studies.

Kephart also suggests that training in visual tracking will positively influence academic success, and in his 1956 text, he advanced methods for evaluation of ocular coordination. (The child is asked to watch a thumbtack fixed to the eraser of a pencil moved by the tester. The failure of the child's eyes to move as smoothly as "ice on a glass of water" is purportedly evidence of an ocular problem.) Again, however, such statements differ from the findings of research conducted over a period of almost 140 years that point out quite clearly that as a child reads his eyes move in rapid starts and stops at a rate too rapid for conscious control (3-8 times per second); and thus problems in fusion or hyperopia, and not binocular tracking, are likely to be found in groups of poor readers (14,15,16,64,65,67).

Several researchers have utilized Kephart's techniques in experimental studies to determine their effects on reading. Generally, the results have been negative. LaPray and Ross, for example, comparing reading improvement, experimented with two groups of first-graders low in reading, one of which was subjected to visual training and large muscle activities, while the other was exposed to practice in reading. The former group improved on perceptual-motor tasks, while the latter improved more in reading (41). Roach (56) and Brown (9) similarly found no significant differences in oral reading on the part of groups exposed to Kephart's techniques. Haring and Stables (27), on the other hand, reported that various perceptual and motor attributes were improved in a Kephart-type program, but no reading measure was obtained in this later investigation.

In summary, most of the available data fail to support the contention that, in groups of normal children and in children with reading problems, significant gains in reading competency will be achieved by participation in the techniques outlined by Kephart in his several publications.

There are facets of the Kephart program that may have value, however. Rutherford (58), for example, studied the influence of Kephart-type activities on scores obtained from kindergarten children in the Metropolitan Readiness test. He found that while the boys had gained significantly, the girls had not. Kephart's rather carefully designed methods of motor training of neurologically impaired youngsters should prove of value when attempting to improve motor functions. Brown, for example, has found that the attributes in Kephart's program that are trained for specifically do improve (9). Additionally, Kephart's suggestion that motor activities during the preschool years may prove to be good preparation for later learning has not been adequately researched, and thus his hypothesis should not be summarily dismissed without further investigation.

NEUROLOGICAL ORGANIZATION

The Delacato method has been much maligned by the medical profession and others (50,54,69) although receiving praise in some of the popular press. Essentially, his theory is based on a view of neural function that suggests that specific "layers" of the brain mediate discrete motor functions. Moreover, Delacato believes that training in specific locomotor tasks will positively influence various brain centers (the midbrain, pons, medulla, cortex), which, in turn, will positively influence other perceptual and cognitive functions that are advanced as being the exclusive purview of these brain centers (10,11,12).

Critical to the theory is the establishment of hemispheric dominance to improve speech and other sensory functions by training in unilateral hand use and monocular activities and the removal of music and other tonal experiences from the child. Tonality, it is hypothesized, is mediated by the nondominant brain hemisphere, and thus listening to music conflicts with the achievement of dominance by the half of the brain that controls speech functions.

This theory and the resultant practices again can be examined critically on theoretical or practical grounds. Most neurologists, as well as the bulk of research emanating from the laboratories of those studying brain function during the past 75 years, fail to support Delacato's theory. For example, complex locomotor functions have been found to be controlled by a number of portions of the brain rather than by a single part as is suggested by the theory.

Delacato's theory dwells at some length on the importance of establishing what is termed cerebral dominance by encouraging similar arm-hand-eye-ear use. It is thus believed important to briefly outline pertinent findings relative to hand-eye preferences in humans and in the lower animals.

Hand-eye preference in humans has been described by Gesell and Ames (19) as a type of functional asymmetry stemming from the tonic neck reflex in infancy. They further explain that it is not a simple trait, but an ever-changing focal symptom of the human action system. Studies of the development of hand preference in infants support the hypothesis that it is a somewhat inconsistent and irregular trait, not stabilizing until about the age of ten (30,31).

Studies of hand, leg, and paw preference among primates, mammals, and insects demonstrate that all mobile organisms function asymmetrically. For example, grasshoppers have a preferred scratching leg, rats manifest paw preferences that cannot be trained out of them, and chimpanzees evidence hand preference (30). A subhuman ancestor of man, the Australopithecus, with a brain approximately a third the size of modern man, evidenced unilateral hand use and was probably right-handed. It is not surprising to find, therefore, that modern man also evidences unilateral hand and eye preference and use.

It is probable that both hand and eye preference are inherited (48,55). Merrell, for example, found that 77 per cent of the offspring of right-eyed parents tend also to prefer their right eye, while only about 46 per cent of all children of parents both of whom are left-eyed tend to be right-eyed (48). Hecaen also reports research that supports the proposition that hand preference is inherited (30). Ramaley suggests that left-hand preference is a mendelian recessive trait (55), and most of the evidence supports this contention.

However, to a lesser degree, functional asymmetries are molded by the culture. Hand preference, in particular, is probably molded to a greater degree by cultural pressures than is eye preference (31). Hildreth, for example, found that it is less likely that children will use their left hands when performing tasks in which they are likely to incur social censure (31). There are fewer left-handers in the older populations of people than in the younger groups sampled, further reflecting the influence of cultural pressures on those whose preferences are not marked (48).

There is a closer association among hand and foot preferences than between hand and eye preferences. It is more likely that an individual will be either left-footed and left-handed or right-footed and right-handed than that he will evidence similar eye-hand preference (48). One-hand use, thus, is seen in a variety of man's early animal ancestors and therefore would not seem to be evidence of the height of neurological development in modern man as is stated within Delacato's theory.

The child development literature also contains extensive evidence suggesting that children do not develop in accordance with the theory. For example, several visual processes mature rather early, prior to the emergence of accurate motor attributes. Ocular processes involved in visual tracking have been found to mature by two years, and perfect gait patterns are not usually seen in children until their fourth year (Chap. 4).

Delacato seems also to ignore social-emotional factors in the application of the method. He suggests, for example, that a child be made to crawl, despite his protestations to the contrary, by the forceful presence of a physical education teacher (10). In contrast, Temple Fay, from whom Delacato has purportedly obtained his basic rationale, has written that the child is "not merely a motor expressive robot to be tuned up or activated as we choose . . . . motivation is in the hoped for and possible purpose that this returning function might serve . . . . the true art of therapy lies not in what is done, but how the patient may receive it" (17).

The techniques inherent in this program have also been questioned on practical grounds. The American Academy of Pediatrics has found the methods fatiguing and disruptive of normal family life. Rabinovitch also stated that the creeping and crawling techniques are regressive and may bring about emotional disturbance (54). Whitsell (69) has similarly offered a medical opinion, in a comprehensive evaluation of the method, that concludes with the suggestion that the Delacato techniques "have not been validated and are not consistent with accepted neurological principles." Furthermore, Whitsell states that "this method may best be regarded as experimental, potentially harmful, and not to be recommended for general use at this time" (69).

A number of studies that might be termed descriptive rather than scientific have been published by the Philadelphia Institute for the Achievement of Human Potential containing data supporting the worth of the programs. Several reviewers, however, have found the methodologies to be something less than sound. Glass's term "of dubious value" has been concurred with by Albert Harris and others (23,28).

Other more scientific tests of the veracity of the methods conducted outside the Institute established for their propagation have produced findings that are not generally supportive. Anderson (2), for instance, tried cross-patterning and creeping on kindergarten children and intermediate grade students and found that children within these groups with lower I.Q.'s and with lower initial reading ability did not improve. A carefully controlled study by Robbins similarly found that the Delacato program produced no significant differences in a variety of measures, including the ability to make left-right judgments (57). Yarborough, using a stereoscopic method intending to lateralize children similar to the Delacato techniques, also found no evidence of significant benefit in reading (71). McCormick, Poetker, and Schnobrich also found no significant changes when employing Delacato procedures with first-grade children (47). These latter investigators disregard a nonsignificant analysis of variance, however, and point out a gain in mean scores to bolster a positive hypothesis.

The author is aware of only the study by Kershner containing findings that purportedly support the Delacato techniques. Using a control and an experimental group of trainable retardates, Kershner found that they improved significantly in their ability to crawl after a program of crawling was engaged in, and a significant improvement of 14 points was exhibited in a test of I.Q. involving the identification of pictures. However, when Kershner found that his *controls* had improved more than his experimental group in extensive battery of perceptual-motor tests (termed the Kershner revision of the Oseretsky), it was claimed that this latter finding supported the viability of the Kephart program (38)!

Within recent months, the Delacato method has been the target of additional criticism. Seven major medical and health organizations * have stated that patterning was "without merit" and chided its supporters for claiming cures without documentation (50). The opinions of medical and research personnel thus seem almost unanimous in their condemnation of the methods and theories advanced by this method of reading remediation.

Several positive outcomes may have possibly arisen from the publicity given to this method, however. Some severely retarded and brain-damaged children have perhaps made some improvement in mobility owing to the kinesthetic and social stimulation they have received at the hands of some adherents of the tech-

* American Academy for Cerebral Palsy, the American Academy of Physical Medicine, the American Congress of Rehabilitation Medicine, the Canadian Association for Children with Learning Disabilities, the Canadian Association for Retarded Children, the Canadian Rehabilitation Council for the Disabled, and the National Association for Retarded Children.

niques. Perhaps with improved and more comprehensive types of sensory stimulation of this nature (tactual, auditory, as well as visual and kinesthetic), more improvement may be achieved with children and adults formerly assigned to the back wards of mental hospitals for the profoundly retarded and physically handicapped.

At the same time, the available evidence makes it clear that normal children and those below average in various academic functions derive little help from the exotic and, at times, punitive procedures advocated within this type of educational therapy.

"PHYSIOLOGICAL OPTICS"

In 1952 Dr. Getman published a monograph titled *How to Develop Your Child's Intelligence*. This initial publication contained theoretical assumptions, coupled with activities geared to improve classroom learning on the part of the child entering school for the first time. The practices outlined were composed primarily of motor activities coupled with visual training. This text was followed in 1963 by a workbook of activities titled *The Physiology of Readiness Experiment*. This publication contained six sections, three of which contain developmental activities primarily involving movement, while the other three contain tasks that might be labeled perceptual-visual in nature.

Like Kephart, Getman proposes that movement is the basis of intellectual development. For example, he states at one point that "this [the development of general movement patterns for action] is a primary process and lays the foundation for all performance and for all learning" and "movement *is* learning; learning *requires* movement" (p. 24). Continuing, he asserts that "foundational to every intellectual activity of the human being is the skill of motor control and coordination." Movement and the efficiency of muscle use are a prerequisite for all knowledge and intellectual performance. It has been said, "Thoughts which do not get into the muscles never fully possess the mind!" (p. 39).

Getman, however, also emphasizes the importance of vision. His term "vision" is a rather global concept, at various times seemingly encompassing ocular and perceptual, as well as intellectual, processes and attributes. Memory for a variety of events, for example, is equated with vision, for Getman states that "visualization is an ability to ignore time and space . . . visual patterns are substitutes for action, speech, and time," and later he remarks,

"Visual-perceptual organization is the ultimate process in the development of the total child."

Claiming that 85 to 90 per cent of a child's learning is acquired through visual processes, Getman further hypothesizes that deficiencies in some component of the visual mechanisms will thus lead to learning difficulties. Thus, he outlines practices in his texts that purport to lead a child through several levels of visual-perceptual development, including:

General Movement Patterns. Involving primarily locomotor activities and movements of the hands and eyes in concert.

Special Movement Patterns of Action. The use of the body and body parts to control and to manipulate things in the world—the combination of hand and eyes in various tasks.

The Development of Eye Movement Patterns. The learning of eye movement skills necessary for the quick and efficient visual exploration of the world. Development of these skills will leave the hands free to become "tools," i.e., to learn writing skills, etc.

Communication Patterns to Replace Action. Learning to use visual and movement experiences to communicate with others.

The Development of Visualization Patterns. Learning visual discriminations, recognitions of numbers and words, and the like are included here. The calling up of visual images constitutes another component of this step in development.

The Development of Visual-Perceptual Organizations. This is conceived by Getman as the ultimate process in the development of the child's intellect and involves the ability to interchange movement for interpretation, understanding, and concept formation.

Getman suggests that each of these six steps, although interwoven with the others, is a stage through which a normal child must pass as he enters school and begins to learn and to read. The motor, visual-motor, and visual activities contained in his texts purport to enhance these various stages of development and thus enable a child to learn better when in the classroom.

Getman further emphasizes perceptual and visual skills necessary when reading. Although stating that "reading is more than seeing words," he also suggests that ocular training involving visual tracking exercises, as well as tasks intended to improve near-point fusion and accommodation, should aid a child to read better as he enters school. Getman writes that "it is now known that most children, age six, have not adequately acquired the neuromuscular controls necessary for advanced learning tasks . . . eye movement skills, the physiological maturities of the visual mechanisms and the integrations of vision, hearing and speech necessary for ultimate success in the reading load, are not yet available to most first grade children" (p. 34). He further contends that if children are introduced to reading too early in life, it may indeed impair their visual-perceptual mechanisms. He undergirds this claim by pointing to evidence collected by D. B. Harmon, and at the Chicago University Hospital, Chicago, showing that, although only 2.4 per cent of all children are born with visual difficulties, this increases from 20 per cent at age five to 40 per cent at age eight.* The stress of near-point reading in school causes this increase in ocular problems, Getman suggests.

Getman also writes that inadequate movement patterns involving skeletal muscles influence a variety of other attributes in children. For example, at one point he states that "better control of muscles anywhere has an effect on speech" (p. 41), and at another point he contends that "dental problems and communicable illnesses (as well as visual problems) are more prevalent in children who lack full freedom of movements. . . ." (p. 62).

A comprehensive evaluation of Getman's theory and practices is made difficult because of the manner in which he blurs distinctions between ocular-visual, visual-perceptual, and cognitive attributes. For example, he states that "reading is more than seeing words" (p. 35), while also stating that "vision is intelligence" (p. 20), and "vision is the dominant factor in human development" (p. 105). Further difficulties arise when interpreting the available research on this topic as one attempts to separate faulty eye movements when reading from eye movements during faulty reading. At the same time, the degree to which a given measure of ocular malfunction detracts from the ability to read well is not clearly outlined in the available literature.

There is, however, a considerable amount of evidence that has clarified relationships between ocular function, motor attributes, visual training, and classroom learning (including reading). Eye movement studies, stemming from the pioneer work of Johannes Muller in 1826, have rather exactly demonstrated just what movements the eyes make as we read. The investigations

---

* D. B. Harmon is an "educationalist" who conducted the study of 160,000 children in Austin, Texas, published in *Medical Women's Journal* in 1942.

of Eames (15,16), Taylor (64), and Tinker (65,67) have explored, with a greater degree of sophistication, relationships between visual function, and academic proficiency.

In general, the available evidence does not support the generalizations made by Getman concerning the close positive, causal relationship between movement, ocular function, and academic success. Good reading, for example, appears greatly dependent on higher mental processes. In every study carried out in which the intelligence of poor and proficient readers is compared, I.Q. differences are apparent (39,40,49). Reading is accomplished with both the eyes and the brain, with the latter probably contributing more than the former to the understanding and interpretation of the printed page.

The close correlation advanced by Getman as existing between ocular function and reading is also not supported by most of the available research evidence. For example, Dingman found that eye movement scores were relatively independent of reading comprehension scores in a factor analysis published in 1958 (13), as did Gruber in 1962 (25). Although it is true that as a child matures he reads more efficiently by engaging in a fewer number of fixations per 100 words, if we train him to fixate less via some kind of visual-training procedure, it is likely that he must then fixate longer each time his eyes come to rest on a word. Thus, his overall reading speed may not improve. Tinker has suggested that improvement of span functions with some training apparatus is no greater than with well-motivated practice in reading itself (65)!

Getman's contention that visual problems are brought on by excessive stress of early exposure to reading is also questionable on consulting the available evidence. Indeed the research suggests that the reverse may be true. Fewer ocular problems are found in groups of poor readers of college age than are found in groups of younger children evidencing reading problems (64). The available evidence thus suggests that exposure to the printed page may train the eyes to engage in better near-point fusion as the child matures.

Difficulty in tracking is not usually found to be related to poor reading (25). More important when reading is efficient fixation, for the child cannot see anything until the eyes are fixed. The manner in which the child fixates and the number of fixations he makes on a group of words are highly individualized characteristics, which to a large degree appear to be inherited and remain relatively constant during maturation (64). Attempting to train eyes to function in a manner at odds with these individual characteristics is not likely to be successful, for the eye fixates while reading from three to five times per second, a rate too rapid to be placed under the conscious control of the learner. As Taylor points out, "Eye movements are neither the cause nor the effect of good or poor reading. The eyes do not dictate to the mind what it should understand nor does the mind dictate to the eyes where they should look" (64).

Three research studies have explored the manner in which Getman's methods may contribute to various parameters of academic performance. One of these is a mimeographed paper mailed with one of his books (21). Halgren (26), following a ten-week program with 31 control and 31 experimental subjects, found that the I.Q.'s of the latter had improved seven points, and they had also improved on the average 2.1 years in reading speed and 2.8 years in reading comprehension. When describing the methods used, however, the writer made it clear that these improvements were gradually modified when individual children's behaviors indicated that a change in methods was called for, thus suggesting that the techniques may be effective only in the hands of a clinician well trained in their use. Halgren also failed to treat his data with anything approaching adequate statistical procedures. No distribution scores accompanied the averages he listed, and thus no test can be made of the statistical significance of the changes he reports. Honzik (32) has found that the I.Q.'s of 60 per cent of the children she studied over a period of years changed 15 points or more due to some combination of experience and/or maturation, whereas the I.Q.'s of one third of the children she investigated changed by 20 or more points. A change of seven points, then, in I.Q., even if occurring only over a ten-month period as reported by Halgren, may have been due to factors other than visual-motor training. Lyons and Lyons (45) also report the influence of visual training on three subjects. Improvement was reported in scores of tests evaluating verbal meaning, reasoning, perception, and the SRA Primary Mental Abilities Test.

The research available that is supportive of Getman's procedures is thus rather sparce indeed, whereas studies containing evidence that groups of children with academic deficiencies may have problems other than those involving eye function are numerous (39,49). It is thus apparent that application of a program of visual training such as that suggested by Getman to large undefined populations of children suffering from mild to moderate educational difficulties is less than sound. Additional evidence is needed before a definitive statement can be made concerning the influence of visual training on *ocular* functioning, and the influence of ocular training on academic achievement has received only infrequent and cursory attention by investigators.

It is probable that some children failing to learn are suffering from various kinds of ocular problems. The usual school evaluation of eye function contains only a test of distance acuity (the Snellen), whereas the ocular problem most frequent in poor readers is near-point fusion. It is thus believed that with additional research, some of the techniques and premises advanced by Getman may prove valid. Even at a later date, however, remedial visual training of this nature should be accompanied by comprehensive pre- and posttests of the ocular capacities of children to whom it is applied. An overreaction to the program and techniques that Getman suggests, without additional evidence of their worth, however, could prove wasteful of the time of most of the children engaged in such training, as well as of the school personnel administering it.

COMPARISONS AND CONCLUSIONS

Upon examining the practices advocated by the three theorists, one may detect more similarities than differences. For example, both Getman and Kephart advocate a body-image exercise termed "angels in the snow" (in a back-lying position, the child sweeps his arms and legs along the floor in various patterned movements). Although all three advocate the use of the trampoline, they do so for different reasons. The activities to heighten directionality and writing skills proposed by Kephart and Getman are similar. Both Getman and Delacato emphasize the importance of encouraging the child to creep prior to walking. Further, all three stress the importance of the acquisition of specific developmental tasks in proper sequence. Both Getman and Kephart propose that there is a motor base to the intellect. However, they take slightly different paths to explain silent thought. Getman suggests the importance of level three "eye movement patterns," which replace the need for constant exploratory movement, and Kephart suggests that even silent thought is accompanied by postural tensions, thus attempting to provide additional evidence that movement is the basis of intelligence.

Both Getman and Delacato suggest that motor training will improve a wide variety of human attributes: Getman includes speech, hearing, sound teeth, and communicable diseases in his list, and Delacato is even more expansive and includes language disorders, specific reading disability, mental deficiency, ocular problems (strabismus, myopia, etc.), athetosis, Parkinson's disease, asphasia, delayed speech, stuttering, and poor spelling.

Delacato and Kephart's writings both evidence a lack of sophistication concerning current knowledge about neural functioning. Kephart's suggestion that the cerebellum mediates balance, for example, is only about one sixth correct, for several other structures such as the motor cortex and the occipital areas take part in this complex behavior. His suggestion that the malfunctioning of a single neuron will result in a large number of neurons "misfiring" (thus interrupting innumerable other functions) is unsupported by any evidence of which the author is aware. It is probable that the average normal child has several hundred thousand damaged neurons within his nervous system that are not reflected in any discernible sensory, motor, or intellectual problems. Kephart's labeling of the Kraus-Weber test as an evaluation of posture and balance (when in truth it is a test of trunk strength and flexibility) leads one also to question his knowledge of motor ability.

Delacato's writings are similarly poorly grounded in neurology, for he suggests that specific motor functions are mediated by identifiable portions of the brain, while also pointing out that athetosis and Parkinson's disease both have their etiology within the midbrain. His discourses on neural function omit references to important cerebral structures such as the corpus callosum, the limbic system, the thalamus, and the reticular formation.

Getman oversimplifies the reading process and the manner in which reading problems are caused (i.e., ocular deficiencies). Delacato is also guilty of oversimplification. He oversimplifies a number of human attributes including spelling and writing ("both are varying degrees of the same problem") and myopia ("caused by the stress of fatigue of using the eyes at near-point, and reading deficiencies, the result of the lack of complete development of binaural abilities").

All three men seem to oversimplify the nature of the developmental processes in children. A number of children development experts, including those who are quoted on some of the theoreticians' texts, would take issue with the neat veridical (Kephart's term) manner in which they suggest infants and children develop. Visual abilities seem to precede motor abilities, and motor abilities fragment into locomotor and manual abilities at a rather early age, unlike the simple picture presented with the theories discussed. Indeed, Kephart's statements seem to reflect incorrect notions of how infants develop because he suggests in one of his films that infantile reflexes "flow from the head to the feet." He continues by stating that these reflexes also evolve into voluntary movement patterns, whereas, in truth, many infantile reflexes terminate prior to the emergence of accurate voluntary movements (33,53).

Delacato's concept of infant reflexes also appears to be somewhat distorted. He insists that training in what he terms the tonic neck reflex is an important first step in the recapitulation of motor experiences. He then proceeds to demonstrate this reflex elicited in a face-down position wherein the arm is flexed toward the side to which the head is turned. However, the tonic neck reflex is elicited in infants in a face-up position! It is difficult to determine, additionally, why this particular reflex was selected by Delacato for training purposes, out of at least 30 from which he might have selected.

Despite the theoretical and practical inadequacies of the writings of these three theoreticians, I believe that the theories and practices have had some positive effects on educational theory and practice. For example, some of the children exposed to some of their programs may have indeed improved, although not perhaps for the reasons contained within the theories. A neurologically impaired child who is looked at, reacted to, and talked to while he is crawling on the floor for several hours a day may begin responding better because of the social stimulation he is receiving, if the physical punishment inherent in the method is not too oppressive. Children who are kept at visual, visual-motor, or motor tasks for increased periods of time may improve in a variety of learning situations because of a prolongation of their attention spans. The literature on transfer suggests that some components of one task are probably aiding the acquisition of a second task while other components are probably impeding it. Thus, the change in the second task (i.e., classroom learning) is probably a result of both the negative and positive qualities of the initial task. Thus, while motor activity itself may not enhance learning in a direct way through movement, there are ancillary components of the motor task (i.e., doing *something* for increased periods of time) that may indeed positivity transfer to academic learning. An increasing number of studies suggest that (1) attention span influences learning, and (2) attention span may be improved by various techniques available to the classroom teacher (46).

Similarly, the practices contained in the program of Getman and Kephart indeed should improve the motor abilities of children to whom they are applied; motor abilities are important in school as they permit the child to accurately guide his hand when writing and to catch a ball when playing. It is believed that increased attention has been paid to the child with minimal neurological problems found within the normal school populations because of the notoriety accorded these theories. These children, constituting from 5 to 20 per cent of most "normal" populations of children, are at a disadvantage, which is obvious to them and to their parents and teachers when they attempt to compete in various ways with their more capable peers.

Further research on these practices contained within these theories should certainly be stressed. In particular, the following problems should be studied.

1. Efforts should be made to delineate the manner in which individual differences in populations of children may be affected by the practices advocated by Getman, Delacato, and Kephart. For example, it is possible that the child from the higher-income home may benefit more from increased exposure to motor activities than the child from the lower socioeconomic areas. The latter may be improved more educationally by exposure to verbal-linguistic tasks and exercises rather than balance-beam walking. The effects of motor activities leading to learning within populations of boys should also be studied. The intellectual functions of children with various levels of arousal, using divergent learning strategies and from different I.Q. groups, should be studied as a function of various kinds of perceptual-motor training.

2. Increased emphasis should be placed on research that at-

tempts to delineate just what components of whose program changes what kinds of children in what ways. For example, if an entire program of the activities advocated by Kephart is applied to a group of children, there is no way, when finished, to determine which of the activities changed what attributes. The attempt, though, should be made to isolate the effects of single variables within a given motor task on academic performances of various kinds. For example, it has been suggested that failure of a child to fixate on the printed page may stem from emotional stress. Thus, balance-beam walking or trampoline jumping ("motor stresses") while watching a point on a wall may habituate the child to fixate under stress, an improvement that may, in turn, positively transfer to the classroom in which he is asked to fixate on a page under academic stresses imposed by his teacher.

3. Increased attempts should be made to incorporate a number of sensory stimulations into programs for the profoundly retarded and physically handicapped. Tactual, auditory, visual, and kinesthetic stimulation combined in the correct tasks to the correct degree may aid the severely retarded adult and child to react more appropriately to the objects, situations, and other stimuli to which he is exposed.

BIBLIOGRAPHY

1 Allen, K. E., L. B. Henke, F. R. Harris, D. M. Baer, and N. J. Reynolds, "Control of Hyperactivity by Social Reinforcement of Attending Behavior," *J. Ed. Psych.*, **58** (1967), 231–37.

2 Anderson, Russell W., *Effects of Neuro-Psychological Techniques on Reading Achievement*, Greeley: Colorado State College, Ed.D., 1965.

3 Ausubel, David P., "A Critique of Piaget's Theory of the Ontogenesis of Motor Behavior," *J. Gen. Psych.*, **109** (1966), 119–22.

4 Ayres, Jean A., "Patterns of Perceptual-Motor Dysfunction in Children: A Factor Analytic Study," *Percept. Mot. Skills, Monograph Suppl.*, I–V20, 1965.

5 Bayley, Nancy, "Behavioral Correlates of Mental Growth—Birth to Thirty-Six Years," *Amer. Psychol.*, **5** (1968), 1–17.

6 Belmont, Lillian, and H. Birch, "Lateral Dominance and

Right-Left Awareness in Normal Children," *Child Dev.*, 34 (1963), 257–70.

7 Bloom, Benjamin S., *Stability and Change in Human Characteristics,* New York: John Wiley & Sons, 1964.

8 Brenner, M. W., and S. Gillman, "Verbal Intelligence, Visuomotor Ability and School Achievement," *Br. J. Ed. Psych.*, 35 (1965), 75.

9 Brown, Roscoe C., "The Effects of a Perceptual-Motor Education Program on Perceptual-Motor Skills and Reading Readiness," Presented at *Research Section* AAHPER, St. Louis, Mo., April 1, 1968.

10 Delacato, Carl H., *Treatment and Prevention of Reading Problems,* Springfield, Ill.: Charles C Thomas, 1959.

11 ———, *The Diagnosis and Treatment of Speech and Reading Problems,* Springfield, Ill.: Charles C Thomas, 1963.

12 ———, *Neurological Organization and Reading,* Springfield, Ill.: Charles C Thomas, 1966.

13 Dingman, H. F., "Factor Analysis of Eye Movements with Reading Scores," *Percept. Mot. Skills,* 8 (1958), 37–38.

14 Eames, T. H., "The Ocular Conditions of 350 Poor Readers," *J. Ed. Res.*, 32 (1938), 10–16.

15 ———, "Comparison of Eye Conditions Among 100 Reading Failures, 500 Ophthalmic Patients and 150 Unselected Children," *Amer. J. Ophth.*, 31 (1948), 713–17.

16 ———, "Visual and Related Factors in Reading," *Rev. Ed. Res.*, 19 (1949), 107–17.

17 Fay, Temple, "Basic Considerations Regarding Neuromuscular and Reflex Therapy," *Spastics Quart.*, Vol. III, No. 3, September, 1954. Published by the British Council for the Welfare of Spastics, 13, Suffolk St., Haymarket, London, S.W. 1.

18 Fleishman, Edwin A., Paul Thomas, and Philip Munroe, "The Dimensions of Physical Fitness: A Factor Analysis of Speed Flexibility, Balance, and Coordination Tests," Technical Report No. 3, The Office of Naval Research, Department of Psychology, Yale University, September, 1961.

19 Gesell, Arnold, and L. B. Ames, "The Development of Handedness," *J. Gen. Psych.*, 70 (1947), 155–75.

20 Getman, G. N., *How to Develop Your Child's Intelligence, A Research Publication,* Luverne, Minnesota: G. N. Getman, 1952.

21 ——, *The Physiology of Readiness Experiment*, Minneapolis: P.A.S.S., Inc., Programs to Accelerate School Success, 1963.

22 Gilbert, Luther C., "Genetic Study of Eye Movements in Reading," *Elementary School J.*, **59** (1963), 328–35.

23 Glass, Gene V., "A Critique of Experiments on the Role of Neurological Oganization in Reading Performance," Monograph, Center for Instructional Research and Curriculum Evaluation, University of Illinois, 1967.

24 Gorelick, Molly C., "The Effectiveness of Visual Form Training in a Prereading Program," *J. Ed. Res.*, **58** (1965), 315–18.

25 Gruber, E., "Reading Ability: Binocular Coordination and the Ophthalmograph," *Arch. Ophth.*, **67** (1962), 280–88.

26 Halgren, M. R., "Opus in See Sharp," *Education*, **81** (1961), 369–71.

27 Haring, Norris G., and Jeanne Marie Stables, "The Effect of Gross Motor Development on Visual Perception and Hand-Eye Coordination," *J. Amer. Phys. Therap. Assn.*, **46** (1966), 129–35.

28 Harris, Albert J., "Diagnosis and Remedial Instruction in Reading," in *Innovation and Change in Reading*, 67th Yearbook, Part II of the National Society for the Study of Education, Chicago: University of Chicago Press, 1968, 159–99.

29 Harris, N. L., and Chester W. Harris, "A Factor Analytic Study of Flexibility," A Paper Presented at the Research Section meeting at the National Convention of the American Association for Health, Physical Education, and Recreation in St. Louis, Mo., on March 30, 1963.

30 Hecaen, H., and J. Ajuriaguerra, *Left-Handedness: Manual Superiority and Cerebral Dominance*, New York: Grune & Stratton, 1964.

31 Hildreth, G., "Manual Dominance in Nursery School Children," *J. Gen. Psych.*, **72** (1948), 29–45.

32 Honzik, M. P., J. W. MacFarlane, and L. Allen, "The Stability of Mental Test Performance Between Two and Eighteen Years", *J. Exp. Ed.*, **17** (1948), 309–24.

33 Illingworth, R. S., *The Development of the Infant and Young Child, Normal and Abnormal*, London: E. & S. Livingstone, Ltd., 1967.

34 Johnson, Dale I., and C. D. Spielberger, "The Effects of Relaxation Training and the Passage of Time on Measures of State and Trait Anxiety," *J. Chem. Psych.*, **24** (1968), 20–23.

35 Keogh, B., and C. E. Smith, "Changes in Copying Ability of Young Children," *Percept. Mot. Skills*, **26** (1967), 773–74.

36 Kephart, Newell C., *The Slow Learner in the Classroom*, Columbus, Ohio: Charles C. Merrill, 1960.

37 ——, "Perceptual-Motor Aspects of Learning Disabilities," *Except. Child.*, **31** (1964), 201–206.

38 Kershner, John R., "An Investigation of the Doman-Delacato Theory of Neuropsychology as It Applies to Trainable Mentally Retarded Children in Public Schools," Monograph, Bureau of Research Administration, Area of Research and Development, Department of Public Instruction, Pennsylvania, May, 1967.

39 Kinsbourne, M., and E. K. Warrington, "Developmental Factors in Reading and Writing Backwardness," *Brit. J. Psych.*, **54** (1963), 145–56.

40 Krippner, Stanley, "Relationship Between Improvement and Ten Selected Variables," *Percept. Mot. Skills*, **19** (1964), 15–20.

41 LaPray, Margaret, and Ramon Ross, "Auditory and Visual Perceptual Training," in *Vistas in Reading*, J. Allen Figurel (ed.), International Association Conference Proceedings, IX, 1966, pp. 530–32.

42 Lederer, J., "The Reading Clinic in Department of Optometry," University of New South Wales, *Aust. J. Optom.*, **43** (1960), 1–6.

43 Lyle, J. G., and J. Gozen, "Visual Recognition, Developmental Lag and Strephosymbolia in Reading Retardation, *J. Abnorm. Psych.*, **73** (1968), 25–29.

44 Lynn, Richard, "Individual Differences in Introversion-Extraversion, Reactive Inhibition and Reading Attainment," *J. Ed. Psych.*, **51** (1960), 318–21.

45 Lyons, C. V., and Emily B. Lyons, "The Power of Visual Training, As Measured in Factors of Intelligence," *J. Amer. Optom. Assn.*, **35** (1954), 255–62.

46 Maccoby, Eleanor E., Edith M. Dowley, and John W. Hagen, "Activity Level and Intellectual Functioning in Normal Pre-School Children," *Child Dev.*, **36** (1965), 761–69.

47 McCormick, Clarence C., Betty Poetker, Janice N. Schnobrich, and S. Willard Footlick, *Improvement in Reading Achievement Through Perceptual-Motor Training*, Chicago: Reading Research Foundation, Inc., July, 1967 (mimeographed).

48 Merrell, D. J., "Dominance of Eye and Hand," *Human Biol.,* **29** (1957), 314–28.

49 Neville, Donald, "A Comparison of the WISC Patterns of Male Retarded and Non-Retarded Readers," *J. Ed. Res.,* **54** (1961), 195–97.

50 Official Statement: "The Doman-Delacato Treatment of Neurologically Handicapped Children," *Arch. Phys. Med. Rehab.,* **49** (1968), 183–86.

51 Orton, S. T., "Visual Functions in Strephosymbolia," *Arch. Ophth.,* **30** (1943), 707–17.

52 Park, G. E., and C. J. Burri, "The Effect of Eye Abnormalities on Reading Difficulties," *J. Ed. Psych.,* **45** (1943), 420–30.

53 Peiper, Albrecht, *Cerebral Function in Infancy and Childhood,* New York: Consultants Bureau, 1963.

54 Rabinovitch, R., "Neuropsychiatric Factors," A Paper Read at the Annual Meeting of the International Reading Assn., Detroit, 1965.

55 Ramaley, F., "Inheritance of Left-Handedness," *Amer. Naturalist,* **47** (1913), 730–38.

56 Roach, Eugene G., "Evaluation of an Experimental Program of Perceptual-Motor Training with Slow Readers," in *Vistas in Reading,* J. Allen Figurel (ed.), International Reading Assn. Conference Proceedings, 1966, pp. 11, 446–50.

57 Robbins, M. P., and G. V. Glass, "The Doman-Delacato Rationale: A Critical Analysis," in *Educational Therapy,* J. Hellmuth (ed.), Seattle Special Child Publications, 1968, Vol. 2.

58 Rutherford, William L., "Perceptual-Motor Training and Readiness," in *Reading and Inquiry,* J. Allen Figurel (ed.), International Reading Assn. Conference Proceedings, X (1965), pp. 194–96.

59 Schaffer, Amy, and J. D. Gould, "Eye Movement Patterns as a Function of Previous Tachistoscope Practice," *Percept. Mot. Skills,* **19** (1964), 701–702.

60 Sinclair, C., "Ear Dominance in Pre-School Children," *Percept. Mot. Skills,* **26** (1968), 510.

61 Smith, Olin W., "Developmental Studies of Spatial Judgments by Children and Adults," *Percept. Mot. Skills,* **22,** Monograph Supp. I–V22 (1966), 3–73.

62 Taylor, E. A., *Controlled Reading: A Correlation of Diagnostic Teaching and Corrective Techniques,* Chicago: University of Chicago Press, 1937.

63 ———, "The Spans: Perception, Apprehension and Recognition," *Amer. J. Ophth.*, **44** (1957), 501–507.

64 Taylor, Stanford E., "Eye Movements in Reading: Facts and Fallacies," *Amer. Ed. Res. J.*, **2** (1965), 187–201.

65 Tinker, M. A., "The Study of Eye Movements in Reading," *Psych. Bull.*, **43** (1946), 93–120.

66 ———, "Perceptual and Oculomotor Efficiency in Reading Materials in Vertical and Horizontal Arrangements," *Amer. J. Psych.*, **68** (1955), 444–49.

67 ———, "Recent Studies of Eye Movement in Reading," *Psych. Bull.*, **55** (1958), 215–31.

68 Wagner, Guy W., "The Maturation of Certain Visual Functions and the Relationship Between These Functions and Success in Reading and Arithmetic," *Psych. Mono.*, **48** (1937), 108–46.

69 Whitsell, Leon J., "Delacato's 'Neurological Organization': A Medical Appraisal," *California School Health*, **3** (1967), 1–13.

70 Wise, James H., "Performance of Neurologically Impaired Children Copying Geometric Stick Designs with Sticks," *Percept. Mot. Skills*, **26** (1968), 763–72.

71 Yarborough, Betty H., *A Study of the Effectiveness of the Leavell Language-Development Service in Improving the Silent Reading Ability and Other Language Skills of Persons with Mixed Dominance*, Charlottesville: University of Virginia, Ed.D., 1964.

72 Zusne, L., and K. Michels, "Nonrepresentational Shapes and Eye Movements," *Percept. Mot. Skills*, **18** (1964), 11–12.

Model for the Study of Human Maturation 11

The material within the previous chapters does not present a simple picture of maturational processes. Thus it would appear that the formulation of a statement to encompass the many facets of human maturation might also be reasonably complex. In the pages that follow an attempt has been made to develop a viable model to explain the many subtle and obvious factors influencing and reflecting the manner in which the human being changes during the early months and years of his life.

Many theories of child development outline a schema that appears to consist of a number of reasonably discrete horizontal layers. Piaget has formulated a conceptual framework acceptable to many in which the sensory-motor period precedes the later acquisition of cognitive skills. Others have written about a reasonably veridical evolution of development, as the child purportedly passes from motor to perceptual and later to cognitive processes (19,23).

The model that will unfold on the following pages, rather than being similar to a layer cake, is more like a "latticework." It encompasses several concepts. The idea of bonds formed horizontally between various channels of development interacts with the idea that the evolution of various vertical classification abilities is at times uneven in nature.

An attempt has been made to explain the statements that follow, the way in which both the normal child and the atypical child mature, as well as the way in which educational programs may modify unfolding attribute patterns.

A theory has been defined as an attempt to explain and thus

273

to predict. A theory of human behavioral development, then, is an attempt to explain and to predict the manners in which the infant and the child change as a function of age. A model, on the other hand, may be viewed as an outline or skeleton of a theory. The extent to which the author was successful in an attempt to construct a viable "skeleton" for the study of processes of human maturation may be judged by the reader by reference to the research literature, as well as through the sensitive observation of children engaged both in thought and in action.

THE DIFFERENTIATION AND INTEGRATION OF BEHAVIOR

Upon consulting the research it appears as if the child's behavioral patterns evidence what might be termed on one hand "diffusion," while at the same time his increasing behavioral system seems to become integrated in various ways.* The processes of diffusion and integration occur simultaneously at times, and to explain these processes several terms have been employed. Reference is made to "attributes." An attribute may be defined as a cluster of scores in similar tasks denoting a relatively specific ability trait. The phrase "classification of ability traits" has also been used and refers to a group of ability traits that are relatively similar. Four general classifications are dealt with in the pages that follow, including the motor, the perceptual, the intellectual, and the verbal. As the chapter unfolds, it will become apparent that these four "simple" classifications become increasingly fragmented as a child ages.

Because of the focus of the text, emphasis is placed on explanations dealing with the interrelationships between the motor and perceptual classifications. However, it is assumed that cognitive processes are important when trying to gain a comprehensive understanding of the growing child. Thus references to cognition and to verbal behavior are made at several points in the discussion.

The second important term in the model is the word "bond." It is suggested that, owing to a number of variables, bonds are formed between various facets of the child's behavioral attributes.

---

* The theory is primarily based on various measures of behavior to be found in the literature with particular emphasis on factor analyses. Additionally the evidence of various research studies has been consulted in which an attempt has been made to evaluate the manner in which experience modifies behavior.

These bonds are conceived of as functional connections between attributes that in the child's life have previously been operating independent of one another. The formation of a bond may often signal the emergence of a new ability trait within a larger classification of attributes.

Another word found in the discussion that follows describes the manner in which attributes may be either retarded, terminated, or otherwise reduced in efficiency or in the incidence with which they occur. It will thus frequently be stated that certain conditions may "blunt" some attribute or classification of attributes.

The term "attribute" is employed with frequency in the conceptual schema that follows. In this context an attribute is taken to mean an ability trait reflected in a score obtained from a test of motor, perceptual, verbal, or cognitive functioning. Separation of motor, perceptual, or verbal from cognitive attributes is of course difficult, and indeed the theory has as one of its primary tenets the bonding of various different ability traits together in the performance of a new type of task reflecting an emerging attribute. At the same time it is possible to determine, much of the time, whether a score derived from a given task is *more* indicative of an individual's verbal ability, his movement competence, his ability to organize and to interpret sensory information, or his ability to think. Most of the time some kind of verbal and/or motor response is required when testing subjects in various kinds of batteries. However, it is equally true that much of the time the motor response (i.e., checking a yes or no answer) is incidental to the validity of the score obtained.

It is believed that the outline that follows may be further illuminated through the formulation of several axioms and postulates that may be derived from these axioms. After each of these generalizations is drawn, examples taken from the research literature, as well as from observations of the behavior of children, will be presented in an attempt to further illuminate the statements presented.

AXIOM 1 Attributes emerge and mature at various rates, and at the same time overlap in time. These attribute families may be classified as cognitive, verbal, motor, and perceptual.

In general, it appears that efficient visual behaviors precede the acquisition of motor accuracy, and that these two classifications in turn are followed by the acquisition of verbal competency coupled with cognitive abilities. To be more specific, a child first becomes able to track moving objects using both eyes in concordance for short periods of time during the first weeks of life. Not until he is several months old, however, can he be expected to evidence motor behavior accurate enough to enable him to intercept a toy swinging on a string by using a crude swiping motion of his hand. He will probably not call the object thrown to him a "ball" until he is about two years of age, and his understanding of the laws of motion governing the trajectory of a thrown missile may not be evidenced until adolescence.

POSTULATE 1 The rate of change evidenced by a given classification of attributes varies at different times in the life of the infant and child.

It is apparent that the greatest change in visual perceptual abilities and in perceptual abilities coupled with motor attributes occurs early in the life of the child from birth to the seventh year. On the other hand, verbal behavior, reflected in vocabulary increase, evidences marked acceleration from the second to the eighth year of life.

POSTULATE 2 The change in a given classification of attributes, which may be expected through the efforts of others such as teachers and parents, will be most pronounced at the time of the child's life during which those attributes are in the greatest state of flux owing to normal maturational processes.

Bloom suggests that political attitudes are likely to be most modifiable in youths between their eighteenth and twentieth years. Research from our laboratory suggests that change in perceptual-motor behavior that may be elicited through training is greater in younger children from four to seven years of age than in children in late childhood, despite the fact that both groups are subjected to the same kind of training for similar periods of time (2).

POSTULATE 3 Exercise of one's capacities may be motivating for its own sake, independent of any apparent material reward for performance.

Children acting as subjects in innumerable experimental studies and taking part in a variety of educational programs have been observed to continue to perform tasks in the absence of any

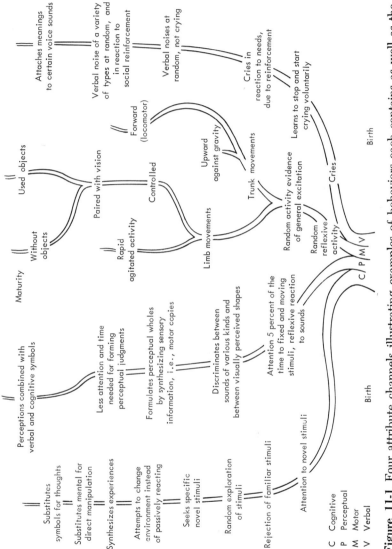

Figure 11-1 Four attribute channels illustrating examples of behaviors each contains as well as the manner in which each tends to branch as a function of age.

obvious reinforcers other than mastery of interesting novel tasks that test their capacities.

POSTULATE 4 Success perceived by the child elicits exercise of groups of attributes and thus is likely to result in marked changes in levels of performances within a given classification. Lack of success leads to less participation in tasks, which in turn is likely to blunt the performance levels of tasks requiring those abilities.

In a study we carried out several years ago we found that groups of atypical children, who evidenced mild coordination problems and who were likely to be aware of the degrees of ineptitude they evidenced, demonstrated performance in late childhood that represented their best efforts. After the ages of 12 and 13 years they were performing as a group at considerably lower levels, similar to the proficiency evidenced in early childhood. It was apparent that a syndrome of failure was reflected in our data, relative to the withdrawal of exercise of abilities and the resultant lack of proficiency in perceptual-motor tasks.

AXIOM 2 As the child matures, the number of individual and relatively independent attributes evidenced within a given classification of abilities will tend to proliferate.

When a child is born his ability to move his hands voluntarily is absent, and increased hand control enables him to evidence general excitation in hand movements and additionally to pair hand movements with objects. Later his ability to deal with objects branches, and he evidences two important abilities: one involves the manipulation of objects, and the other involves the making of marks with objects, such as scribbling with crayons.

By either the end of his second year or the beginning of his third year this scribbling again branches into two subattributes: one represents relatively free movements of the arms, and the other represents the growing tendency to draw accurately, as geometrical figures appear in his drawings. Again in his fourth year the ability to draw geometrical figures subdivides: on the one hand he begins to draw letters and numbers, and on the other hand he continues to draw geometrical shapes.

These two abilities will be seen to split, as later in childhood geometrical figure drawing continues and becomes more complex, while at the same time the simple circles and squares come to represent faces and houses. The child's effort to print continues, but he will also evidence another branch, that of cursive writing. In late childhood his inclination to translate cognitive symbols into the written word may take the form of typing.

Big muscle activity also undergoes this same process of division as a function of maturation. At birth the child is generally either active or inactive. Upper limb movements soon become observably different from leg and trunk movements. The latter subclassification of movements begins to separate into those showing that the upright is being sought and those involving some kind of movement forward in a horizontal plane. Following the acquisition of walking behavior the child begins to devise innumerable ways of moving forward.

This process of division of attributes as a function of maturation, using two subclassifications of motor abilities, is depicted in Figures 11-2 and 11-3.

POSTULATE 1 Severe and/or moderate intellectual deficits are likely to impede the proliferation of attributes and to render the total attribute structure less specific and complex.

Studies of retarded children indicate that the lower on the intellectual scale that performances are sampled, the less likely one is to obtain high correlations between performance traits. It has been hypothesized by more than one researcher that retarded children's ability trait structures stop becoming diffuse by the age of ten years. On the other hand, as normal children continue to mature, they evidence an attribute structure indicative of increased specificity and complexity (4).

AXIOM 3 A "blunting" either of a total classification of attributes or of individual attributes may occur for a variety of reasons.

POSTULATE 1 If some subattributes within a classification are found to be relatively ineffectual in coping with the environment, they may tend either to disappear or to be evidenced very seldom as the child matures.

Simple arm waving due to excitation by the presence of an object is likely to disappear from an infant's motor ability repertoire when he finds that more effective uses can be made of the hands and arms. Crawling gives way to effective means of locomotion as he acquires the upright and learns to walk.

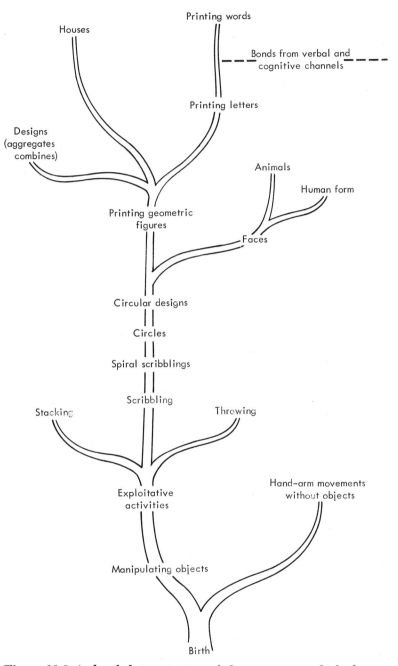

Figure 11-2 A detailed examination of the manner in which the attribute channel containing arm, manipulative, and drawing abilities tends to diffuse.

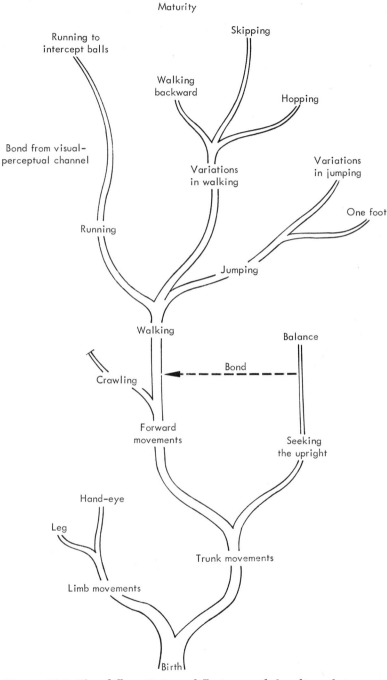

Figure 11-3 The differentiation, diffusion, and bonding that occur within the attribute branch containing locomotor and trunk behaviors.

POSTULATE 2 Moderate and severe sensory, motor, and intellectual deficits may tend to either blunt or accelerate another classification of attributes, depending on the type and the severity of the defect.

The child with moderate motor problems may tend to compensate by seeking scholarly outlets for his efforts, rather than to incur social punishment for his ineptitudes at play. However, if the motor problem is serious enough, his efforts to coordinate his hands when writing may be so constrained as to make much of his classroom work either difficult or impossible.

The child who is born blind, in the absence of cognitive deficits, will tend to learn about space in other ways. Results of studies of the blind, unlike those of the sighted, show that there are close relationships between measures of kinesthesis, manual competencies, and scores gained from tasks involving spatial orientation of the total body (17).

POSTULATE 3 Not only does there seem to be an optimum time for the insertion of educational experiences to elicit the most improvement in an attribute or group of attributes, but the reverse also seems to be true.

The extent to which some kind of either environmental or nutritional deprivation is likely to negatively affect an attribute or classification of attributes is dependent on the time in the child's life during which this deprivation occurs. When the negative factor is inserted, the greatest blunting of ability is likely to occur during that time of life in which that attribute or classification of attributes evidences the greatest amount of change caused by normal maturation processes.

Thus cortical cell proliferation is likely to be more negatively affected during the early months of life by dietary deficiencies. However, if the child experiences a similar deprivation of nutritional (protein) intake later in life when the growth of the central nervous system has stabilized, little or no damage is likely to occur to his central nervous system.

The early deprivation of normal visual experiences is likely to produce more marked changes in the infant's visual-motor behaviors than if this occurs later in life. If the infant is permitted to move when his capacities for action mature, any early deprivation of movement experiences will not likely exert a marked effect on motor development (10).

POSTULATE 4 An overexercise of a group of attributes may tend either to blunt the emergence of ability traits within another classification or to delay their appearance to some degree.

The hyperactive child is likely to have learning problems because his overzealous exercise of movement capacities may block intellectual growth to some extent. Early enriched visual environments may tend to delay slightly the beginnings of hand-eye coordinations.

The contemplative infant may appear relatively immobile in the play yard.

AXIOM 4 Many attributes within several channels, particularly those involving an observable response, may be "taken over" via mental functions as a child matures. A child may become able to "mentally manipulate" his environment without the need for direct experience after he has stored a number of types and classifications of experiences.

Contemplative babies between the ages of 15 and 18 months have been found to evidence better intelligence later in life (1). One important criterion of intelligence may be the appearance of this more efficient type of coping behavior.

Kilpatrick, Judd, French, and others have identified the ability of individuals to formulate perceptual judgments via analytical processes (thought) without the need for direct action (12,16, 20). Even animals (cats) have been found to be able to learn escape problems through observation, rather than through actual practice.

AXIOM 5 As maturation proceeds, innumerable bonds are formed between previously independent attributes residing either within the same or within separate classifications. At times this pairing signals the emergence of a new attribute within a classification of attributes.

As visual regard becomes bonded to crude voluntary hand movements, visually monitored manipulative and rudimentary drawing behaviors are triggered.

Later, as the maturing child is increasingly confronted with the necessity of catching balls, his previously formed abilities to track moving objects and to run become welded together, and he is able to anticipate and to intercept the illusive missiles.

As the child becomes able to draw more precisely in later childhood and early adolescence, his previously acquired and little used abilities to scribble may again be "called up" and employed as he depicts shadows and shadings on the landscapes he produces.

POSTULATE 1 *At times a bond may be formed between three or more attributes in different classifications. This bond may not become established between all three attributes at the same time in the life of a child.*

POSTULATE 2 *Some bonds formed early in life either may become less distinct with disuse as the child matures or may disappear entirely as their continuance may tend to impede his efficient functioning.*

Several of the important bonds pairing movements with vision formed early in the life of the child will become less distinct. Visually directed walking is important to the child of one and two years but is of little use to the child of four and five years.

POSTULATE 3 *The problem of the educator is at times to aid the child to form useful bonds between previously unassociated attributes and is at other times to aid him in terminating useless bonds.*

The child may need aid in pairing movement with vision as he begins to draw and to write. On the other hand, he may need to be aided to observe the goal he is approaching when walking, rather than to watch the alternate placement of his feet.

As a child first learns to read, he usually pairs lip movements representing vocalizations of the words he sees with his attempts to decipher the printed page. However, if his intellect is normal, these will usually "drop out" later as he finds that his reading speed will be impaired and/or as his reading speed tends to exceed his ability to match the slower lip movements with each word.

The young child, and later the older individual, may need to watch his hand as it approaches, contacts, picks up, and returns the water glass to his mouth. However, this type of commonly performed task is seldom accompanied by the same degree of visual monitoring when performed by the older child, adolescent, and adult in the middle years of life.

The child of five and six similarly needs to observe his hand in constant motion as he learns to write, whereas adolescents and adults pay considerably less attention to each movement of their pen when engaged in the same kind of task.

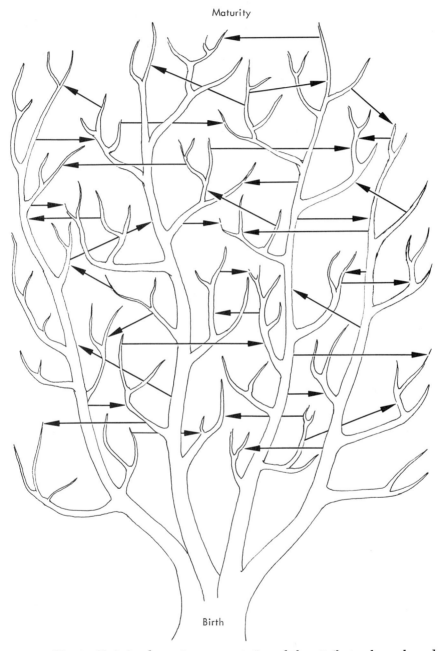

Figure 11-4 A schematic representation of the attribute channels and the bonds that tie appropriate abilities together.

POSTULATE 4 The educator at times must aid in the formation of bonds that would not normally be formed, in order to enhance the emergence of a given set of attributes.

The author has formulated a program of total body movements that have been found to aid a number of cognitive operations and classroom skills (7). Montessori and others have utilized a variety of sensory experiences to aid children in acquiring concepts of weight, size, texture, and the like (22). These types of programs may prove inefficient with the normal child because he may be forming quickly and easily subtle cognitive bonds between various classifications of stimuli and may not need this kind of "artificial" bond building. The atypical child, on the other hand, is often in need of programs that may lead toward the enrichment of associations between cognitive, perceptual, motor, and verbal activities by using "new routes."

POSTULATE 5 The formation of one bond leads toward the formation of other bonds. The formation of bonds between facets of behavior proceeds in a reasonably orderly manner in normal children.

A child usually crawls before he walks, and on walking he will engage in a variety of modifications of locomotor activity. A child must see his hand prior to using it, but once he begins to use it in primitive ways, he soon discovers innumerable variations of manipulative behavior in which he may engage.

POSTULATE 6 Failure to form a bond may be due to a lack of appropriate proliferation within classifications of attributes between which the bond must be formed, due to a lack of cognitive ability to perceive relationships, due to a lack of experience at observing others, due to a lack of motivation, and/or due to a lack of appropriate educational experiences.

If a helpful bond is not being formed in a child, it should be determined whether perceptual, cognitive, motor, or attitudinal deficits or some combination of these deficits is present. The three- and four-year-old child may not evidence efficient drawing behavior forming a visual-manual bond because he may not feel that it is important (attitude); he either may not have observed other individuals drawing or may lack drawing implements at home (cultural deprivation); either he may not realize that it can be done with crayons and pencils (cognitive), or he may lack the ability to guide his hand with his vision on a reasonably accurate course.

POSTULATE 7 The bonds formed by a child may be basic, necessary for his survival and for efficient performance of all children within a culture. On the other hand, a bond may be unique to an individual. Both types of bonds are formed in children under most circumstances.

As a normal child matures, more unique bonds are formed as experience becomes more specific. It must be determined in atypical children which bonds are important to form, that is, which bonds are basic and which bonds are less important. Early in life a child forms bonds between classifications of attributes that enable him to walk; to think through basic processes, such as to remember items in a series; to write; and to form verbal connections to common objects, movements, and situations in his environment. Unique bonds would be connections formed, for example, as the son of a naturalist learns the names of various waterfowl.

POSTULATE 8 The effectiveness of educators, of curriculum developers, and of parents when attempting to deal with children lies in the facility with which they can identify those bonds that are dependent on other bonds. In the life of a normal child various types of bonds and the manner in which various subattributes may be expected to appear within a given classification of attributes should emerge.

POSTULATE 9 At times educators must aid a child to strengthen bonds between facets of his behavior that may be indistinct either because of some kind of maturational delay or sensory-motor or cognitive deficits or because of lack of practice.

AXIOM 6 With maturation and the evolution of intelligent behavior, the child will become able to quickly select from the several clusters of attributes at his command those which will enable him to deal effectively with situations he faces. The facility with which he "calls up" attributes may be an important index of intelligence and emotional stability.

There is less time delay between the presentation of stimuli and the appropriate reactions by older people than there is by younger people. Learned response patterns are more quickly reacted to than are new response patterns. Several authors have cited the development of efficient work methods as important to efficient motor and perceptual-motor performance, as are basic movement and perceptual capacities.

POSTULATE 1 With maturation the "calling up" of appropriate attributes is carried out with less and less conscious effort. Exercise of capacities and learned experience results in efficient selection of appropriate work methods from an individual's storehouse of attributes.

The theory outlined could be elaborated on by reference to the expanding literature in neurology, and in particular by texts such as those by Konorski (21) and by others who have attempted to relate neurological function to behavior (13). Konorski, similarly, utilizes the concept of bonds formed between various components of the human personality; however, his theoretical assumptions are more static and at the same time are more global than are the assumptions contained in the model outlined on the previous pages. Hebb's concept of cell linkages written 20 years ago, as well as John's more recent exposition of more contemporary and more molecular trends in biochemistry of neural functioning, also offer physiological and anatomical support for the statements made on the previous pages (13,15).

It is believed, however, that a model of the type sketched here may rest simply on supports formed by data collected from various studies of *behavior,* and that it need not be made more "respectable" by allusions to neurological "models," which in themselves are to a great extent speculative in nature. Rather it has been attempted to formulate a series of statements that, hopefully, weld themselves into a cogent and rational raft of thought. It has been said that the worth of a theoretical posit may be assessed by consulting the evidence that has inspired it, as well as by inspecting the quality of the research that, in turn, has seemed to provide the impetus. My purposes will be served if the reader, after reviewing the previous paragraphs, is encouraged to engage in either endeavor.

SUMMARY

The "latticework" of bonds and channels that has been only briefly sketched in may to some degree be supported by the summaries of the neurological literature by John (15) and by the theoretical speculations of Hebb (13), Illingworth (14), and others. In general, the theory rests on the measurement of behavior and, in particular, on the admittedly scarce factorial of human ability traits. Particularly data from the studies of Cumbee (9), Carpenter (3), Fleishman (11), Smith (24),

Keogh (18), and Clausen (4), as well as those emanating from our own laboratory, have proved helpful (5,6,7,8).

Those familiar with the research literature have realized by this time the flimsiness of the evidence supporting some of the statements found on the preceding pages. At the same time it is believed that the available evidence does attest to the validity of most of the axioms and postulates presented in the model outlined.

It is believed that further research should attempt to determine the manner in which unique attributes emerge in the several classifications as the child matures. There are few factorial studies employing children under the ages of five years as subjects, and I am not aware of an extensive and detailed research program in which the emergence of various factors of either perceptual or motor ability traits have been studied as a function of sex and of age.

The manner in which bonds are formed between various attributes in children is a topic that has been studied by educators for years. The concept of bond formation utilized within the previous paragraphs is closely similar to the concept of learning as used by many behavioral scientists.

The clinician, it is hoped, may also gain some guidance from the careful consideration of the theoretical pronouncements within this final section. It is believed that, to successfully modify the behavior of both normal and atypical children, constructive and helpful educators and others purporting to elicit change should evidence a cognizance of the complexities of human development and of the numerous variables that modify this development, rather than merely grasping at naive theoretical guidelines, which may result in the formulation of simple-minded and ineffective curricula.

BIBLIOGRAPHY

1 Bayley, Nancy, "Behavioral Correlates of Mental Growth—Birth to Thirty-Six Years," *Amer. Psych.*, **23** (1968), 1–17.

2 Bloom, Benjamin S., *Stability and Change in Human Characteristics*, New York: John Wiley & Sons, 1964.

3 Carpenter, Aileen, "The Differential Measurement of Speed in Primary School Children," *Child Dev.*, **12** (1941), 1–7.

4 Clausen, Johs., *Ability Structure and Subgroups in Mental*

Retardation, Washington: Spartan Books; London: Macmillan and Co., Ltd., 1966.

5 Cratty, Bryant J., *The Perceptual-Motor Attributes of Mentally Retarded Children and Youth,* Monograph, sponsored by Mental Retardation Services Board of Los Angeles County, Los Angeles, Calif., 1966.

6 ———, *Movement Behavior and Motor Learning,* 2nd ed., Philadelphia: Lea & Febiger, 1967.

7 ———, *Perception, Motion and Thought,* Palo Alto, Calif.: Peek Publications, 1969.

8 ———, and M. M. Martin, *Perceptual-Motor Efficiency in Children,* Philadelphia: Lea and Febiger, 1969.

9 Cumbee, F. Z., "A Factorial Analysis of Motor Coordination," *Res. Quart.,* 25 (1954), 412–28.

10 Dennis, W., "Infant Development under Conditions of Restricted Practice and of Minimum Social Stimulation: A Preliminary Report," *J. Genet. Psych.,* 53 (1938), 149–58.

11 Fleishman, Edwin A., and Walter E. Hempel, Jr., "Factorial Analysis of Complex Psychomotor Performance and Related Skills," *J. Appl. Psych.,* 40 (1956), 2.

12 French, J. W., "The Relationship of Problem-Solving Styles to Factor Composition of Tests," *Educ. Psych. Measmt.,* 25 (1965), 9–28.

13 Hebb, D. O., *The Organization of Behavior,* New York: John Wiley & Sons, 1949.

14 Illingworth, R. S., *The Development of the Infant and Young Child,* 3rd ed., Edinburgh and London: E. & S. Livingstone, Ltd., 1967.

15 John, E. Roy, *Mechanisms of Memory,* New York and London: Academic Press, 1967.

16 Judd, C. H., "The Relationship of Special Training to General Intelligence," *Educ. Rev.,* 26 (1908), 28–42.

17 Juurmaa, Jyrki, "On Interrelations of Auditory, Tactual and Visual Spatial Performances," Helsinki, Finland: Reports from the Institute of Occupational Health, Mono. No. 54, September, 1967.

18 Keogh, J. F., *Motor Performance of Elementary School Children,* Monograph, University of California, Los Angeles, Physical Education Dept., 1965.

19 Kephart, Newell C., *The Slow Learner in the Classroom,* Columbus, Ohio: Charles E. Merrill Books, Inc., 1960.

20 Kilpatrick, F. P., "Two Processes in Perceptual Learning," *J. Exp. Psych.*, **36** (1946), 187–211.

21 Konorski, Jerzy, *Integrative Activity of the Brain—An Interdisciplinary Approach*, Chicago and London: University of Chicago Press, 1967.

22 Montessori, Maria, *Dr. Montessori's Own Handbook*, New York: Frederick A. Stokes, 1914.

23 Piaget, Jean, *The Construction of Reality in the Child*, New York: Basic Books, Inc., 1954.

24 Smith, Olin W., and Patricia C. Smith, "Developmental Studies of Spatial Judgments by Children and Adults," *Percept. Mot. Skills*, Mono. Suppl. 1–V22, 1966.

25 White, Burton L., and Richard Held, "Plasticity of Sensorimotor Development in the Human Infant," in *Biological and Biochemical Bases of Behavior*, H. Harlow and C. Woolsey (eds.), Madison: University of Wisconsin Press, 1958.

Index

Abnormalities, 1

Academic performance, motor ability, 247

visual training, 260

Accommodations in infants, 70

Accuracy, jumping in children, 194

throwing, age trends, 207

Activity, levels, at birth, 10

children, 36

needs and I.Q., 174

Adams, N., 119

Adolescence, leadership at play, 231

Adult intelligence, prediction from children's motor scores, 172

Age trends, ball interception, 208

ball skills, 204

bodily integrations, 202

cable jump, 202

hopping, 196

running speed, 200

throwing accuracy, 207

throwing mechanics, 204

Agility, 199

runs in children, 189

sex differences, 202

Ajuriaguerra, J., 40, 41, 63, 121, 254, 268

Allen, K., 266

Allen, L., 63, 215

Allen, S., 237, 241

Ames, L., 32, 40, 62, 97, 107, 109, 121, 166, 267

Amnionic fluid, 1

Anastasiow, N., 228, 241

Anderson, D., 237, 240

Anderson, H., 119, 241

Anderson, J., 213

Anderson, R., 266

Animal drawings, by children, 221

Arm pull-up reflex, 18

Arm-supporting reflex, 16

Arnoult, M., 119

Aronfreed, J., 237

Arrington, R., 230, 241

Arrowhead, A., 238, 244

Asymmetries, motor performance, 254

movement, 32, 39

Attention and stimulus complexity, 74

infants, 73

Attention span, learning, 265

Attitudes about physical activity, mother-father correlations, 226

Attneave, F., 119

Attributes, blunting, 279

bond between, 283

changes due to teaching efforts, 276

patterns in infants, 39

Auditory and verbal functions, hand preference, 40
Auditory imprinting, 1
Austin, M., 228, 241
Australopithecus, hand preference, 254
Ausubel, D., 266
Ayres, J., 95, 119, 250, 266
Azrin, N., 235, 241

Baer, D., 266
Baird, J., 84, 95
Balance, 170, 171, 184
  academic performance, 187
  children, 48, 212
  intelligence, 249
  measurement, 185
  reading, 2
  sex differences in children, 186
  static balance, measures, 50
  visual-motor system, 52
  walking lines, 48
Baldwin, A., 241
Ball, bouncing, 59, 170
  catching, reaction time, 183
  handling, kicking, and batting, 209
  interception, 89
    age trends, 208
    sex differences, 208
  skills, 204
    in children, 53
Baseball, distance throw, 170
Basketball, selection of team captains, 233
Bass, R., 123, 185
Batting balls, 209
Bauer, J., 139
Bayley, N., 29, 43, 49, 62, 173, 213, 251, 266, 289
Beach, F., 75, 95
Beam walking, 185
Beck, L., 83, 97
Bell, R., 221, 245
Belmont, L., 32, 62, 266
Bender, L., 154, 166, 221, 241
Benton, A., 107, 118

Berges, J., 111, 121
Bernstein, L., 96
Bielianskos, V., 223, 241
Binocular cues in infants, 82
Biochemical changes, imprinting, 76
Bioelectronics, 1
Birch, H., 32, 62, 266
Birdwhistell, R., 221, 241
Birth reflexes, 1, 28
Bishop, B., 222, 241
Block building, competition among children, 235
Block handling, 33
Bloom, B., 36, 62, 172, 213, 251, 276, 289
Bloom, M., 267
Bodily integrations, 202
Bodily proportions of children, 35
Body build, nursery school children, 35
  performance, 60
Body cathexis, 103
Body-image concept, 102
  development, 101
  letter reversal, 118
  perception, 250
  self-concept, 103
  testing, 105
  verbal ability, 107
  testing via gesture imitation, 110
  verbal identification of body parts, 107
Boser, J., 125
Bossom, J., 97
Bowell, C., 242
Bower, T., 68, 69, 81, 95
Brackett, C., 241
Brandt, H., 119, 241
Brengelmann, J., 121
Brenner, J., 166, 247
Bridges, J., 95, 241
Bridges, K., 223, 229, 232
Broadbeck, A., 76, 95
Broad jump, children 6 to 12 years old, 170
  standing, 192

Brody, S., 77, 95
Brown, D., 223, 241
Brown, R., 252, 267
Buhler, C., 234, 242
Bullis, G., 96
Burn, C., 270

Caldwell, W., 119
Campbell, W., 122
Carey, R., 194, 213
Carpenter, A., 170, 189, 213, 288
Castler, L., 95
Catching, 55
    balls, 89
    behavior, stages, 58, 207
    reaction time, 183
Cattel, P., 213
Cavanaugh, M., 213
Cells of the eye, 70
Cerebellum, functioning and balance, 249
Challman, R., 228, 242
Child development, history of study, 1
Childhood, gross motor ability, 31
    hand preference, 31
    manual dexterity, 132
    preferences for manual activities, 135
    running, 44
    sex differences, manipulative behavior, 132
    structural changes, 35
Children, activity level, 36
    balancing ability, 48
    ball bouncing, 170
    ball catching, 89
    ball skills, 53
    body-image development, 101
    developmental trends, 62
    dynamic balance, 185
    fantasies, 221
    flexibility in 6 to 12 year-olds, 212
    improvement of ability with age, 170
    letter reversal and inversion, 80

locomotor abilities, 189
    perceptual development, 67
    reaction time, 182
    scribbling and drawing, 141
    strength measures, 179
    vertical jumping, 190
    visual development, 94
    whole-part perception, 85
Children's ability to print letters and numbers, 161
Children's art, mental test, 142
    pictorial stage, 155
Children's performance, interest in the task, 237
Children's play, parental supervision, 222
Chromosomes, 1
Circle drawing, 147
Circles and squares, early attempts at drawing, 152
Clarke, H., 178, 180, 213, 220, 242
Clausen, J., 179, 189
Cleveland, S., 102, 121
Climbing, 52
    movements, 22
    reflex, 20
Coan, R., 130, 138
Cockrell, D., 221, 229, 230, 242
Cognitive functions and hand preference, 40
Cognitive skills, development, 273
Cognition and movement at birth, 10
Cohen, E., 62
Competition, children's play, 234
    development, 240
    infancy, 220
    performance level, 234
Conel, J., 125, 138
Cones in the eye, 71
Contacting objects, 138
Cooperation in children, 235
Correlation, balance and academic performance, 187
    mental and motor abilities, 172
    motor ability scores of fathers and sons, 178

Correlation (*Cont.*)
  strength measures in children, 182
Cowan, E., 213
Cowell, C., 215
Cox, F., 220, 238, 242
Cratty, B. J., 32, 62, 68, 76, 95, 102, 104, 121, 166, 178, 187, 189, 207, 208, 214, 225, 242, 289, 290
Crawling, 24
  reflex, 18, 20
Creeping, stages, 23
Cross-dominance and intelligence, 41
Cruickshank, R., 68, 81, 83, 95
Cues for visual perception, 67
Cumbee, F., 170, 200, 214, 290

Davidson, H., 80, 95, 118, 121
Davitz, J., 242
Degtyar, E., 126
Delacato, C., 253, 267
  program reading, 256
  theory, medical opinion, 255
Dennis, M., 62
Dennis, W., 34, 62, 282, 290
Dental problems and motor ability, 259
Denver Developmental Screening, 167
Deprivation, motor development, 282
  movement experiences, 34
Depth perception in infants, 83
Development, children's drawings, 165
  effects of trauma or deprivation, 282
  infants, 28
  manipulative behaviors, 123, 136–37
  motor abilities of children, 60, 61
  scribbling, 144–47
  social abilities, 219

trends in body image development, 112, 113
  visual perception, 67
Developmental sequences, motor ability, 6 to 12 year-olds, 212
Diagram phase in drawing, 148
Dillon, D., 121
Ding, G., 243
Dingman, H., 10, 30, 260, 267
Distance throwing in children, 57
Dodds, J., 167, 214
Doll, E., 242
"Doll-eye" reflex, 14
Dowley, E., 265, 269
Draw-a-person test, 105, 156
Drawing, ability and I.Q., 148
  aggregate phase, 156
  animal drawings by children, 221
  diagram phase, 147
  geometric figures, 149
  letters and numbers, 161
  pictorial stage, 155
  tests, 6
  three-dimensional figures, 163
Dubanosky, R., 75, 98
Dunsing, J., 129, 138
Dynamic balance in children, 185

Eames, T., 252, 260, 267
Eckert, H. M., 8, 43, 62
Educators, 7
Electric activity in the brain, 4
Elkind, D., 85, 95
Emotional development, draw-a-person test, 106
  prediction in childhood, 36
Espenschade, A., 6, 8, 43, 62
Evaluating, body image, 102, 105
  game choice in children, 209
  hopping, 47
  manipulative abilities in children, 132
  motor ability in children 6 to 12 years old, 177

visual attention in infants, 73
visual motor ability, 87
Evolution and reflexes, 10
Exploration of objects, 130
Eye, fixations and reading, 260
    preference, 39

Face regard, infants, 73
Factor analyses, children 6 to 12
        years old, 171
    infants' abilities, 251
    motor ability, 169
    visual perception, 67
Factors of visual perception, 67,
        90
Family influences, upon infants,
        221
Fantz, R., 9, 29, 67, 73, 95
Fathers and sons, comparisons of
        motor abilities, 178
Fay, T., 255, 267
Fetal activity, 10
Fetal movement, recording, 23
Fetology, 1
Fibrillations, eye, 71
Figure drawing, children, 147
Fine versus gross control in in-
        fants, 28
Finger opposition in children,
        132
Fisher, L., 99
Fisher, S., 102, 121
Fitness and reading, 175
Five-year-old, motor ability, 32,
        44
Fleishman, E., 8, 169, 179, 214,
        251, 267, 288, 290
Flexibility, children 6 to 12 years
        old, 212
Flick, G., 32, 40, 62
Foot preference, 39
    hand preference, 42, 254
Footlick, W., 269
Forlands, F., 245
Form, discrimination, 79
    perception, 78

infants, 82
Frankenberg, W., 167, 214
Freedman, H., 245
Friedman, H., 228
French, J., 91, 96, 283, 290

Gait, 249
Gallifret-Granjon, N., 121
Galloping, 45
Game choices, children, 223
    6 to 12 years old, 209
Games Choice Test, 209
Gender identification, gestures,
        224
    infants and children, 223
General activity level in children,
        36
Geometric figure drawing in chil-
        dren, 149
Gesell, A., 32, 33, 40, 62, 67, 96,
        125, 138, 267
Gesture imitation, children, 110
    test, 111
Gestures, masculine and feminine,
        224
Getman, G., 257, 267
Ghent, L., 68, 79, 80, 96
Gibson, E., 68, 83, 96, 98
Gibson, J., 120, 125, 139
Gieseck, M., 63
Gilbert, L., 268
Gillman, S., 166
Glass, G., 255, 256, 268, 270
Glassow, R., 206, 214
Goetzinger, C., 185, 214
Goldfarb, W., 96, 220, 242
Goodenough, F., 121, 166, 243,
        299
Gorelick, M., 268
Gould, J., 270
Gozen, J., 269
Graves, E., 234, 236, 243
Gray, P., 76
Green, E., 221, 229, 243
Green, R., 96
Greenberg, P., 234, 243

Grip strength, 212
    children, 6 to 12 years, 179
    sex differences, 180
Gross motor ability in early child-
    hood, 31
Group interaction of children, in-
    structions, 235
Growth changes in childhood, 34
Gruber, E., 260, 268
Gruber, J., 215
Guilford, J., 214
Guttridge, M., 48, 63, 214

Hacaen, H., 40, 41, 63, 254, 268
Hacaen, J., 121
Hagen, J., 265, 269
Haines, H., 68
Haith, M., 70, 96
Halgren, M., 261, 268
Halverson, H., 125, 139
Hamachek, D., 121
Hand-eye preference, 254
Hand preference, 39, 253
    animals and primates, 254
    auditory verbal and cognitive
        functions, 40
    childhood, 31
    culture, 254
    evaluation, 42
    foot preference, 42, 254
    infants, 128
    inheritance, 40, 254
Hand regard, environment, 127
Harborough, B., 256
Hardy, M., 243
Haring, N., 252, 268
Harmon, D., 259
Harris, A., 255, 268
Harris, D., 103, 122
Harris, L., 139
Harrison, J., 214
Hartman, D., 214
Hartrup, W., 223, 243
Hayes, B., 236
Hayes, M., 67, 68
Haynes, H., 73
Haynes, J., 97

Head-body reflexes, 14
Head-neck control, infants, 28
Heath, S., 215
Heathers, G., 225, 243
Hebb, D., 288, 290
Hein, A., 97
Heise, B., 243
Held, R., 67, 68, 69, 73, 77, 91,
    99, 125, 127, 128, 139,
    291
Hemispheric dominance, 254
Henke, L., 266
Herbert, E., 245
Hershenson, M., 97
Hicks, J., 33, 63
Hildreth, G., 63, 254, 268
Hilgard, J. R., 33, 63
Hill, K., 243
Hindmarch, R., 215
History of the study of child de-
    velopment, 1
Holbrook, S., 47, 50, 63, 133, 139
Honzik, M., 36, 63, 215, 268
Hopping, 45, 47
    accuracy, 198
    distance, 198
    grid patterns, 194
    rhythmically, 32, 196
Horowitz, F., 236, 243
Howard, I., 97, 121
Humans, imprinting, 75
Hunt, J., 228, 232, 243
Hupprich, F., 215
Hurdle jump, 45, 193
    age trends, 196
    sex differences, 194
Hurlock, E., 243

Ilg, F., 96, 97, 107, 109, 121,
    139, 166
Illingworth, R. S., 11, 30, 264,
    268, 288, 290
Imitation, infancy, 220
Imprinting, animals, 75
    biochemical changes, 76
    perceptual, 75
    periods in life of humans, 76

Infancy, competition, 221
  fixation time, 73
  neural changes, 6
  parallel play, 221
  sex differences in throwing, 220
  smiling, 220
  social development, 220
  social responsiveness, 37
  upper and lower limb move-
    ments, 278
Infant, abilities, factor analysis,
    251
  binocular cues, 82
  crawling, 24
  creeping, 23
  depth perception, 83
  developmental trends, 27
  drawing circles and squares,
    152–53
  family influences, 221
  form perception, 82
  gender identification, 223
  hand preference, 128
  institution reared, 220
  locomotion, 23
  manipulative behavior, 123
  manual dexterity, 38
  movements, 9
  ocular characteristics, 70
  perception, form, 78
  three dimensions, 83
  perceptual cues, 82
  perceptual discrimination, 9
  reflexes, 10
  sliding movements, 24
  standing, 25
  visual attention, 73
  visual behavior, 77
    at birth, 126
  visual tracking, 70
  vocalization, 10
  walking, 26
Infantile behavior, components,
    37
Institution-reared infants, 220
Instructions in group interaction,
    235
Integration of behavior, 274

bodily movements, 202
Intelligence, cross-dominance, 41
  draw-a-person test, 157
  infancy, adult intelligence, 39
  leadership at play, 232
  motor performance in children
    6 to 12 years old, 171, 172
  movement ability, 248
  physical fitness, 174
  prediction, childhood, 36, 251
  motor ability scores in child-
    hood, 173
  visual perceptual abilities, 283
I.Q., drawing abilities in children,
    148
  physical fitness, 174
Irwin, O. C., 10, 30, 76, 95
Ismail, O., 171, 172, 187, 215, 242

Jack, L., 233, 243
Jaynes, J., 75, 95
Jeffrey, W., 79, 97
Jenkins, L., 44, 63
Jersild, A., 122, 243
John, E., 288
John, R., 290
Johnson, B., 97
Johnson, D., 268
Johnson, G., 167, 189, 215
Johnson, R., 83, 215
Jones, H., 104, 215, 243
Jones, M., 122, 230, 243, 288
Jones, T., 63
Jordan, D., 178, 180, 213, 242
Jourard, M., 103
Judd, C., 283, 290
Jumping, 44
  accuracy, 194
  children, 45, 190
  leg power, 190
Juurmaa, Jyrki, 282, 290

Kagan, J., 37, 63, 73, 97, 220, 243
Kagan, K., 223
Kalafat, J., 97
Kane, R., 215

Kanzer, P., 238, 246
Katsui, A., 79, 97
Keiley, R., 236, 243
Kellogg, R., 141, 142, 158, 166
Keogh, B., 269
Keogh, F., 290
Keogh, J., 47, 50, 53, 63, 64, 132, 133, 179, 189, 194, 195, 197, 199, 201, 207, 215, 289
Kephard, N., 106, 122, 129, 131, 138, 216, 248, 257, 269, 290
Kephard, N. C., 97
Kershner, J., 269
Kicking balls, 209
Kilpatrick, F., 283, 291
Kinsbourne, M., 262, 269
Klafat, J., 73
Klein, R., 98
Koegler, E., 85, 95
Koegler, R., 85, 95
Koppitz, E., 154, 166
Koronsky, J., 6, 8, 288, 291
Krippner, S., 269
Kruse, P., 206, 214

Labyrinthine reflexes, 17
Labyrinthine righting reflex, 15
Ladder climbing, 52
Lambercier, M., 68, 88, 98
LaPray, M., 252, 269
Latane, B., 239, 244
Latchaw, M., 216
Laterality, 114, 115, 250
Leadership, development in childhood play, 240
  experimental manipulation, 233
  intelligence, 232
  play, 230
    adolescence, 231
  rating by observers, 231
  selection of basketball captains, 233
  social level, 231
Learning, maturation, 33
  vision, 258

Lederer, J., 269
Left-right discrimination, 107
  stages in development, 109
Leg power, jumping, 190
Lehman, H., 230, 231, 243
Letter inversion, 80
Letter reversal in children, 80
  motor ability, 250
Letters, drawing, 160
Levin, H., 241, 245
Lewis, M., 73, 97, 237
Lézine, I., 111, 121
Lindsley, O., 234, 241
Line, W., 87, 97
Line walking, 48
Ling, B., 78, 79, 97
Lippman, H., 64
Lipsitt, L., 244
Locomotion, 249
  infants, 23
  variations, 44
Locomotor abilities, 189
  fathers and sons, 178
Locomotor reflexes, 18, 29
Longitudinal studies, children, 223
  motor ability in children 6 to 12 years old, 178
Lumbar curve when walking, 26
Lyle, J., 269
Lynn, R., 139, 269
Lyons, C., 261
Lyons, E., 261, 269

Maccoby, E., 4, 8, 245, 265, 269
MacFarlane, J., 63, 215
Manipulative behavior, 123
  examination phase, 131
  social development, 131
Manipulative development, 129
Manual activity, childhood preferences, 135
  visual behavior in infants, 77
Manual dexterity, childhood, 132
  infants, 38
Martin, M., 68, 95, 166, 207, 208
Masculine gestures, 224

Maturation, intelligence, 287
  learning, 33
  model for study, 273
  visual perception, 82
Maturity and motor ability, 227
McCormick, C., 269
McCormick, D., 257
McGraw, M., 11, 21, 30, 34, 64
McKee, L., 225, 245
McKee, R., 180, 216
Measurement, balance in children, 185
  motor ability in children 6 to 12 years old, 168
Medford Study, 178, 180
Medical opinion, Delacato method, 255
Medinnus, G., 224, 243
Mental-motor relationships in retarded children, 174
Mental testing, using children's art, 142
Meredith, H., 215, 216
Merrell, D., 254, 270
Metheny, E., 64, 179, 180, 216
Meyers, C. E., 10, 30
Meyers, J., 122
Michaels W., 214
Michels, K., 271
Milner, E., 6, 8, 30
Minerva, A., 34, 64
Missiuro, W., 236, 244
Misumi, J., 84, 97
Money, J., 96
Montessori, M., 286, 291
Moro reflex, 11, 12, 28
Morris, D., 166
Moss, H., 37, 63, 220, 223, 243
Motivation, motor training, 255
Motor ability, factor analysis, 169
  fathers and sons, 178
  intelligence in children, 36
  maturity, 227
  6 to 12 years old, 212
  social ability, 219
  when it can be changed, 276
Motor attributes, diffusion, 276

Motor copy theory, 129
Motor generalizations, 250
Motor learning, 6
  childhood, 31
Motor performance, academic performance comparison of theories, 262
  children and parental attitudes, 225
  definition, 4
  influence of social reinforcement, 240
  intelligence, 172
  social reinforcement, 236
  social success, 228
Motor training in children, 34
Movement, imprinting, 75
  perception, 88
    space, 81
  reading, 2
Movement behavior, 4
Movement parallax cues, 69
  visual perception of infants, 82
Moyes, F., 64
Mukerji, N., 238, 244
Munroe, P., 251, 267
Murphy, G., 236, 244
Murphy, L., 236, 244
Mussen, P., 122, 224, 244
Myers, J., 118

Needs for activity and I.Q., 174
Nelson, D., 224
Neural changes in infancy, 6
Neurological, dysfunction and infant reflexes, 13
  organization, 253
Nevia, S., 96
Neville, D., 270
Newberry, H., 30
Noer, D., 238, 244
Normal children, 6 to 12 years old, 169

Object exploration, 130
Object regard in infants, 126

Ochs, E., 167
Ocular characteristics of infants, 70
O'Dell, S., 155, 166
Olum, V., 68, 96
Orton, S., 270
Oseretsky test, 133

Palermo, D., 244
Palmar grasp reflex, 13, 22
Parallel play, 229
  infancy, 221
Parental attitudes, children's performance, 225
Parental control of children, 222
Parental correlations between attitudes about physical activity, 226
Parental imitation by children, 223
Park, G., 270
Parten, M., 221, 229, 230, 232, 244
Pathological reflexes, 11
Patterson, G., 237, 244
Payne, D., 224, 244
Peiper, A., 139
Perception, definition, 4
  developmental trends, 92
  form, 78
  left and right, 108
  movement, 5, 88
  three dimensions in space, 81, 83
  upright, 79
  whole-part, 85
Perceptual abilities, 5
  motor abilities, 2
Perceptual changes through experience, 77
Perceptual development, 67, 273
  general trends, 69
Perceptual discrimination of infants, 9
Perceptual interest in infancy, 37
Perceptual judgments and intelligence, 283

Perceptual-motor behavior, definition, 5
  functioning, individual differences, 265
Performance and academic performance, 248
  theories and educational practice, 264
  training, 248
  when it can be changed, 277
Perceptual selection, 69
Perceptual sequences in children, 79
Perceptual types, 91
Performance, sex of onlookers, 237
  social reinforcement, 236
Personality and perception, 2
Philip, A., 234, 237, 244
Physical fitness and I.Q., 174
Physical maturity and social success, 227
Physical restraint of children at play, 222
Physiological optics, 257
Piaget, J., 68, 88, 98, 127, 139, 291
Pick, A., 98
Pick, H., 98
Pictorial stage in children's drawings, 155
Pieper, Albrecht, 11, 30, 69, 71, 98, 264, 270
Piers, E., 103, 122
Pigors, P., 231, 232, 245
Pintney, R., 228, 245
Plantar reflex, 13
Play, leadership of children, 230
  social organization, 240
Poetker, B., 257, 269
Polikanina, R., 126, 139
Posture, 249
Poyntz, L., 217
Pratt, B., 194, 213
Prebirth movements, 9
Prediction, intelligence, 251
  mental ability from motor ability scores in children, 173
Preferences, hand-eye-foot, 39

Prenatal movements, 9
Primates and infant reflexes, 13
Printing, children's, 161
Probotova, L., 126, 139
Puffer, J., 228, 245
Pull-up reflex, 18
Pupillary fibrillations, 71

Rabinovitch, R., 253, 255, 270
Rage, childhood, 221
Railo, W., 174, 175, 216
Ralph, C., 63
Ralph, D., 33
Ramaley, F., 254, 270
Rappaport, J., 221, 241
Rarick, G., 64, 180, 216, 225, 245
Reaction time, 182
    simple and complex responses,
        183
Reading, balance, 2
    fitness, 175
    letter reversal, 251
    motor ability, 250
    ocular functioning, 259
    perceptual-motor improvement,
        252
    visual tracking, 260
Reading improvement, Delacato
        method, 256
    Kephart's program, 252
Reaney, M., 232, 245
Reflexes, birth, 28
    climbing, 20, 22
    crawling, 20
    doll-eye, 14
    evolution, 10
    head-body, 14
    infancy, 10
    labyrinthine righting, 15
    locomotor, 18, 229
    Moro, 11
    optic stimulation, 16
    palmar grasp, 13
    pathological, 11
    plantar, 13
    pull-up, 18
    righting, 14

startle, 11
    supporting reflex, 16
    swimming, 21
    tonic-neck, 12
    walking, 18, 19
Research, Delacato method, 255
    manipulative behavior, 125
    motor performance, 7
Retarded children, Delacato
        method, 256
    motor ability, 174
Reynolds, N., 266
Rhythmic hopping, 47
    sex differences, 196
Rhythmical walking, children, 43
Richards, T. W., 30
Riesen, A., 98
Righting reflex, 14
Roach, E., 216, 252, 270
Robbins, M., 256, 270
Rooting reflex, 11
Rosenberg, B., 223, 225, 245
Ross, R., 252, 269
Rowe, A., 122
Rudel, R., 98
Running, childhood, 44, 170
    speed, 199
        children 6 to 12 years old,
            212
        sex differences, 200
Rutherford, W., 270

Sanders, A., 98
Sandusky, A., 245
Scarr, S., 10, 30, 36, 64
Schaefer, E., 122
Schaffer, A., 270
Schilder, P., 122
Schnobrich, J., 257, 269
Scribbling and drawing, 141
    stages, 141
Seashore, H., 216
Sears, 220, 221, 245
Secord, P., 103, 122
Seils, L., 217
Self-concept, body image, 103
    physical performance, 104

Sensory-motor deficits, 282
Sersen, E., 99
Sex differences, 3, 60
  agility, 202
  balance ability of children, 186
  ball kicking and batting, 209
  cable jump, 202
  children's drawings, 163
  children 6 to 12 years old, 171, 212
  complex bodily integrations, 202
  game choices, 209
  hopping accuracy for distance, 198
  hurdle jump, 194
  manipulative behaviors in childhood, 132
  play characteristics, 229
  rhythmic hopping, 196
  standing broad jump, 192
  static balance, 188
  strength, children 6 to 12 years old, 180
  throwing, accuracy, 207
    distance, 204
    infancy, 220
    velocity, 205
  vertical jump, 191
  visual attention, 74
  walking, 43
Sheldon, W., 122
Shirley, M., 64
Sigherseth, P., 215
Sinclair, C., 270
Size of play groups, 229
Skill with balls, 53, 204
Skipping, 32, 38, 45, 48
Sliding of infants, 25
Sloan, W., 139, 168, 217
Smiling in infancy, 220
Smith, C., 269
Smith, O., 67, 84, 91, 130, 139, 251, 288, 291
Smith, P., 98, 291
Social development, 219, 240
  infancy, 220

manipulative behavior in infants, 131
Social emotional factors, Delacato method, 255
Social responsiveness in infancy, 37
Social rewards, 236
Social status and friendships, 228
Social success, physical maturity, 227
Sociocultural level and leadership in children, 230
Solokov, E., 129, 139
Solomon, R., 158
Spatial judgment and balance, 249
Special educators, 7
Speech and hemispheric dominance, 253
Spielberger, D., 269
Spitz, R., 98, 245
Spool winding in children, 132
Stables, J., 252, 268
Standing broad jump, 192
Standing up, 25
Startle reflex, 11
Static balance in children, 185
  sex differences, 188
Status and performance of children, 228
Stephens, M., 236, 243
Stevenson, H., 238, 245
Strength, children 6 to 12 years old, 179
  intercorrelations of measures, 182
Strephosymbolia, 250
Stott, D., 47, 64, 133, 139
Structural changes in childhood, 35
Studies of motor performance, 7
Subirana, A., 122
Success and attribute changes, 278
Supporting reflex, 16, 17
Sutton-Smith, B., 223, 225, 245
Swenson, C., 106, 122
Swimming reflex, 18
  mammals, 21

Taylor, E., 270
Taylor, S., 252, 260, 271
Team captains in basketball, 233
Templeton, W., 97, 121
Teuber, H., 98
Theories, development, 275
  perceptual-motor performance, intelligence, 248
    comparison, 262
  visual perception, 92
Thomas, P., 251, 267
Thompson, G., 228
Thompson, H., 33, 63
Thompson, W., 75, 98
Thought and movement, 32
Threading beads, 133
Three-dimensional figure drawing, 163
Three dimensions, perception, 83
Throwing, 32, 54
  accuracy, sex differences, 207
  age trends in throwing distance, 205
  catching balls, 276
  children 6 to 12 years old, 212
  distance, 56, 170
  form, age trends, 207
  patterns by age, 204
  sex differences in young children, 220
  spatial perception, 250
  stages in development, 55
  velocity, 206
Tinker, M., 252, 260, 271
Tonic-neck reflex, 12
Tracking, visual, 70
Training, motor in children, 33
  visual perceptual abilities, 258
Two-year-old children, walking, 43

Updergraff, R., 65, 245
Upper and lower limb movements, development, 279
Uzgiris, I., 131, 139

Vandenberg, S., 171, 217
Vane, J., 166
Verbal ability, 275
Vernon, M., 71, 98
Vertical jump, 170, 190
  sex differences, 191
Vickers, V., 167, 217
Victors, E., 65
Vision and learning, 258
Visual abilities, training, 258
Visual attention, infants, 73
Visual behavior, at birth, 126
  infants, 77
Visual discrimination, infants, 69
Visual following, infants, 37
Visual-motor, system and balance, 52
  integration of vision and movement, 87
Visual perception, 2
  cognition, 90, 91
  cues, 67
  research trends and issues, 91
Visual perceptual development, 67, 94
  attributes, 251
  research summary, 93
Visual tracking, evaluation, 251
  infants, 71
  reading, 260
Visual training, academic performance, 260
Vocalization at birth, 10, 38

Wagner, G., 271
Walk, R., 83, 96, 98
Walker, R., 31, 35, 65, 223, 245
Walking, infants, 26
  reflex, 18
  rhythm, 43
  sex differences, 43
  stages in development, 43
Wall, M., 237
Walters, E., 9, 30, 122
Wapner, S., 88, 99, 122
Wardweel, E., 246
Warrington, E., 262, 269

Washburn, R., 246
Watson, J., 79, 99
Watt, N., 217
Weiner, M., 99
Weinstein, S., 99
Weisinger, M., 99
Welker, W., 129, 139
Wellman, B., 49, 55, 65
Werner, H., 122
White, B., 67, 77, 97, 99, 127, 139, 291
White, R., 68, 69, 73
Whiting, H., 184, 217
Whitsell, L., 253, 255, 271
Whittaker, J., 238, 244
Whole-part perception, 85
    visual motor tasks, 87
Wiener, H., 88, 99
Wild, M. R., 31, 54, 65, 221, 246
Williams, G., 217

Williams, H., 65, 89, 99, 208
Wilner, M., 121
Wise, J., 271
Witty, P., 230, 231, 244
Wohlwill, J., 99
Wolf, K., 98, 245
Wolf-child histories, 76
Wylie, R., 122

Yarborough, B., 271
Yarmolenko, A., 217

Zeller, J., 225, 246
Ziegler, E., 238, 246
Zig-zag run, 189
Zimmerman, H., 217
Zunich, M., 222, 246
Zusne, L., 271